METHUEN LIBRARY REPRINTS

SBN/416 32510 6/33

THE COMPLETE WORKS

OF

WALTER SAVAGE LANDOR

———

VOLUME VI

Walter Savay Landor

THE
COMPLETE WORKS
OF
WALTER SAVAGE
LANDOR

EDITED BY
T. EARLE WELBY

VOLUME VI

BARNES & NOBLE, Inc.
New York
METHUEN & CO. Ltd
London

This edition, published in 1969

by Barnes & Noble, Inc., New York
and Methuen & Co., Ltd. London

is reproduced from the edition
published by Chapman & Hall, Ltd.
between 1927 and 1936

Manufactured in the United States of America

CONTENTS

IMAGINARY CONVERSATIONS

ENGLISH (*continued*)

PAGE

XXXIII. The Duke of Wellington and Sir Robert Inglis . 1

XXXIV. Martin and Jack 9

XXXV. Archdeacon Hare and Walter Landor . . . 12

SCOTTISH

I. William Wallace and King Edward I. 43

II. Mary and Bothwell 50

IRISH

I. Essex and Spenser 57

II. Archbishop Boulter and Philip Savage 64

III. Duke de Richelieu, Sir Firebrace Cotes, Lady Glengrin, and Mr. Normanby 73

IV. Lord Coleraine, Rev. Mr. Bloombury, and Rev. Mr. Swan 161

V. Cavaliere Puntomichino and Mr. Denis Eusebius Talcranagh 170

AMERICAN

I. William Penn and Lord Peterborough 187

IMAGINARY CONVERSATIONS

ENGLISH—(continued)

XXXIII. THE DUKE OF WELLINGTON AND
SIR ROBERT INGLIS

(*Wks.*, ii., 1846 ; *Wks.*, iii., 1876.)

DUKE. Good morning, Sir Robert Inglis, I am glad to see you.

INGLIS. Your Grace is extremely obliging in fixing so early an hour for the audience I requested.

DUKE. We cannot meet too early for business, long or short.

INGLIS. The present is most important to the Administration of which your Grace is the main support.

DUKE. If you think so, we will dispatch it at once. I presume you mean the matter of Lord Ellenborough.

INGLIS. Exactly, my lord duke.

DUKE. Your objections, I think, rest on something which wounded your feelings on the side of religion ?

INGLIS. Not mine only, may it please your Grace.

DUKE. It neither pleases nor displeases me, Sir Robert Inglis. I am an impartial man ; and this is a matter that lies among the bishops.

INGLIS. I fear they will not stir in the business.

DUKE. The wiser men they.

INGLIS. But surely it is most offensive to pay twenty thousand men, and two millions of money, for a pair of sandal-wood gates,[1] which are not of sandal-wood, in order to fix them again to a temple which does not exist ; a temple which, while it did exist, was dedicated to the most immoral and impure of worship ; which afterward

---

[1] The gates of Somnath. Ellenborough boasted publicly that the victorious British forces were bringing back to India the spoils of Mahmud of Ghazni after eight centuries. Inglis protested in the House of Commons against the use by a Christian Governor of language such as no Mahomedan Governor would have suffered himself to use.

was converted to a mosque, and is now the receptacle of all the filth in the city that is ever removed at all.

DUKE. You say the gates are not of sandal-wood ; yet Lord Ellenborough is accused by the Radicals of setting up sandal-wood gates. This is frivolous.

INGLIS. He made a proclamation in the style of Buonaparte.

DUKE. Not he, indeed ; he is no more like Buonaparte than you are ; another frivolous objection. I do assure you, Sir Robert Inglis, he always thought Buonaparte a miserably poor creature in comparison with himself ; for, even in his best days, or (to use the word well for once) his *palmy* days, Buonaparte had notoriously little hair, and wore it quite flat. Then, after he made a peace, which to many, who pull back the past to overlay the present, seems as glorious as that which Lord Ellenborough has just concluded ; what did Buonaparte ? Mind ! I am speaking now his lordship's sentiments ; for I never speak in disparagement of any person I have been in the habit of meeting in society ; but what, in his lordship's opinion, did he, which could excite his envy or imitation ? Instead of turning his sword into a pruning-hook, which would have been ostentation and folly in one who never left behind him anything to prune, and scarcely a pruner, he neglected the only use to which Lord Ellenborough might reasonably have expected him to apply it ; he overlooked the obvious utility of its conversion into curling-irons. The cannon his lordship has taken from the enemy, no doubt, will be so employed ; at least, they may contribute to it, as far as they go. I do not expect it will be thought advisable, in the present state of her Majesty, to discharge them in the Park. Really, I see no reason why, after their remounting, they should not enter on another career of conquest. And where better than against the artillery on the crested heights of Almack's ? Do not look so grave, my good Sir Robert Inglis. We are both of us on half-pay in the same department, and our laurels grow rigidly cold upon us.

INGLIS. I protest, my lord duke, I do not comprehend your Grace.

DUKE. Then we will converse no longer on a subject of such intricacy, in which only one of us has had any practice.

INGLIS. He was desirous of ingratiating himself with the Hindoos.

DUKE. So he should be. A third frivolous objection.

INGLIS. But at the danger of alienating the Mahometans.

2

WELLINGTON AND SIR ROBERT INGLIS

DUKE. They hate us as you hate the devil ; therefore they are not to be alienated. A fourth frivolous objection.

INGLIS. My lord duke, I pretend to no knowledge of the parties in India, or their inclinations.

DUKE. Then why talk about them ?

INGLIS. My zeal for the religion of my country.

DUKE. What have they to do with the religion of our country, or we with theirs ?

INGLIS. We, as Englishmen and Christians, have very much to do with theirs.

DUKE. Are they then Christians and Englishmen ? We may worry those who are near us for believing this and disbelieving that ; but, until there are none to worry at home, let the people of India fight and work for us, and live contentedly. You live contentedly. But you are too grave and of too high standing to be bottle-holder to conflicting religions. I am sure, Sir Robert Inglis, I would wish fair play and no favour.

INGLIS. I trust, my lord duke, I never wish anything unfair.

DUKE. And if I have any reputation in the world, it is for loving all that is most fair.

INGLIS. Such is your Grace's character.

DUKE. Well then, let Somnauth and Juggernauth share and share alike.

INGLIS. In the bottomless pit !

DUKE. Wherever is most convenient to the parties. Juggernauth, I must confess to you, has been taken most into consideration by us, being an old ally, in a manner ; and our Government has always paid six thousand a-year toward his maintenance.

INGLIS. I deplore it.

DUKE. Every man is at liberty to deplore what he likes ; but really I do not see why you should hit upon this in particular. Not a bishop or archbishop rose from his seat in Parliament to denounce or censure or discommend it : therefore I am bound in conscience as a member of the Church of England, in duty as a peer, and in honour as a gentleman, to believe it all right.

INGLIS. Surely not, my lord duke. I yield to no man in veneration for the Church as by law established, or for those descendants of the Apostles, nevertheless.

DUKE. Better that I should be wrong in my theology than they :

but I can not well be wrong when I agree with lords so learned, particularly now you remind me of their unbroken descent from the Apostles. They are the fairest and most impartial men in the world : they let all religions thrive that do not come too near their own. They never cry " stand back," on slight occasions : and I firmly believe you could never engage more than a couple of them to lend a hand at the car of Juggernauth, even in cool weather. Some of them, whose skirts the reformers have been clipping, would be readier than the rest ; but they must have a very high minster in view before they would let you buckle on the harness.

INGLIS. I respect their motives. In like manner they abstained from voting on the question of the slave-trade. It behoves them to avoid all discussion and disquisition on the policy of Ministers.

DUKE. So it does you and me. I lean to neither of the contending Gods in particular : they are both well enough in their way : if they are quiet with us, let them do as they like with their own people, who certainly would not have worshipped them so long if they had misbehaved. Do not encourage men, ignorant men particularly, to throw off any restraint you find upon them : it is no easy matter to put another in the place, well-looking as it may be, and clever as you may think yourself in cutting it out and fitting it to the wearer.

INGLIS. These wretched men have souls, my lord duke, to be saved from the flames of hell.

DUKE. I hope so : but I am no fire-man. I know what good, meanwhile, may be done with them in the hands of the priests, if you let the priests have their own way : but if you stop their feeds what work can you expect out of them ?

INGLIS. So long as they have their way, Christianity will never be established in Hindostan.

DUKE. Bad news, indeed ! Upon my life, I am sorry to hear it ; especially, when other most religious men have taken the trouble to assure me that it would prevail against the devil and all his works. We must not be hasty, Sir Robert Inglis. There are some things at which we may make a dash ; others require wary circumspection and slow approaches. I would curtail the foraging ground of an enemy, never of an ally. We must wink upon some little excesses of theirs, while we keep our own men strictly to duty. Beside, we are hard-driven, and cannot give up patronage.

4

WELLINGTON AND SIR ROBERT INGLIS

INGLIS. If your Grace's conscience is quite satisfied that the service of Government requires a certain relaxation in what we consider vital essentials, we must submit.

DUKE. Our consciences may not be quite so easy as one could wish, nor are our places ; but we must take into consideration the necessity of collecting the revenue in Hindostan ; and the priests in all countries can make it difficult or easy. Lord Ellenborough is affable ; and I trust he will hang a religion in each ear, so that neither shall hang higher than the other.

INGLIS. We are taught and commanded to judge not hastily. Now, I would not judge hastily my Lord Ellenborough ; but certainly it does bear hard on tender consciences, to believe he entertains that lively faith which——

DUKE. Pooh, pooh ! If he has any faith at all, I will answer for him it is as lively as a turtle ; which, you know, is proverbial : no advertisement calls the thing otherwise. You may call Ellenborough a silly fellow, but never a dull one, unless when wit and humour are required ; and business wants none of their flashes to show its path.

INGLIS. Belief in his Creator——

DUKE. He believes in all of these, better than they believe in him, from those who created him Secretary of State, to those who created him Governor-General.

INGLIS. I meant to signify his religion.

DUKE. He might ask you what that signifies ?

INGLIS. We require from all the servants of her Majesty, from all who are in authority under her, as our Church service most beautifully expresses it——

DUKE. Well, well ! what would you have ? I will speak from my own knowledge of him ; I know he believes in a deity ; I heard him use the very name, in swearing at his groom ; and, on the same occasion, he cried aloud, " The devil take the fellow ! " Can you doubt, after this, that his religion is secure on both flanks ?

INGLIS. God has, from the beginning, set his face against idolatry.

DUKE. I don't wonder. I am persuaded you are correct in your statement, Sir Robert Inglis.

INGLIS. He reproved it, in his wrath, as one among the most crying sins of the Jews.

DUKE. They have a good many of that description : but they

5

must have been fine soldiers formerly. Do you think, Sir Robert Inglis, they are likely, at last, to get into the Houses of Parliament ?

INGLIS. God forbid !

DUKE. For my own part I have no voice on the occasion. Other rich folks, quite as crying, and craving, and importunate, lawyers more especially, crowd both yours and ours. But I think a sprinkling of Jews might help you prodigiously just at present ; for, by what I hear about them, there are nowhere such stiff sticklers against idolatry, at the present day, as those gentlemen ! We both are connected, to a certain extent, with the University of Oxford. Now, people do tell me that many of those who voted for us, as well as many of those who did not, are inclined to a spice of it.

INGLIS. They deny the charge.

DUKE. Of course they do : so do the people of Hindostan, even those among them who possess no pluralities, no preferment. They all tell you there is something at the bottom of it which you do not see, because you are blind and stupid and unbelieving. They all, both here and there, tell you that, to learn things rightly, you must become a child once more. Now, against the child's doctrine I have nothing to say, but I have a serious objection, in my own person, to certain parts of the discipline.

INGLIS. Your Grace is grave apparently, which could not surely be the case if such abomination were about to be tolerated in our principal seats of learning.

DUKE. In truth I was not thinking about the seats of learning : nor indeed do I see any danger in pious men erecting the Cross to elevate their devotion. I fear more the faggot than the solid timber : and, when I know they came out of the same wood, I am suspicious they may be travelling the same road. But until an evil intention is manifest, I would let people have their own way, both in Oxfordshire and Hindostan. In regard to giving them money, I leave that matter entirely to the discretion of their votaries.

INGLIS. I grieve for this lukewarmness in your Grace.

DUKE. It is high time for me to be lukewarm, and hardly that.

INGLIS. I did not enter upon politics, or question an officer, a high, a very high functionary of her Majesty, in regard to the expediency of favouring one religion of the Hindoos against the other and that professed by the more warlike and powerful.

DUKE. Did not you ? Then what can you question ?

6

WELLINGTON AND SIR ROBERT INGLIS

INGLIS. I question, and more than question, the correctness of his views in winking at impurity ; for the worship of the Lingam is most impure.

DUKE. We do wink at such things, Sir Robert ; we do not openly countenance them. I am no worshipper of the Lingam. I speak as an unprejudiced man ; and, depend upon it, if Lord Ellenborough had any tendency to that worship, the priests would make him undergo a rigorous examination, and probably would reject him after all. Nothing in his past life lays him open to such an imputation.

INGLIS. God forbid I should imply such an obscenity.

DUKE. Do not embarrass by this implication, or any other, the march of a Ministry which not only has pointed stakes at every ten yards, but a toll-bar at every twenty. I tell you from my own knowledge, that Ellenborough is only a coxcomb. Respect him, for he is the greatest in the world : and the head of every profession should be respected. What would you have ? whom would you have ? You are an aristocrat ; you have your title ; and, no doubt, your landed estate. Would you send to govern India, as was done formerly, such men as Clive and Hastings ? They could conquer and govern empires : what then ? Could they keep Ministers and the friends of Ministers in their places ? No such thing. Therefore, my good worthy Sir Robert Inglis, do not let us talk any more nonsense together. Our time is valuable ; we have not too much left.

INGLIS. Whatever, by God's Providence, we may still look forward to, let us devote to his service, repressing to the utmost of our power all attempts to aid or comfort a false and most impure religion.

DUKE. A bargain ! we will ; that is, you and I. Let us enter into a compact, this very hour, never to worship the Lingam in word or deed. We will neither bow down to it nor worship it, nor do anything in word or deed which may point to such a conclusion. I promise, furthermore, to use all my interest with her Majesty's Ministers, that they will immediately send a dispatch to Lord Ellenborough, ordering him not to set up the gates again in a temple which has ceased to exist for many centuries ; but that, as the gates have been carried about a thousand miles, and as we have lost about as many men (to say nothing of field-pieces) in conveying them back, his Excellency do issue another proclamation, empowering six of the

Generals and six of the Supreme Council to leave India forthwith, bearing with them, to show the devotion both of Mahometans and Hindoos to her Majesty, a toothpick-case and twelve tooth-picks, made therefrom, for the use of her Majesty and her successors. Do you ride, Sir Robert Inglis ?

INGLIS. I have no horses in town.

DUKE. My horse is waiting for me in the courtyard, and I think it proper to set my servants an example of punctuality. Perhaps I may have the pleasure of meeting you in the park.

INGLIS. I have occupied too much of your Grace's time ?

DUKE. Very little.

INGLIS. I would only beg of your Grace that you prevail on Ministers to hesitate before——

DUKE. I never tell any man to hesitate. Right or wrong, to hesitate is imbecility. How the deuce can a man fall while he is going on ? If Peel stops suddenly, the Whigs will run in and cut his brush off.

INGLIS. God forbid !

DUKE. They don't mind what God forbids, not they. A man is never quagmired till he stops ; and the rider who looks back has never a firm seat. We must cast our eyes not at all behind nor too much before, but steadily just where we are. Politicians are neither lovers nor penitents. I see, Sir Robert Inglis, you are in haste. I will lay before Peel, and the rest of them, all your suggestions. In the meantime be a little patient ; Juggernauth is not coming down St. James's Street.

8

XXXIV. MARTIN AND JACK

(*Last Fruit*, 1853 ; *Wks.*, v., 1876.)

[Lord Peter, Martin, and Jack, brought the people much about them in a disturbance long ago. Lord Peter, the proudest, most intolerant, most exclusive, of his order, suddenly grew condescending and bland. Martin had little confidence in this demonstration ; so little indeed that he ordered the locksmith to alter the locks of his cellar and larder, well knowing that, however different in stature and features, there was a marvellous family-likeness in appetite and quickness of digestion. Jack, whose house was smaller, was contented with a cellar of proportionate dimensions ; and, if you only sent him a simple calf's head toward the close of January, cared little for any other delicacy of the larder. When Peter spoke to him, which was seldom, he pretended that he was ignorant of his language, and avowed that neither father nor mother had taught it to any of their children. Martin had caught a few words of it from Peter, and was somewhat fond of displaying his acquisition. Jack, who kept aloof from both brothers, was more scandalized at Martin. At last, taciturn as was his nature, he zealously burst forth in this brotherly expostulation.]

JACK. Brother Martin, friends we have met, whatever were our feuds formerly, and friends, in God's name, let us part. We have been somewhat too much given to the holding forth of long discourses ; and perhaps I, in this particular, have been the more censurable of the two. Let me now come to the point and have done with it. I always knew that Peter was an impostor and a bastard : I always knew he was neither our father's son nor our mother's son. Had he been, would he ever have attempted to strangle us in our cradles ? Would he not rather have helped us in our sickness and infirmity ? would he not rather have fed us with pure fresh milk and unfermented bread in it ? would he not rather have taken us by the hand, and guided our tottering steps, patiently and cautiously ? Instead of which, he blew out the rush-light, because it was *only* a rush-light ; he set fire to our cribs, and burnt us cruelly.

MARTIN. I have heard all this story from our nurse ; but, Jack ! Jack ! thou wert always a froward child.

JACK. Too true, brother ! but age hath sobered and softened me : I trust it continues to render me, day by day, a little more like our father. If this aspiration be too high, if this expression be too

9

presumptuous, permit me to correct it, and only to say that, as I advance in life, I do heartily hope, I do anxiously desire, that my steps be more prone and more direct toward him.

MARTIN. Give me thy hand, brother Jack ! This is manly ; this is true-hearted.

JACK. Can you then bear questioning and reproof, brother ?

MARTIN. Not very well, as you know, my old boy. But come ; let me try ; out with it ; out at once.

JACK. Martin ! Martin ! the hottest air taints and corrupts our viands no more certainly, nor more intimately, nor more perniciously, than the lukewarm. So is it, my brother, with the sustenance of the spirit. I have lived where the flocks are scattered and healthy, and where the life of the shepherd is innocent and laborious. You have been spending your days where there is no true shepherd at all, and where the crowded fold is a sad congestion of ordure, scab, and foot-rot. You are grown angry, I hear, at certain new impertinences of the proud bastard whom you never have ventured to disclaim as brother. Shall I reveal to you the secret of this anger ?

MARTIN (*yawning*). With all my heart.

JACK. Indifferent as usual ! Well then ; continue this indifference until the close of our conversation. The audacious bastard, who dared to spit in our father's face when he forbade any to call him *lord*, sees many of his spawn grown recently, from wriggling black little tadpoles, into party-coloured, puffy, croaking frogs ; and he claims the whole fat marsh for his own property. The neighbouring lords assumed the livery of our Lord Peter, and imitated his voice and bearing. But no sooner had he laid claim to the whole fat marsh, and had driven into it their cattle for his own use, than they raised an outcry throughout the land.

MARTIN. Methinks it was time, brother Jack.

JACK. Brother Martin ! it was time long before. The dissolute old bastard collected those spies and assassins who had, even when nations were thought to be less civilized, been driven forth from every kingdom. He now stocks every kingdom with them again, and mounts every throne with them, vicariously. Well do I remember the time, my brother, when I reproved you for a tendency to what is called philosophy. It is true, you laughed in my face : certainly, you will never laugh in it again for any similar reproof. If priests there must be, let them keep their proper station : let the king have

MARTIN AND JACK

his palace, not the priest. When you have assigned to the endow
ment of schools the many millions which pamper your hierarchs,
those burly bellies, swaying some one way, some another, then,
Martin, we shall meet in brotherly love, and shall say (what I wish
we could say sooner, instead of the contrary), " This is verily God's
work, and it is marvellous in our eyes."

MARTIN. There is only one set of men in Europe who are avowedly
adverse to the propagation of knowledge, aware that the propaga
tion of knowledge is adverse to their dominion. My friends, I am
sorry to say it, are almost as much given to lying as these are. Both
parties call themselves *Catholic*, which neither is. Nor indeed, my
dear Jack, between ourselves, is it desirable that either should be.
Every sect is a moral check on its neighbour. Competition is as
wholesome in religion as in commerce. We must bid high for heaven ;
we must surrender much, we must suffer much ; we must make way
for others, in order that in our turn we may succeed. There is but
one guide : we know him by the gentleness of his voice, by the
serenity of his countenance, by the wounded in spirit who are
clinging to his knees, by the children whom he hath called to him,
and by the disciples in whose prosperity he hath shared.

XXXV. ARCHDEACON HARE AND WALTER LANDOR [1]

(Last Fruit, 1853 ; Wks., v., 1876.)

ARCHDEACON HARE. In some of your later writings, I perceive, you have not strictly followed the line you formerly laid down for spelling.

WALTER LANDOR. I found it inexpedient ; since whatever the pains I took, there was, in every sheet almost, some deviation on the side of the compositor. Inconsistency was forced on me against all my struggles and reclamations. At last nothing is left for me but to enter my protest, and to take the smooth path instead of the broken-up highway.

ARCHDEACON HARE. It is chiefly in the preterites and participles that I have followed you perseveringly. We are rich in having two for many of our verbs, and unwise in corrupting the spelling, and thereby rendering the pronunciation difficult. We pronounce " astonish*t* " ; we write astonish*ed* or astonish'*d* ; an unnecessary harshness. Never was spoken drop*ped*, or lop*ped*, or hop*ped*, or prop*ped;* but drop*t*, &c. ; yet with the choice before us, we invariably take the wrong. I do not resign a right to " astonish*ed* " or " diminish*ed*." They may, with many like them, be useful in poetry ; and several such terminations add dignity and solemnity to what we read in our church, the sanctuary at once of our faith and of our language.

WALTER LANDOR. In more essential things than preterites and participles I ought rather to have been your follower than you mine. No language is purer or clearer than yours. Vigorous streams from the mountain do not mingle at once with the turbid lake, but retain their force and their colour in the midst of it. We are sapt by an influx of putridity.

ARCHDEACON HARE. Come, come ; again to our spelling-book.

WALTER LANDOR. Well then, we differ on the spelling of *honour*,

[1] In part a reply to De Quincey's *Notes on Walter Savage Landor.*

12

ARCHDEACON HARE AND LANDOR

favour, &c. You would retain the *u* : I would eject it, for the sake of consistency. We have dropt it in *author, emperor, ambassador.* Here again, for consistency and compliancy, I write " *embassador,"* because I write, as all do, " embassy." I write thea*ter,* sepulch*er,* met*er,* in their english form rather than the french. The best authors have done it ; all write " hexamet*er* " and " pentamet*er."*

ARCHDEACON HARE. It is well to simplify and systematize wherever we can do it conveniently.

WALTER LANDOR. And without violence to *vested rights ;* which words have here some meaning. Why "*amend,"* if "*emendation"*? Why not " pont*if,"* if " cait*if* " ?

ARCHDEACON HARE. Why then should grand*eur* be left in solitary state ? The Englishman less easily protrudes his nether jaw than the Frenchman, as " grand*eur* " seems to require. Grand*our* (or grand*or,* if you will have it so) sounds better.

WALTER LANDOR. I *will* have it so ; and so will you and others at last.

ARCHDEACON HARE. Meanwhile, let us untie this last knot of Norman bondage on the common-law of language in our land.

WALTER LANDOR. Set about it : no authority is higher than yours : I will run by the side of you, or be your herald, or (what better becomes me) your pursuivant.

There is an affectation of scholarship in compilers of spelling-books, and in the authors they follow for examples, when they bring forward *phenomena* and the like. They might as well bring forward *mysteria.* We have no right to tear greek and latin declensions out of their grammars : we need no *vortices* when we have *vortexes* before us ; and while we have *memorandums, factotums, ultimatums,* let our shepherd-dogs bring back to us by the ear such as have wandered from the flock.

ARCHDEACON HARE. We have " stimul*ant* " ; why " stimul*us* " ? why " stimul*i* " ? Why " recip*e* " ? why " rece*ipt* " ? we might as reasonably write " dece*ipt* " and " conce*ipt.*" I believe we are the only people who keep the *Dramatis Personæ* on the stage, or announce their going off by " *exeunt*": " *exit* " for *departure,* is endurable, and kept in countenance by *transit :* let us deprecate the danger of hearing of a friend's *obit,* which seems imminent : a " *post-obit* " is bad enough : an *item* I would confine to the ledger. I have no mind for *animus.*

WALTER LANDOR. Beside these there are two expressions either of which is quite enough to bring down curses and mortality on the poet. " *Stand confest* "[1] (even if not written " conf*ess'd* ") is one : " *unbidden tears* "[2] the other. I can imagine no such nonsense as *unbidden tears*. Why do we not write the verb control with an *e* at the end, and the substantive with *u* as *soul ?* we might as reasonably write *whol* for whole : very unreasonably do we write *wholly* with a double *l* ; *wholy* and *soly* might follow the type of *holy*. We see printed, *befal* with one *l*, but never *fal*, and yet in the monosyllable we should not be doubtful of the accentuation. It is but of late that we contro*l*, reca*l*, appa*l*, we do not yet ro*l*. Will anyone tell me who put such a lazy beast to our *munition*-train, and spelt on the front of the carriage *am*munition ? We write *enter* and *inter* equally with a single final *r* : surely the latter wants another.

ARCHDEACON HARE. What is quite as censurable, while we reject the good of our own countrymen, we adopt the bad of the forener. We are much in the habit of using the word *flibustier*. Surely we might let the French take and torture our *freebooter*. In our fondness for making verbs out of substantives, we even go to the excess of *flibustering*. And now from coarse vulgarity let us turn our eyes toward inconsiderate refinement. When I was a boy every girl among the poets was a *nymph*, whether in country or town. Johnson countenanced them, and, arm-in-arm with Pope, followed them even into Jerusalem. " Ye nymphs of Solyma," &c.

WALTER LANDOR. Pity they ever found their way back !

ARCHDEACON HARE. Few even now object to Muse and Bard.

WALTER LANDOR. Nor would I in their proper places : the Muse in Greece and Italy ; the Bard on our side of the Alps, up almost as far as Scandinavia, quite as far as the Cimbrian Chersonese. But the Bard looks better at nine or ten centuries off than among gentlemen in roquelaures or paletots. Johnson, a great reprehender, might fairly and justly have reprehended him in the streets of London, whatever were his own excesses among the " Nymphs of Solyma." In the midst of his gravity he was not quite impartial, and, extraordinary as were his intellectual powers, he knew about as much of

---

[1] Compare Swinburne's protest against Rossetti's use of this phrase, in the correspondence over correction of Rossetti's proofs for the volume of 1870.

[2] See Landor's other outburst against " unbidden tears " in the Second Conversation of Southey and Landor.

ARCHDEACON HARE AND LANDOR

poetry as of geography. In one of his letters he talks of Guadaloupe as being in another hemisphere. Speaking of that island, his very words are these : " Whether you return hither or stay in another hemisphere." At the commencement of his Satire on the *Vanity of Human Wishes* (a noble specimen of declamation), he places China nearer to us than Peru.

ARCHDEACON HARE. The negligences of Johnson may easily be forgiven, in consideration of the many benefits he has conferred on literature. A small poet, no great critic, he was a strenuous and lofty moralist. Your pursuers are of another breed, another race. They will soon tire themselves, hang out their tongues, and drop along the road. Time is not at all misapplied by you in the analysis and valuation of Southey's and Wordsworth's poetry, which never has been done scrupulously and correctly. But surely gravel may be carted and shot down on the highway without the measure of a Winchester bushel. Consider if what you have taken in hand is worthy of your workmanship.

WALTER LANDOR. The most beautiful tapestry is workt on extremely coarse canvas. Open a volume of *Bayle's Biographical Dictionary ;* and how many just and memorable observations will you find on people of no " note or likelihood."

ARCHDEACON HARE. Unhappily for us, we are insensible of the corruptions that creep yearly into our language. At Cambridge or Oxford (I am ignorant which of them claims the glory of the invention) some undergraduate was so facetious as to say, " Well, while you are *discussing* the question, I will *discuss* my wine." The gracefulness of this witticism was so captivating, that it took possession not only of both universities, but seized also on " men about town." Even the ladies, the vestals who preserve the purity of language, caught up the expression from those who were libertines in it.

WALTER LANDOR. Chesterfield and Horace Walpole, who are among the most refined of our senators, have at present no more authority in language than in dress. By what we see, we might imagine that the one article is to be cast aside after as short a wear as the other. It occurs to me at this moment, that, when we have assumed the habiliments of the vulgar, we are in danger of contracting their coarseness of language and demeanour.

ARCHDEACON HARE. Certainly the Romans were *togati* in their

15

tongue, as well as in their wardrobe. Purity and gravity of style were left uncontaminated and unshaken by the breath of Tiberius and his successor. The Antonines spoke better latin than the Triumvir Antonius ; and Marcus Aurelius, altho on some occasions he preferred the greek, was studious to maintain his own idiom strong and healthy. When the tongue is paralyzed, the limbs soon follow. No nation hath long survived the decrepitude of its language.

There is perpetually an accession of slang to our vernacular, which is usually biennial or triennial.

WALTER LANDOR. I have been either a fortunate or a prudent man to have escaped for so many years together to be " pitched into " among " *giant* trees," " *monster* meetings," " *glorious* fruit," " *splendid* cigars, dogs, horses, and *bricks*," " *palmy* days," " *rich* oddities "; to owe nobody a farthing for any other fashionable habits of rude device and demi-saison texture ; and above all, to have never come in at the " *eleventh hour*," which has been sounding all day long the whole year. They do me a little injustice who say that such a good fortune is attributable to my residence in Italy. The fact is, I am too cautious and too aged to catch disorders, and I walk fearlessly through these epidemics.

ARCHDEACON HARE. Simply to *open* is insufficient : we " open *up* " and " open *out*." A gentleman *indues* a coat ; it will be difficult to *exue* if he tries ; he must lie down and sleep in it.

" *Foolery* " was thought of old sufficiently expressive : nothing short of *tom*foolery will do now. To *repudiate* was formerly to put away what disgraced us : it now signifies (in America at least) to reject the claims of justice and honour. We hear people *re-read*, and see them *re-write ;* and are invited to a *spread*, where we formerly went to a dinner or collation. We cut down *barracks* to a single *barrack ;* but we leave the " stocks " in good repair. We are among *ambitions*, and among *peoples*, until Sternhold and Hopkins call us into a quieter place, and we hear once again

All people that on earth do dwell.

Shall we never have done with " *rule and exception*," " *ever and anon*," " *many a time and oft* " ?

WALTER LANDOR. It is to be regretted that Horne Tooke and Bishop Lowth were placed so far apart, by many impediments and

16

ARCHDEACON HARE AND LANDOR

obstructions, that they never could unite in order to preserve the finials and pinnacles of our venerable fabric, to stop the innovations and to diminish the anomalies of our language. Southey, altho in his youth during their time, might have assisted them; for early in life he had studied as sedulously the best of our old authors as they had, and his judgment was as mature at twenty-five as theirs at fifty. He agreed with me that *mind, find, kind, blind, behind,* should have a final *e,* in order to signify the sound, and that the verb *wind* should likewise for the same reason. I brought Fairfax's *Tasso* with me, and showed him that Fairfax had done it, and had spelt many other words better than our contemporaries, or even than the most-part of his own.

ARCHDEACON HARE. There are two expressions of frequent occurrence, equally wrong: " incorrect *orthography* " and " vernacular *idiom.*" Distempers in language, as in body, which rise from the crowded lane, creep up sometimes to where the mansions are higher and better ventilated. I think you once remarkt to me that you would just as properly write pill*anger* for pillager, as mess*enger* for messager. The more excusable vulgar add to these dainties their *sausenger.* Have you found anything more to notice where you have inserted those slips of paper in your Fairfax ?

WALTER LANDOR. Much : to run over all would be tedious. He writes with perfect propriety *dismaid, applie, chefe, hart, wisht, husht, spred.* Southey was entirely of my opinion that if *lead* in the present is *led* in the preterite, *read* should be *red.* There is no danger of mistaking the adjective for the verb by it. He ridiculed the spelling of Byron *redde ;* which is quite as ridiculous as the conceit of that antiquarian society which calls itself the " Roxburgh*e* Club " ; *e* was never added to *burgh.*

Howell, a very careful writer, an excellent authority, writes *forren, frend, Mahometism, toung, extemporal, shipwrack, cole, onely, sutable, plaid, askt, begger, apparance, brest, yeer, lanch, peece, tresure, scepter, incertain, kinde, perle.*

Drayton and Daniel may be associated with Howell. Drayton in his prose wrote *red,* and there is no purer or more considerate author. He writes also ransack*t,* distinguish*t,* dispers*t,* worship*t,* admonish*t,* tax*t,* deck*t,* wrack*t,* profes*t,* extol*d,* purchas*t.* He writes *fained, tuch, yeers, onely, dore.*

Sir Thomas More writes *lerned, clereness, preste* (priest), *sholde, wolde, leve, yere, harte, mynde, here* (hear), *herer* (hearer), *appere, speker, seke, grevous, fynde, doute, wherof, seme, dede, nede, tethe* (teeth), *precher, peple, sene* (seen), *eres* (ears), *toke, therfor, mete* (meat), *frend, therin, fere* (fear), a *wever, rede* (read). A host of these words only show that the best authors avoided the double vowel.

Chaucer, in consecutive verses, writes *were* (wear), and *bere* (bear), and *heven* and *foule.*

> Upon her thombe or in her purse to bere.

> There is no foule that flieth under heven.

Camden writes *forraine* and *iland.*

It was late before *ea* was employed in place of the simple vowel *e.* Chaucer writes " *eny pecock.*" *Shal* and *wil,* so written by him, are more proper than *shall* and *will,* by avoiding the form of substantives. Caxton writes, as many of his time, *werk* not " work." Tyndal, long after, writes *doo* for *do.* Spenser writes *dore* instead of *door.* Sackville writes *pearst.* Dryden is less accurate than Cowley, and Waller, and Sprat. Speaking of Cowley, he says " he never could forgive a conceit," meaning *forego.* In our own age many, Burke among the rest, say, " By *this* means." It would be affectation to say " By this *mean*," in the singular ; but the proper expression is " By these means."

ARCHDEACON HARE. In regard to terminations, it is difficult to account for the letter *e* when we say " by and bye." There is none in accounting for it in " Good *bye,*" which is the most comprehensive of all contractions : it is " Good be with ye ! " or " God be with ye ! " which in effect is the same. Formerly *ye* was more universal than *you.* Ignorant critics reprehend it wrongly in such a position as " I would not hurt *ye.*" But it is equally good english as " *Ye* would not hurt me." No word is more thoroughly vernacular, from of old to this present day, among the people throughout the land. We should keep our homely well-seasoned words, and never use the grave for light purposes.

Among the many we misapply is the word *destiny.* We hear of a man controling the destiny of another. Nothing on earth can controle the *destined,* whether the term be applied strictly or laxly. *Element* is another, meaning only a *constituent.* Graver stil is *incar-*

18

nation. We hear about the *mission* of fellows whose highest could be only to put a letter into the post-office.

We usually set ' before '*neath:* improperly : the better spelling is *nethe,* whence *nether.* We also prefix the same ' to '*fore.* We say (at least those who swear do) " '*fore* God "; never " *before* God." *Cause* in like manner is a word of itself, no less than " *because.*" But this form is properer for poetry.

Chaucer writes *peple,* as we pronounce it.

Skelton writes *sault* and *mault,* also in accordance with the pronunciation, and there is exactly the same reason for it as in *fault.* It would not be going far out of our way to bring them back again, and then cry *hault,* which we do only with the pen in hand.

We are in the habitude of writing onward*s,* backward*s,* toward*s,* afterward*s* ; he more gracefully drops the final *s.* We write strip*t,* whip*t,* yet hesitate at trip*t* and worship*t.* We possess in many cases two for one of the preterites, and, to show our impartiality and fairness, we pronounce the one and write the other. We write *said* and *laid,* but never *staid* or *plaid.* We write offi*c*ial ; why not influen*c*ial, circumstan*c*ial, differen*c*ial ? We write *entrance* the substantive like *entrànce* the verb. Shakespeare wisely wrote

> That sounds the fatal enter*a*nce of Duncan, &c.

Wond*e*rous is a finer word than *wondrous.*

It is not every good scholar, or every fair poet, who possesses the copiousness and exhibits the discrimination of Shakespeare. Even when we take the hand he offers us, we are accused of innovating.

WALTER LANDOR. So far from innovating, the words I propose are brought to their former and legitimate station ; you have sanctioned the greater part, and have thought the remainder worth your notice. Every intelligent and unprejudiced man will agree with you. I prefer high authorities to lower, analogy to fashion, a *Restoration* to a *Usurpation.* Innovators, and worse than innovators, were those Reformers called, who disturbed the market-place of manorial Theology, and went back to Religion where she stood alone in her original purity. We English were the last people to adopt the reformed style in the kalendar, and we seem determined to be likewise the last in that of language. We are ordered to please the public ; we are forbidden to instruct it. Not only publishers and booksellers are against us, but authors too ; and even some of them who are not regularly in the service of those masters. The outcry is, " *We* have not ventured to alter what we find in use, and why should *he ?* "

ARCHDEACON HARE. If the most learned and intelligent, in that age which has been thought by many the most glorious in our literature, were desirous that the language should be settled and fixt, how much more desirable is it that its accretion of corruptions should be now removed ! It may be difficult ; and stil more difficult to restore the authority of the ancient dynasty.

WALTER LANDOR. We never have attempted it. But there are certain of their laws and usages which we would not willingly call obsolete. Often in the morning I have lookt among your books for them, and I deposit in your hands the first fruits of my research. It is only for such purposes that I sit hours together in a library. Either in the sunshine or under the shade of trees, I must think, meditate, and compose.

ARCHDEACON HARE. Thoughts may be born in a room above-stairs or below, but they are stronger and healthier for early exercise in the open air. It is not only the conspirator to whom is appropriate the " modo citus modo tardus incessus " ; it is equally his who follows fancy, and his also who searches after truth.

WALTER LANDOR. The treasures of your library have sometimes tempted me away from your pictures ; and I have ceast for a moment to regret that by Selections and Compendiums we had lost a large portion of the most noble works, when I find so accurate a selection, so weighty a compendium, carried about with him who is now walking at my side.

ARCHDEACON HARE. I would have strangled such a compliment ere it had attained its full growth : however, now it is not only full-grown but over-grown, let me offer you in return not a compliment, but a congratulation, on your courage in using the plural " compendi*ums* " where another would have pronounced " compendi*a.*"

WALTER LANDOR. Would that other, whoever he may be, have said muse*a* ? All I require of people is consistency, and rather in the right than in the wrong. When we have admitted a greek, or latin, or french word, we ought to allow it the right of citizenship, and induce it to comply and harmonize with the rest of the vocular community. " Pindari*que* " went away with Cowley, and died in the same ditch with him ; but " obli*que* " is inflexible, and stands its ground. He would do well who should shove it away, or push it into the ranks of the new militia. " Antique " is the worst portion of Gray's heritage. His former friend, Horace Walpole, had many *antiques*, and other trifles at Strawberry-hill, but none so worthless as this. In honest truth, we neither have, nor had then, a better and purer writer than he, although he lived in the time of the purest and best, Goldsmith, Sterne, Fielding, and Inchbald. He gave up his fashionable french for a richer benefice. He would not use " *rouge* " but " *red* " ; very different from the ladies and gentlemen of the present day, who bring in entremets, and lardès, casting now and then upon the lukewarm hearth a log of latin, and in the sleeping-room they have prepared for us, spread out as counterpane a remnant of etruscan from under a courier's saddlebag.

Chaucer, who had resided long in France, and much among courtiers, made english his style. Have you patience to read a list of the words he spelt better than we do ? and not he only but his remote successors.

ARCHDEACON HARE. I have patience, and more than patience, to read, or hear, or see, whatever is better than ourselves. Such investigations have always interested me, you know of old.

WALTER LANDOR. Rare quality ! I scarcely know where to find another who possesses it, or whose anger would not obtain the mastery over his conscience at the imputation.

Let your eyes run down this catalogue. Here are *swete* and *swote*, *finde, ther, wel, herken, herk, gilt* (guilt), *shal, don* (done), *werks* (works), *weping, clene, defaulte, therof, speking, erthe, bereth* (beareth), *seate, mete* (meat), *shuld* (should), *hevy, hevn, grevous, grete, hete, yere, fode* (food) ; we still say *fodder*, not fooder ; *ete* (eat), *lede, throt, wel, drede, shal, gess* (guess), *ful, wheras, trespas, betwene, repe, slepe, shete, frend, dedly, delites, teres, hering, clereness, juge, plese, speke, wold* (would), *ded, tred, bereve, thred, peple, dore, dreme, deme, reson, indede, meke, feble, wede, nede, fele, cese, pece, dedly, deme, resonable, slepe, titel, refrein, preeste.*

ARCHDEACON HARE. In adding the vowel, he makes it available for verse. *Covetise*, how much better than *covetousness !* Among the words which might be brought back again to adorn our poetical diction is *beforne*, before. Here is *distemperament* (for inclemency of season) ; *forlet*, forgive, another good word ; so is *wanhope*, despair. Has no poet the courage to step forth and to rescue these

21

maidens of speech, unprotected beneath the very castle-walls of Chaucer?

WALTER LANDOR. If they are resolved to stitch up his rich old tapestry with muslin, they would better let it stay where it is.

ARCHDEACON HARE. Several more words are remaining in which a single vowel is employed where we reduplicate. *Sheres, appere, speche, wele, bereth, reson, mening, pleasance, stele, coles, mekeness, reve* (bereave), *rore, tong, corageous, forbere, kepe, othe* (oath), *cese, shepe, dreme, werse* (worse), *reken* (reckon). Certainly this old spelling is more proper than its substitute. To *reken* is to *look over* an account before casting it up. Here are *grevance, lerne, bete, seke, speke, freze* (freeze), *chese, clense, tretise, meke.* Here I find *axe* (ask), which is now a vulgarism, though we use *tax* for *task.* With great propriety he writes *persever;* we, with great impropriety, *persevere.* He uses the word *spiced* for *overnice,* which in common use is *gingerly.* I think you would not be a stickler for the best of these, whichever it may be.

WALTER LANDOR. No indeed : but there are in Chaucer, as there are in other of our old, yet somewhat later writers, things which with regret I see cast aside for worse. I wish every editor of an author, whether in poetry or prose, would at least add a glossary of his words as he spelt and wrote them, without which attention the history of a language must be incomplete. Heine in his Virgil, Wakefield in his Lucretius, have preserved the text itself as entire as possible. Greek words do not appear in their spelling to have been subject to the same vicissitudes as latin.

I have not been engaged in composing a grammar or vocabulary, nor is a conversation a treatise ; so with your usual kindness you will receive a confused collection of words, bearing my mark on them and worthy of yours. They are somewhat like an Italian pastry, of heads and necks and feet and gizzards off a variety of birds of all sorts and sizes. If my simily is undignified, let me go back into the Sistine Chapel, where Michel Angelo displays the same thing more gravely and grandly in his *Last Judgment.*

ARCHDEACON HARE. Do not dissemble your admiration of this illustrious man, nor turn into ridicule what you reverence. Among the hardy and false things caught from mouth to mouth is the apothegm that " there is only a step from the sublime to the ridiculous." There was indeed but a step from Bonaparte's.

ARCHDEACON HARE AND LANDOR

WALTER LANDOR. I perceive you accept the saying as his. It was uttered long before his birth, and so far back as the age of Louis the Fourteenth. Another is attributed to him, which was spoken by Barrère in the Convention. He there called the English " cette nation *boutiquière.*"

ARCHDEACON HARE. Well, now empty out your sack of words, and never mind which comes first.

WALTER LANDOR. Probably there are several of them which we have noticed before. Here are a few things which I have markt with my pencil from time to time ; others are obliterated, others lost.

There is a very good reason why *ravel* and *travel* should be spelt with a single *l*, pronunciation requires it ; equally does pronunciation require a double *l* in befell, expell, compell, rebell.

We often find *kneeled* instead of *knelt*, yet I do not remember *feeled* for *felt*. Shaftesbury, and the best writers of his age and later, wrote *cou'd, shou'd, wou'd :* we do not, although in speaking we never insert the *l*. Hurd writes, " *Under* the *circumstances.*" Circumstances are *about* us, not *above* us.

" Master of the situation," is the only expression we have borrowed lately of the Spanish, and it is not worth having.

I have observed *rent* as preterite of *rend :* improper : as *ment* would be of *mend.*

All too well, &c., the word *all* used needlessly   *All* the greater, &c. These expressions are among the many which have latterly been swept out of the servants' hall, who often say (no doubt), " I am all the better for my dinner."

Daresay is now written as one word.

Egotist should be *egoist :* to *doze* should not be written *dose,* as it often is.

I once was present when a scholar used the words *vexed question :* he was not laughed at, although he was thought a pedant for it ; many would willingly be thought pedants who never can be ; but they can more cheaply be thought affected, as they would be if they assumed this latinism. In our english sense, many a question vexes, none is vext. The sea is *vexatum* when it is tost hither and thither, to and fro ; but a question, however unsettled, has never been so called in good english.

" *Sought* his bedchamber " ; improper, because he knew where it was.   To *seek* is to go after what may or may not be found.   *Firstly* is no English.   To *gather* a rose is improper.   To gather *two* roses would be proper.   Better to *cull*, which may be said of choosing one out of several ;   *cull* is from the italian *cogliere*, originally in latin *colligare*.   But to us in our vernacular, the root is invisible : not so to *gather*, of which we are reminded by " *together*."

There is a bull of the largest Irish breed in nearly the most beautiful of Wordsworth's poems.[1]

> I lived upon what casual bounty yields,
> Now coldly given, *now utterly refused*.

The Irish need not cry out for their potatoes, if they can live upon what they can not get.

> The child is father of the man,

says Wordsworth, well and truly.   The verse animadverted on must have been written before the boy had begotten his parent.

What can be sillier than those verses of his which many have quoted with unsuspicious admiration ?

> A maid whom there was none to praise,
> And very few to love.

He might have written more properly if the rhyme and meter had allowed it,

> A maid whom there were none to love,
> And very few to praise.

For surely the few who loved her would praise her.   Here he makes love subordinate to praise : there were some who loved her, none (even of these) who praised her.   Readers of poetry hear the bells, and seldom mind what they are ringing for.   Where there is laxity there is inexactness.

Frequently there are solid knolls in the midst of Wordsworth's morass, but never did I expect to find so much animation, such vigour, such succinctness, as in the paragraph [2] beginning with

> All degrees and shapes of spurious form,

and ending with

> Left to herself, unheard of and unknown.

---

[1] " The Female Vagrant," *Lyrical Ballads*.   [2] The *Prelude*, iii.

ARCHDEACON HARE AND LANDOR

Here indeed the waggoner's frock drops off, and shows to our surprise the imperial purple underneath it. Here is the brevity and boldness of Cowper; here is heart and soul; here is the εἰκὼν βασιλική of Poetry.

I believe there are few, if any, who enjoy more heartily than I do, the best poetry of my contemporaries, or who have commended them both in private and in public with less parsimony and reserve. Several of them, as you know, are personally my friends, although we seldom meet. Perhaps in some I may desiderate the pure ideal of what is simply great. If we must not always look up at Theseus and the Amazons, we may however catch more frequent glimpses of the Graces, with their zones on, and their zones only. Amplification and diffuseness are the principal faults of those who are now standing the most prominent. Dilution does not always make a thing the clearer ; it may even cause turbidity.

ARCHDEACON HARE. Stifness is as bad as laxness. Pindar and Horace, Milton and Shakespeare, never caught the cramp in their mountain-streams : their movements are as easy as they are vigorous.

WALTER LANDOR. The strongest are the least subject to stifness. Diffuseness is often the weakness of vanity. The vain poet is of opinion that nothing of his can be too much : he sends to you basketful after basketful of juiceless fruit covered with scentless flowers.

ARCHDEACON HARE. Many an unlucky one is like the big and bouncing foot-ball, which is blown up in its cover by unseemly puffing, and serves only for the game of the day. I am half-inclined to take you to task, my dear friend, feeling confident and certain that I should do it without offence.

WALTER LANDOR. Without offence, but not without instruction. Here I am ready at the desk, with both hands down.

ARCHDEACON HARE. To be serious. Are you quite satisfied that you never have sought a pleasure in detecting and exposing the faults of authors, even good ones ?

WALTER LANDOR. I have here and there sought that pleasure, and found it. To discover a truth and to separate it from a falsehood, is surely an occupation worthy of the best intellect, and not at all unworthy of the best heart. Consider how few of our countrymen have done it, or attempted it, on works of criticism : how few of them have analyzed and compared. Without these two processes

25

there can be no sound judgement on any production of genius. We are accustomed to see the beadel limp up into the judge's chair ; to hear him begin with mock gravity, and to find him soon dropping it for his natural banter. He condemns with the black cap on, but we discover through its many holes and dissutures the uncombed wig. Southey is the first and almost the only one of our critics who moves between his intellect and his conscience, close to each.

ARCHDEACON HARE. How much better would it be if our reviewers and magazine-men would analyze, in this manner, to the extent of their abilities, and would weigh evidence before they pass sentence. But they appear to think that unless they hazard much they can win little ; while in fact they hazard and lose a great deal more than there is any possibility of their recovering. One rash decision ruins the judge's credit, which twenty correcter never can restore. Animosity, or perhaps something more ignoble, usually stimulates rampant inferiority against high desert.

I have never found you disconcerted by any injustice toward yourself ; not even by the assailants of this our Reformation.

WALTER LANDOR. If we know a minor, whose guardians and trustees have been robbing him of his patrimony, or misapplying it, or wearing out the land by bad tillage, would we not attempt to recover for him whatever we could ; and especially if we were intimate with the family, if we had enjoyed the shade of its venerable woods, the refreshing breezes from its winding streams, and had in our early days taken our walks among them for study, and in our still earlier gone into the depths of its forests for our recreation ?

ARCHDEACON HARE. Next in criminality to him who violates the laws of his country, is he who violates the language. In this he is a true patriot, and somewhat beside,

Qui consulta patrum qui leges juraque servat.[1]

Byron is among the defaulters. On Napoleon he says " Like *he* of Babylon." [2] " The *annal* of Gibbon." " I have *eat*," &c. There is a passage in Tacitus on a vain poet, Luterius, remarkably applicable to our lately fashionable one. " Studia illa, ut plena vecordiæ, ita inania et fluxa sunt : nec quidquam grave ac serium ex eo metuas qui, suorum ipse flagitiorum proditor, non virorum animis sed muliercularum adrepit." [3]

[1] Hor., *Ep.*, I, xvi. 41. [2] " Ode to Napoleon." [3] *Ann.*, iii. 50.

ARCHDEACON HARE AND LANDOR

WALTER LANDOR. It suits him perfectly. I would however pardon him some false grammar and some false sentiment, for his vigorous application of the scourge to the two monsters of dissimilar configuration who degraded and disgraced, at the same period, the two most illustrious nations in the world. The Ode against Napoleon is full of animation : against the other there is less of it ; for animation is incompatible with nausea. Byron had good action, but he tired by fretting, and tossing his head, and rearing.

ARCHDEACON HARE. Let reflections for a moment give way to recollections. In the morning we were interrupted in some observations on the aspirate.

WALTER LANDOR. Either I said, or was about to say, that the aspirate, wherever it is written, should be pronounced. If we say " *a* house," why not say " *a* hour " ? if " *a* horse," why not " *a* honour " ? Nobody says " *an* heavy load," " *an* heavenly joy," " *an* holy man," " *an* hermit," " *an* high place," " *an* huge monster," " *an* holly-bough," " *an* happy day." Let the minority yield here to the majority. Our capriciousness in admitting or rejecting the service of the aspirate was contracted from the French. The Italians, not wanting it, sent it off, and called it back merely for a mark discriminatory, for instance in the verb *Ho, hai, ha.*

ARCHDEACON HARE. You have been accused of *phonetic* spelling.

WALTER LANDOR. Inconsiderately, and with even less foundation than falsehood has usually under it. Nothing seems to me more grossly absurd, or more injurious to an ancient family, the stem of our words and thoughts. Such a scheme, about fourscore years ago, was propounded by Elphinstone : it has lately been reproduced, only to wither and die down again.

ARCHDEACON HARE. I always knew, and from yourself, that you are a " good hater " of innovation, and that your efforts were made strenuously on the opposite side, attempting to recover in our blurred palimpsests what was written there of old. We have dropt a great deal of what is good, as you just now have shown, and we have taken into our employment servants without a character, or with a worthless one. We adorn our new curtains with faded fringe, and embellish stout buckskin with point-lace.

WALTER LANDOR. After this conversation, if it ever should reach the public ear, I may be taken up for a brawl in the street, more serious than an attack on the new grammar-school.

27

ARCHDEACON HARE. What can you mean ? Taken up ? For a brawl ?

WALTER LANDOR. Little are you aware that I have lately been accused of a graver offence, and one committed in the dark.

ARCHDEACON HARE. And in the dark you leave me. Pray explain.

WALTER LANDOR. I am indited for perpetrating an *epic*.

ARCHDEACON HARE. Indeed ! I am glad to hear the announcement. And when does the cause come into court ? And who is the accuser ? And what are his grounds ?

WALTER LANDOR. Longer ago by some years than half a century, I wrote *Gebir*. The cause and circumstances I have detailed elsewhere.

ARCHDEACON HARE. Is this the epic ?

WALTER LANDOR. It appears so.

ARCHDEACON HARE. Already you look triumphant from that ancient car.

WALTER LANDOR. No truly ; I am too idle for a triumph : and the enemy's forces were so small that none could legitimately be decreed.

> Exoriare aliquis nostris ex ossibus ultor
> Qui façe barbaricos calamoque sequare colonos.[1]

> Surely shall some one come, alert and kind,
> With torch and quill to guide the blundering hind.

ARCHDEACON HARE. Clowns and boys and other idlers, if they see a head above a garden-wall, are apt to throw a pebble at it, which mischief they abstain from doing when the head is on their level and near.

WALTER LANDOR. Nobody reads this poem, I am told ; and nothing more likely.

ARCHDEACON HARE. Be that as it may. The most disappointed of its readers would be the reader who expected to find an epic in it. To the *epic* not only its certain spirit, but its certain form, is requisite ; and not only in the main body, but likewise in the minute articulations. I do not call *epic* that which is in lyric meter, nor indeed in any species of rhyme. The cap and bells should never surmount the helmet and breastplate ; Ariosto and Tasso are lyrical

---

[1] Virgil, *Æn.*, iv. 625; which reads: " Dardanios ferroque."

romancers. Your poem, which Southey tells us he took for a model, is in blank verse.

WALTER LANDOR. Southey, whom I never had known or corresponded with, hailed it loudly in the *Critical Review*, on its first appearance. He recommended it to Charles Wynne, Charles Wynne to the Hebers ; they to your uncle Shipley, Dean of St. Asaph's. Southey's splendid criticism, whatever may be the defects and deficiencies of the poem, must have attracted at the time some other readers ; yet I believe (though I never heard or inquired) that they were not numerous. Frere, Canning, and Bobus Smith were among them. Enough for me.

Within these few months, a wholesale dealer in the brittle crockery of market criticism has pickt up some shards of it, and stuck them in his shelves. Among them is my *Sea-shell*, which Wordsworth clapt into his pouch. There it became incrusted with a compost of mucus and shingle ; there it lost its " pearly hue within," and its memory of where it had abided.

ARCHDEACON HARE. But Wordsworth had the industry and skill to turn everything to some account.

WALTER LANDOR. Perfectly true. And he is indebted to me for more than the value of twenty *Shells :* he is indebted to me for praise, if not more profuse, yet surely more discriminating, than of those critics who were collected at wakes and hired by Party. Such hospital-nurses kill some children by starving, and others by pampering with unwholesome food.

ARCHDEACON HARE. I have often heard you express your admiration of Wordsworth ; and I never heard you complain, or notice, that he owed any thing to you.

WALTER LANDOR. Truly he owes me little. My shell may be among the prettiest on his mantelpiece, but a trifle it is at best. I often wish, in his longest poem, he had obtained an Inclosure-act, and subdivided it. What a number of delightful Idyls it would have afforded ! It is pity that a vapour of metaphysics should overhang and chill any portion of so beautiful a plain ; of which, however, the turf would be finer and the glebe solider for a moderate expenditure in draining and top-dressing.

ARCHDEACON HARE. Your predilections led you to rank Southey higher.

WALTER LANDOR. Wordsworth has not written three poems so

excellent as *Thalaba*, the *Curse of Kehama*, and *Roderic* ; nor indeed any poem exhibiting so great a variety of powers. Southey had abundance of wit and humour, of which Wordsworth, like greater men, such for instance as Goethe and Milton, was destitute. The present age will easily pardon me for placing here the German and the Englishman together : the future, I sadly fear, would, without some apology, be inexorable. If Wordsworth wants the diversity and invention of Southey, no less than the humour, he wants also the same geniality belonging in the same degree to Cowper, with terseness and succinctness.

ARCHDEACON HARE. You have often extolled, and in the presence of many, the beauty of his rural scenes and the truth of his rural characters.

WALTER LANDOR. And never will I forego an opportunity. In the delineation of such scenes and characters, far, infinitely far beneath him are Virgil and Theocritus. Yet surely it is an act of grievous cruelty, however unintentional, in those who thrust him into the same rank and file with Milton. He wants muscle, breadth of shoulder, and highth.

ARCHDEACON HARE. Sometimes he may be prosaic.

WALTER LANDOR. He slithers on the soft mud, and can not stop himself until he còmes down. In his poetry there is as much of prose as there is of poetry in the prose of Milton. But prose on certain occasions can bear a great deal of poetry : on the other hand, poetry sinks and swoons under a moderate weight of prose ; and neither fan nor burnt feather can bring her to herself again.

It is becoming and decorous that due honours be paid to Wordsworth ; undue have injured him. Discriminating praise mingled with calm censure is more beneficial than lavish praise without it. Respect him ; reverence him ; abstain from worshipping him. Remember, no ashes are lighter than those of incense, and few things burn out sooner.

ARCHDEACON HARE. It appears that you yourself, of late, have not suffered materially by the wafting of the thurible.

WALTER LANDOR. Faith ! I had quite forgotten what we were speaking about last.

It was about myself, I suspect, and the worthy at Edinburgh who *reviews* me. According to him, it appears that only two had read *Gebir*, namely, Southey and Mr. De Quincey. I have mentioned a

30

ARCHDEACON HARE AND LANDOR

few others ; I might have added Coleridge, to whom Southey lent it, and who praised it even more enthusiastically, until he once found Southey reciting a part of it in company : after which, I am told, he never mentioned it, or slightly. In the year of its publication Cary, translator of Dante, had praised it. His opinion of it I keep to myself, as one among the few which I value. This was long before Mr. De Quincey knew Southey. It is marvelous that a man of so retentive a memory, as Southey, should have forgotten a thing to which he himself had given its importance : it is less so that Mr. De Quincey imagined it, under the influence of that narcotic the effects of which he so ingenuously and so well described, before he exhibited this illustration.

He had another *imaginary conversation* with Southey, in which they agree that *Gebir* very much resembled the *Argonautics* of Valerius Flaccus. Hearing of this, about a twelvemonth ago, I attempted to read that poem, but was unsuccessful. Long before, and when my will was stronger, I foundered in the midst of Statius. Happily in my schooldays, I had mastered Lucan and Juvenal.

ARCHDEACON HARE. They are grandly declamatory : but declamation overlays and strangles poetry, and disfigures even satire.

WALTER LANDOR. Reserving the two mentioned, and Martial, I doubt whether the most speculative magazine-man would hazard five pounds for the same quantity of *english* poetry (rightly called *letter-press*) as all the other post-Ovidian poets have left behind. After the banishment of Ovid hardly a breath of pure poetry breathed over the *Campagna di Roma*. Declamation was spouted in flood-gate verse : Juvenal and Lucan are high in that school, in which, at the close of the poetical day, was heard the street cow-horn of Statius.

ARCHDEACON HARE. Even for the company of such as these, I think I would have left the Reeker in *Auld Reekie*. Flies are only the more troublesome and importunate for being driven off, and they will keep up with your horse, however hard you ride, without any speed or potency of their own.

WALTER LANDOR. True : but people who sell unsound wares, and use false scales and measures, ought to be pointed out and put down, although we ourselves may be rich enough to lose an ounce or two by their filching.

ARCHDEACON HARE. No one ever falls among a crowd of literary men without repenting of it sooner or later. You may encounter a

31

single hound outside the kennel, but there is danger if you enter in among them, even with a kind intention and a bland countenance.

WALTER LANDOR. It must be a dog in the distemper that raises up his spine at me. I have spoken favourably of many an author, undeservedly of none : therefore both at home and abroad I have received honorary visits from my countrymen and from foreners.

ARCHDEACON HARE. Possibly there may be some of them incontinent of the acrimonious humour pricking them in the paroxism of wit. I know not whether there be any indication of it in the soil under your shovel. Grains of wit, however, may sometimes be found in petulance, as grains of gold in quartz ; but petulance is not wit, nor quartz gold.

Are you aware how much thought you have here been throwing away ?

WALTER LANDOR. My dear friend ! thought is never thrown away : wherever it falls, or runs, or rests, it fertilizes. I speak not of that thought which has evil in it, or which tends to evil, but of that which is the exercise of intellect on the elevated and healthy training-ground of truth. We descend ; and as we descend, we may strike off the head of a thistle, or blow away the wandering seed of a dandelion which comes against the face, but, in a moment forgetting them totally, we carry home with us freshness and strength.

ARCHDEACON HARE. I have never known you, at any former time, take much trouble about your literary concerns.

WALTER LANDOR. Never have I descended to repell an attack, and never will ; but I must defend the understanding and consistency of a wiser and better man in Southey. Never have I feared that a little and loose petard would burst or unhinge the gates of my fortress, or that a light culverine at a vast distance below would dismantle or reach the battlements.

ARCHDEACON HARE. It is dangerous to break into a park where the paling is high, for it may be difficult to find the way out again, or to escape the penalty of transgression. You never before spoke a syllable about your *Shell.*

WALTER LANDOR. The swallow builds her nest under a Doric architrave, but does not build it of the same materials.

ARCHDEACON HARE. It is amusing to observe the off-hand facility and intrepid assurance with which small writers attack the greater, as small birds do, pursuing them the more vociferously the higher the flight. Milton stoopt and struck down two or three of these obstreperous chatterers, of which the feathers he scattered are all that remains ; and these are curiosities.

It is moroseness to scowl at the levity of impudence ; it is affability, not without wisdom, to be amused by it. Graver men, critics of note, have seen very indistinctly, where the sun has been too bright for them. Gifford, the translator of Juvenal, who was often so grave that ordinary people took him for judicious, thought wit the better part of Shakespeare, and in which alone he was superior to his contemporaries. Another finds him sadly deficient in his female characters. Johnson's ear was insensible to Milton's diapason ; and in his Life of Somervile he says,

" If blank verse be not tumid and gorgeous, it is crippled prose."

WALTER LANDOR. Johnson had somewhat of the medlar in his nature ; one side hard and austere, the other side unsound. We call him *affected* for his turgidity : this was not affected ; it was the most natural part of him. He hated both affectation and tameness.

ARCHDEACON HARE. Two things intolerable, whether in prose or poetry. Wordsworth is guiltless at least of affectation.

WALTER LANDOR. True ; but he often is as tame as an abbess's cat, which in kittenhood has undergone the same operation as the Holy Father's choristers.

ARCHDEACON HARE. Sometimes indeed he might be more succinct. A belt is good for the breath, and without it we fail in the long run. And yet a man will always be more lookt at whose dress flutters in the air than he whose dress sits tight upon him : but he will soon be left on the roadside. Wherever there is a word beyond what is requisite to express the meaning, that word must be peculiarly beautiful in itself or strikingly harmonious ; either of which qualities may be of some service in fixing the attention and enforcing the sentiment. But the proper word in the proper place seldom leaves anything to be desiderated on the score of harmony. The beauty of health and strength is more attractive and impressive than any beauty conferred by ornament. I know the delight you feel, not only in Milton's immortal verse, but (although less) in Wordsworth's.

WALTER LANDOR. A Mozart to a Handel ! But who is not charmed by the melody of Mozart ? Critics have their favourites ; and, like the same rank of people at elections, they chair one candidate and pelt another

IMAGINARY CONVERSATIONS : ENGLISH

ARCHDEACON HARE. A smaller object may be so placed before a greater as to intercept the view of it in its just proportions. This is the favourite manœuvre in the Review-field. Fierce malignity is growing out of date. Nothing but fairness is spoken of; regret at the exposure of faults, real or imaginary, has taken the place of derision, sarcasm, and arrogant condemnation. Nothing was wanting to Byron's consistency when he had exprest his contempt of Shakespeare.

WALTER LANDOR. Giffords, who sniffed at the unsavory skirts of Juvenal, and took delight in paddling among the bubbles of azote, no longer ply the trade of critics to the same advantage. Generosity, in truth or semblance, is expected and required. Chattertons may die in poverty and despair ; but Keatses are exposed no longer to a lingering death under that poison which paralyzes the heart, contempt.

ARCHDEACON HARE. In youth the appetite for fame is strongest. It is cruel and inhuman to withhold the sustenance which is necessary to the growth, if not the existence, of genius ; sympathy, encouragement, commendation. Praise is not fame ; but the praise of the intelligent is its precursor. *Vaticide* is no crime in the statute-book ; but a crime, and a heavy crime, it is : and the rescue of a poet from a murderous enemy, although there is no oaken crown decreed for it, is among the higher virtues.

WALTER LANDOR. Many will pass by ; many will take the other side ; many will cherish the less deserving ; but some one, considerate and compassionate, will raise up the neglected : and, where a strong hand does it, several less strong will presently be ready to help. Alas ! not always. There is nothing in the ruins of Rome which throws so chilling a shadow over the heart as the monument of Keats.

Our field of poetry at the present time is both wider and better cultivated than it has ever been. But if the tyrant of old who walked into the growing corn, to inculcate a lesson of *order* by striking off the heads of the higher poppies, were to enter ours, he would lay aside his stick, so nearly on a level is the crop. Every year there is more good poetry written now, in this our country, than was written between the *Metamorphoses* and the *Divina Commedia*. We walk no longer in the cast-off clothes of the ancients, often ill sewn at first, and now ill fitting. We have pulpier flesh, stouter

34

limbs, we take longer walks, explore wider fields, and surmount more craggy and more lofty eminences. From these let us take a leisurely look at Fancy and Imagination. Your friend Wordsworth was induced to divide his minor Poems under the separate heads of these two ; probably at the suggestion of Coleridge, who persuaded him, as he himself told me, to adopt the name of *Lyrical Ballads.* He was sorry, he said, that he took the advice. And well he might be ; for *lyre* and *ballad* belong not to the same age or the same people. It would have puzzled Coleridge to have drawn a strait boundary-line between the domains of Fancy and those of Imagination, on a careful survey of these pieces ; or perhaps to have given a satisfactory definition of their qualities.

ARCHDEACON HARE. Do you believe you yourself can ?

WALTER LANDOR. I doubt it. The face is not the same, but the resemblance is sisterly ; and, even by the oldest friends and intimates of the family, one is often taken for the other, so nearly are they alike. Fancy is Imagination in her youth and adolescence. Fancy is always excursive ; Imagination, not seldom, is sedate. It is the business of Imagination, in her maturity, to create and animate such Beings as are worthy of her plastic hand ; certainly not by invisible wires to put marionettes in motion, nor to pin butterflies on blotting-paper. Vigorous thought, elevated sentiment, just expression, developement of character, power to bring man out from the secret haunts of his soul, and to place him in strong outline against the sky, belong to Imagination. Fancy is thought to dwell among the Faeries and their congeners ; and they frequently lead the weak and ductile poet far astray. He is fond of playing at *little-go* among them ; and, when he grows bolder, he acts among the Witches and other such creatures ; but his hankering after the Faeries still continues. Their tiny rings, in which the intelligent see only the growth of fungusses, are no arena for action and passion. It was not in these circles that Homer and Æschylus and Dante strove.

ARCHDEACON HARE. But Shakespeare sometimes entered them, who, with infinitely greater power, moulded his composite and consistent Man, breathing into him an immortality never to be forfeited.

WALTER LANDOR. Shakespeare's full strength and activity were exerted on Macbeth and Othello : he trifled with Ariel and Titania ; he played with Caliban ; but no other would have thought of playing

35

with him, any more than of playing with Cerberus. Shakespeare and Milton and Chaucer have more imagination than any of those to whom the quality is peculiarly attributed. It is not inconsistent with vigour and gravity. There may be a large and effuse light without

the motes that people the sunbeams.

Imagination follows the steps of Homer throughout the Troad, from the ships on the strand to Priam and Helen on the city-wall : Imagination played with the baby Astyanax at the departure of Hector from Andromache, and was present at the noblest scene of the *Iliad,* where, to repeat a verse of Cowper's on Achilles, more beautiful than Homer's own,

his hand he placed
On the old man's hand, *and pusht it gently away.*

No less potently does Imagination urge Æschylus on, from the range of beacons to the bath of Agamemnon ; nor expand less potently the vulture's wing over the lacerated bosom on the rocks of Caucasus. With the earliest flowers of the freshly created earth Imagination strewed the nuptial couch of Eve. Not Ariel, nor Caliban, nor Witches who ruled the elements, but Eve, and Satan, and Prometheus, are the most wonderous and the most glorious of her works. Imagination takes the weaker hand of Virgil out of Dante's who grasps it, and guides the Florentine exile thro the triple world.

ARCHDEACON HARE. Whatever be your enthusiasm for the great old masters, you must often feel, if less of so strong an impulse, yet a cordial self-congratulation in having bestowed so many eulogies on poetical contemporaries, and on others whose genius is apart from poetry.

WALTER LANDOR. Indeed I do. Every meed of Justice is delivered out of her own full scale. The poets, and others who may rank with them, indeed all the great men, have borne toward me somewhat more than civility. The few rudenesses I have ever heard of, are from such as neither I nor you ever meet in society, and such as warm their fingers and stomachs round less ornamental hearths.

When they to whom we have been unknown, or indifferent, begin to speak a little well of us, we are sure to find some honest old friend ready to trim the balance. I have had occasion to smile at this.

36

ARCHDEACON HARE AND LANDOR

ARCHDEACON HARE. We sometimes stumble upon sly invidiousness and smouldering malignity, quite unexpectedly, and in places which we should have believed were above the influence of such malaria. When Prosperity pays to Wisdom her visit in state, would we not, rather than halloo the yard-dog against her, clear the way for her, and adorn the door with garlands ? How fond are people in general of clinging to a great man's foibles ! they can climb no higher. It is not the solid, it is the carious, that grubs feed upon.

WALTER LANDOR. The practice of barring out the master is still continued in the world's great schoolroom. Our sturdy boys do not fear a flogging ; they fear only a book or a lecture.

ARCHDEACON HARE. Authors are like cattle going to a fair ; those of the same field can never move on without butting one another.

WALTER LANDOR. It has been my fortune and felicity, from my earliest days, to have avoided all competitions. My tutor at Oxford could never persuade me to write a piece of Latin poetry for the Prize, earnest as he was that his pupil should be a winner at the forthcoming *Encœnia*. Poetry was always my amusement, prose my study and business. I have publisht five volumes of *Imaginary Conversations :* cut the worst of them thro the middle, and there will remain in this decimal fraction quite enough to satisfy my appetite for fame. I shall dine late ; but the dining-room will be well lighted, the guests few and select.

In this age of discovery it may haply be discovered, who first among our Cisalpine nations led Greek to converse like Greek, Roman like Roman, in poetry or prose. Gentlemen of fashion have patronized them occasionally, have taken them under the arm, have recommended their own tailor, their own perfumer, and have lighted a cigar for them from their own at the door of the *Traveler's* or *Athenæum :* there they parted.

ARCHDEACON HARE. Before we go into the house again, let me revert to what you seem to have forgotten, the hasty and inaccurate remarks on *Gebir*.

WALTER LANDOR. It is hardly worth our while. Evidently they were written by a very young person, who with a little encouragement, and induced to place his confidence in somewhat safer investment than himself, may presently do better things.

ARCHDEACON HARE. Southey too, I remember, calls the poem in some parts obscure.

37

IMAGINARY CONVERSATIONS : ENGLISH

WALTER LANDOR. It must be, if Southey found it so. I never thought of asking him where lies the obscurity: I would have attempted to correct whatever he disapproved.

ARCHDEACON HARE. He himself, the clearest of writers, professes that he imitated your versification : and the style of his *Colloquies* is in some degree modified by yours.

WALTER LANDOR. Little cause had he for preferring any other to his own.

Perhaps the *indictum ore alio* is my obscurity. Goethe is acknowledged by his highest admirers to be obscure in several places ; which he thinks a poet may and should be occasionally. I differ from him, and would avoid it everywhere : he could see in the dark. This great poet carries it with him so far as into *Epigram*. I now regret that I profited so little by the calm acuteness of Southey. In what poet of the last nineteen centuries, who has written so much, is there less intermixture of prose, or less contamination of conceit ? in what critic, who has criticized so many, less of severity or assumption ?

I would never fly for shelter under the strongest wing : but you know that commentators, age after age, have found obscurities in Pindar, in Dante, and in Shakespeare.

ARCHDEACON HARE. And it is not in every place the effect of time. You have been accused, I hear, either by this writer or some such another, of *turgidity*.

WALTER LANDOR. Certainly by this : do not imagine there is anywhere such another.

ARCHDEACON HARE. Without a compliment, no poet of ours is less turgid. Guests may dispense with potage and puff-paste, with radishes and water-cresses, with salad and cream-cheese, who " *implentur veteris bacchi pinguisque ferinæ*."

WALTER LANDOR. Encouraged by your commendation, let me read to you (for I think I placed it this evening in my pocket) what was transcribed for me as a curiosity out of the same *Article*. Yes ; here it is.

" His great defect is a certain crudeness of the judgment, implied in the selection of the subject matter, and a further want of skill and perspicuity in the treatment. Except in a few passages, it has none of those peculiar graces of style and sentiment which render the writings of our more prominent modern authors so generally delightful."

38

ARCHDEACON HARE AND LANDOR

ARCHDEACON HARE. Opinion on most matters, but chiefly on literary, and above all on poetical, seems to me like an empty egg-shell in a duck-pond, turned on its stagnant water by the slightest breath of air ; at one moment the crackt side nearer to sight, at another the sounder, but the emptiness at all times visible.

Is your detractor a brother poet ?

WALTER LANDOR. An incipient one he may be. Poets in that stage of existence, subject to sad maladies, kick hard for life and scratch the nurse's face. Like some trees, fir trees for instance, they must attain a certain highth and girth before they are service-able or sightly.

ARCHDEACON HARE. The weakest wines fall soonest into the acetous fermentation ; the more generous retain their sweetness with their strength. Somewhat of this diversity is observable in smaller wits and greater, more especially in the warm climate where poetry is the cultivation.

WALTER LANDOR. The ancients often hung their trophies on obtruncated and rotten trees : we may do the like at present, leaving our enemies for sepulture.

ARCHDEACON HARE. Envy of pre-eminence is universal and ever-lasting. Little men, whenever they find an opportunity, follow the steps of greater in this dark declivity. The apple of Discord was full-grown soon after the Creation. It fell between the two first brothers in the garden of Eden : it fell between two later on the plain of Thebes. Narrow was the interval, when again it gleamed portentously on the short grass of Ida. It rolled into the palace of Pella, dividing Philip and " Philip's godlike son " : it followed that insatiable youth to the extremities of his conquests, and even to his sepulcher ; then it broke the invincible phalanx and scattered the captains wide apart. It lay in the gates of Carthage, so that they could not close against the enemy : it lay between the generous and agnate families of Scipio and Gracchus. Marius and Sulla, Julius and Pompeius, Octavius and Antonius, were not the last who ex-perienced its fatal malignity. King imprisoned king, emperor stabbed emperor, pope poisoned pope, contending for God's vicegerency. The roll-call of their names, with a cross against each, is rotting in the lumber-room of History. Do not wonder then if one of the rabble runs after you from the hustings, and, committing no worse mischief, snatches at the colours in your hatband.

39

IMAGINARY CONVERSATIONS : ENGLISH

WALTER LANDOR. Others have snatcht more. My quarry lies upon a high common a good way from the public road, and everybody takes out of it what he pleases " with privy paw, and nothing said " beyond " *a curse on the old fellow ! how hard his granite is, one can never make it fit.*" This is all I get of quitrent or acknowledgment. I know of a poacher who noosed a rabbit on my warren, and I am told he made such a fricassee of it that there was no taste of rabbit or sauce. I never had him taken up : he is at large, drest in new clothes, and worth money.

ARCHDEACON HARE. Your manors are extensive, comprehending

> Prata, arva, ingentes sylvas, saltusque paludesque
> Usque ad oceanum.[1]

WALTER LANDOR. I never drive the poor away if they come after dry sticks only, but they must not with impunity lop or burn my plantations.

ARCHDEACON HARE. I regret that your correspondent was sickened or tired of transcribing.

WALTER LANDOR. Here is another slip from the same crabtree. It is objected that most of my poems are occasional.

ARCHDEACON HARE. In number they may be, but in quantity of material I doubt whether they constitute a seventh. We will look presently, and we shall find perhaps that the gentleman is unlucky at his game of hazard.

WALTER LANDOR. Certainly his play is not deep. We who are sober dare not sit down at a table where a character may be lost at a cast : they alone are so courageous who have nothing to be seized on.

ARCHDEACON HARE. The gentleman sweeps the cloth with little caution and less calculation. Of your poems the smaller alone are occasional : now not only are the smaller, but the best, of Catullus and Horace, and all of Pindar. Were not the speeches of Lysias, Æschines, Demosthenes, occasional ? Draw nearer home. What but occasional were the *Letters of Junius ?* Materiam superabat opus.[2]

WALTER LANDOR. True. The ministers and their king are now mould and worms ; they were little better when above-ground ; but

---

[1] Catullus, cxv. 5.   [2] Ovid, *Metam.*, ii. 5.

ARCHDEACON HARE AND LANDOR

the bag-wig and point-lace of *Junius* are suspended aloft upon a golden peg for curiosity and admiration.

ARCHDEACON HARE. Regarding the occasional in poetry; is there less merit in taking and treating what is before us, than in seeking and wandering through an open field as we would for mushrooms ?

WALTER LANDOR. I stand out a rude rock in the middle of a river, with no exotic or parasitical plant on it, and few others. Eddies and dimples and froth and bubbles pass rapidly by, without shaking me. Here indeed is little room for pic-nic and polka.

ARCHDEACON HARE. Praise and censure are received by you with nearly the same indifference.

WALTER LANDOR. Not yours. Praise on poetry, said to be the most exhilarating of all, affects my brain but little. Certainly I never attempted to snatch " the peculiar graces so generally delightful." My rusticity has at least thus much of modesty in it.

ARCHDEACON HARE.

> The richest flowers have not most honey-cells.
> You seldom find the bee about the rose,
> Oftener the beetle eating into it.
> The violet less attracts the noisy hum
> Than the minute and poisonous bloom of box.
> Poets know this ; Nature's invited guests
> Draw near and note it down and ponder it ;
> The idler sees it, sees unheedingly,
> Unheedingly the rifler of the hive.

Is your critic wiser, more experienced, and of a more poetical mind than Southey ? *Utri horum creditis, Quirites ?*

Vanity and presumption are not always the worst parts of the man they take possession of, although they are usually the most prominent. Malignity sticks as closely to him, and keeps more cautiously out of sight. Sorry I have often been to see a fellow Christian, one of much intellect and much worth, one charitable to the poor, one attendant on the sick, one compassionate with the sufferer, one who never is excited to anger but by another's wrongs, enjoying a secret pleasure in saying unpleasant things at no call of duty ; inflicting wounds which may be long before they heal ; and not only to those who are unfriendly or unknown, but likewise to the nearest and the friendliest. Meanwhile those who perhaps are less observant of our ritual, not only abstain from so sinful an indulgence, but appear to be guided in their demeanour by the less imperative and less authoritative dictate of Philosophy. I need not exhort or advise you, who have always done it, to disregard the insignificant and obscure, so distant from you, so incapable of approaching you. Only look before you at this instant; and receive a lesson from Nature, who is able and ready at all times to teach us, and to teach men wiser than we are. Unwholesome exhalations creep over the low marshes of Pevensey, but they ascend not to Beachyhead nor to Hurstmonceaux.

IMAGINARY CONVERSATIONS

SCOTTISH

I. WILLIAM WALLACE AND KING EDWARD I.

(*Imag. Convers.*, iv., 1829 ; *Wks.*, i., 1846 ; iii., 1876.)

EDWARD. Whom seest thou here ?

WALLACE. The King of England.

EDWARD. And thou abasest not thy head before the majesty of the sceptre !

WALLACE. I did.

EDWARD. I marked it not.

WALLACE. God beheld when I did it ; and he knoweth, as doth King Edward, how devoutly in my heart's strength I fought for it.

EDWARD. Robber ! for what sceptre ? who commissioned thee ?

WALLACE. My country.

EDWARD. Thou liest : there is no country where there is no king.

WALLACE. Sir, it were unbecoming to ask in this palace, why there is no king in my country.

EDWARD. To spare thy modesty, then, I will inform thee. Because thy kingdom is mine. Thou hast rebelled against me ; thou hast presumed even to carry arms against both of those nobles, Bruce and Cummin, who contended for the Scottish throne, and with somewhat indeed of lawyer's likelihood.

WALLACE. They placed the Scottish throne under the English.

EDWARD. Audacious churl ! is it not meet ?

WALLACE. In Scotland we think otherwise.

EDWARD. Rebels do, subverters of order, low ignorant knaves, without any stake in the country. It hath pleased God to bless my arms : what further manifestation of our just claims demandest thou ? Silence becomes thee.

43

WALLACE. Where God is named. What is now to the right bank of a river, is to the left when we have crossed it and look round.

EDWARD. Thou wouldst be witty truly! Who was wittiest, thou or I, when thy companion Menteith delivered thee into my hands?

WALLACE. Unworthy companions are not the peculiar curse of private men. I chose not Menteith for his treachery, nor rewarded him for it. Sir, I have contended with you face to face; but would not here: your glory eclipses mine, if this be glory.

EDWARD. So, thou wouldst place thyself on a level with princes!

WALLACE. Willingly, if they attacked my country; and above them.

EDWARD. Dost thou remember the Carron-side, when your army was beaten and dispersed?

WALLACE. By the defection of Cummin and the arrogance of Stuart.

EDWARD. Recollectest thou the colloquy that Bruce condescended to hold with thee across the river?

WALLACE. I do, sir. Why would not he, being your soldier, and fighting loyally against his native land, pass the water, and exterminate an army so beaten and dispersed? The saddle-skirts had been rather the stiffer on the morrow, but he might have never felt them. Why not finish the business at once?

EDWARD. He wished to persuade thee, loose reviler, that thy resistance was useless.

WALLACE. He might have made himself heard better if he had come across.

EDWARD. No trifling; no arguing with me; no remarks here, caitiff! Thou canst not any longer be ignorant that he hath slain his competitor, Cummin; that my troops surround him; and that he perhaps may now repent the levity of his reproaches against thee. I may myself have said a hasty word or two—but thou hast nettled me. My anger soon passes. I never punish in an enemy anything else than obstinacy. I did not counsel the accusations and malignant taunts of Bruce.

WALLACE. Sir, I do not bear them in mind.

EDWARD. No?

WALLACE. Indeed I neither do nor would.

EDWARD. Dull wretch! I should never forget such. I can make

allowances ; I am a king. I would flay him alive for half of them, and make him swallow back the other half without his skin.

WALLACE. Few have a right to punish, all to pardon.

EDWARD. I perceive that thou hast at last some glimmering of shame ; and adversity makes thee Christian-like.

WALLACE. Adversity then, in exercising her power, loses her name and features. King Edward ! thou hast raised me among men. Without thy banners and bows in array against me, I had sunk into utter forgetfulness. Thanks to thee for placing me, eternally, where no strength of mine could otherwise have borne me ! Thanks to thee for bathing my spirit in deep thoughts, in refreshing calm, in sacred stillness ! This, O king, is the bath for knighthood : after this it may feast, and hear bold and sweet voices, and mount to its repose.

I thought it hard to be seized and bound and betrayed, by those in whom I trusted. I grieved that a valiant soldier (such is Menteith) should act so. Unhappily ! he must now avoid all men's discourses. 'Twill pierce his heart to hear censures on the disloyal ; and praises on the loyal will dry up its innermost drop. Two friends can never more embrace in his presence, but he shall curse them in the bitterness of his soul, and his sword shall spring up to cleave them. " Alas ! " will he say to himself, " is it thus ! was it thus when I drew it for my country ! "

EDWARD. Think now of other matters : think, what I suggested, of thy reproaches.[1]

WALLACE. I have none to make myself.

EDWARD. Be it so : I did not talk about that any longer.

WALLACE. What others then can touch or reach me ?

EDWARD. Such as Bruce's.

WALLACE. Reproaches they were not : for none were ever cast against me : but taunts they were, not unmingled with invitations.

EDWARD. The same invitations, and much greater, I now repeat. Thou shalt govern Scotland for me.

WALLACE. Scotland, sir, shall be governed for none : she is old enough to stand by herself, and to stand upright : the blows she hath received have not broken her loins.

EDWARD. Come, come, Wallace ! thou hast sense and spirit :

[1] 1st ed. reads : " reproaches, which no doubt thou deemest unmerited. WALLACE. I have none," etc.

45

confess to me fairly that, if thou wert at liberty, thou wouldst gladly make Bruce regret his ill-treatment of thee.

WALLACE. Well then, I do confess it.

EDWARD. Something would I myself hazard ; not too much ; but prudently and handsomely. Tell me now plainly, for I love plain-speaking and everything free and open, in what manner thou wouldst set about it ; and perhaps, God willing, I may provide the means.

WALLACE. Sir, you certainly would not : it little suits your temper and disposition.

EDWARD. Faith ! not so little as thou supposest. Magnanimity and long-suffering have grown upon me, and well become me ; but they have not produced all the good I might have expected from them. Joyfully as I would try them again, at any proper opportunity, there is nothing I am not bound to do, in dearness to my people, to rid myself of an enemy.

In my mind, no expressions could be more insulting than Bruce's, when he accused thee, a low and vulgar man (how canst thou help that ?), of wishing to possess the crown.

WALLACE. He was right.

EDWARD. How ! astonishment ! Thou wouldst then have usurped the sovereignty !

WALLACE. I pòssessed a greater power by war than peace could ever give me ; yet I invited and exhorted the legitimate heir of the throne to fight for it and receive it. If there is any satisfaction or gratification in being the envy of men, I had enough and greatly more than enough of it, when even those I love envied me : what would have been my portion of it, had I possessed that which never should have been mine !

EDWARD. Why then sayest thou that Bruce was right ?

WALLACE. He judged, as most men do, from his own feelings. Many have worn crowns ; some have deserved them : I have done neither.

EDWARD. Return to Scotland ; bring me Bruce's head back ; and rule the kingdom as viceroy.

WALLACE. I would rather make him rue his words against me, and hear him.

EDWARD. Thou shalt.

WALLACE. Believe me, sir, you would repent of your permission.

EDWARD. No, by the saints !

46

WALLACE AND KING EDWARD I.

WALLACE. You would indeed, sir.

EDWARD. Go, and try me : do not hesitate : I see thou art half inclined : I may never make the same offer again.

WALLACE. I will not go.

EDWARD. Weak wavering man ! hath imprisonment in one day or two wrought such a change in thee ?

WALLACE. Slavery soon does it : but I am, and will ever be, unchanged.

EDWARD. It was not well, nor by my order, that thou wert dragged along the road, barefooted and bareheaded, while it snowed throughout all the journey.

WALLACE. Certainly, sir, you did not order it to snow from the latter days of December till the middle of January ; but whatever else was done, if my guard spake the truth——

EDWARD. He lied, he lied, he lied.

WALLACE. —or the warrant he showed me is authentic, was done according to your royal order.

EDWARD. What ! are my officers turned into constables ? base varlets ! It must have seemed hard, Wallace !

WALLACE. Not that indeed ; for I went barefooted in my youth, and have mostly been bareheaded when I have not been in battle. But to be thrust and shoven into the court-yard ; to shiver under the pent-house from which the wind had blown the thatch, while the blazing fire within made the snow upon the opposite roof redden like the dawn ; to wax faint, ahungered and athirst, when, within arm's length of me, men pushed the full cup away, and would drink no more ; to that I had never been accustomed in my country. The dogs, honester and kinder folks than most, but rather dull in the love of hospitality, unless in the beginning some pains are taken with them by their masters, tore my scant gear ; and then your soldiers felt their contempt more natural and easy. The poor curs had done for them what their betters could not do ; and the bolder of the company looked hard in my face, to see if I were really the same man.

EDWARD. O the rude rogues ! that was too bad.

WALLACE. The worst was this. Children and women, fathers and sons, came running down the hills, some sinking knee-deep in the incrusted snow, others tripping lightly over it, to celebrate the nativity of our blessed Lord. They entreated, and the good priest likewise, that I might be led forth into the church, and might kneel

47

down amid them. " Off," cried the guard ; " would ye plead for Wallace the traitor ? " I saw them tremble, for it was treason in them, and then came my grief upon me, and bore hard. They lifted up their eyes to heaven ; and it gave me strength.

EDWARD. Thou shalt not, I swear to thee, march back in such plight.

WALLACE. I will not, I swear to thee, march a traitor.

EDWARD. Right ! right ! I can trust thee—more than half already. Bruce is the traitor ; the worst of the two ; he raises the country against me. Go ; encompass him, entrap him, quell him.

Sweetheart ! thou hast a rare fancy, a youth's love at first sight, for thy chains : unwilling to barter them for liberty, for country, for revenge, for honour.

WALLACE. Honour and revenge,[1] such as I have carried in my bosom, are very dear to me ! For liberty and country I have often shed my blood, and, if more is wanting, take it. My heart is no better than a wooden cup, whereof the homely liquor a royal hand would cast away indifferently. There once were those who pledged it ! where are they ? Forgive my repining, O God ! Enough, if they are not here.

EDWARD. Nay, nay, Wallace ! thou wrongest me. Thou art a brave man. I do not like to see those irons about thy wrists : they are too broad and tight : they have bruised thee cruelly.

WALLACE. Methinks there was no necessity to have hammered the rivets on quite so hard : and the fellow who did it, needed not to look over his shoulder so often while he was about it, telling the people, " This is Wallace." Wrist or iron he and his hammer cared not.

EDWARD. I am mightily taken with the fancy of seeing thee mortify Bruce. Thou shalt do it : let me have thy plan.[2]

---

[1] 1st ed. reads : " The two latter " (for " Honour and revenge ") and " the two former " (for " liberty and country ").

[2] 1st ed. reads : " plan. WALLACE. Sir, I have none worthy of your participation. EDWARD. Thou formest the best possible in one moment, and executest them in another. WALLACE. Peradventure the only one I could devise and execute, in this contingency, might not please you. EDWARD. It would, beyond measure, I promise thee : set about it instantly : I must enjoy it before I rest. Tell it me, tell it me. WALLACE. Must I ? EDWARD. Thou must : I am faint with waiting. WALLACE. I would go unto him bareheaded : I would kiss his hand. EDWARD. Nothing can be better : wary, provident, deep. WALLACE. I would lead him before the altar, if my entreaty could do it.—EDWARD. No, no, no !— unless in case of necessity. WALLACE. I would adjure him by the Lord of Hosts,

WALLACE AND KING EDWARD I.

the preserver of Scotland—— EDWARD. No harm in that. WALLACE. —to pity his country—— EDWARD. Ay ; it would vex him to reflect on what a state it is in at present. WALLACE. —and to proclaim a traitor to his king and God every Scotchman who abandons or despairs of her. EDWARD. What is this ? Why would it hurt him ? I comprehend not half the stratagem. How ! thy limbs swell longer, thy stature higher.—Thou scornest, thou scoffest, thou defiest me ! a prisoner ! a bondman ! By the Holy Ghost ! the hurdle shall croak under thee tomorrow. WALLACE. Tomorrow ! EDWARD. Tomorrow ; I repeat it. WALLACE. So soon ? EDWARD. Yea, by the rood ! no later. WALLACE. King Edward, I never thought to thank thee. EDWARD. What audacious insurgent pride ! what villanous loftiness ! By all the saints of heaven ! every town in England shall have a fair sight of thee, more or less ; hand or foot, brisket or buttock, heart or liver. WALLACE. They should have seen me, King of England, to greater advantage, if thy sword alone had been against me. EDWARD. To-morrow thy tongue, I trow, shall wag less bravely, tho' it have a good spear to support it. I will render thee a terror to thy riotous gang. The raven shall take a text from thee and preach over thee, and merry Carlisle shall ring the bells after the service. WALLACE. Thou needest not send branch nor bough nor cutting to Carlisle : that city, from autumn to spring, hath beheld the tree nod in its glory, and feared lest it sweep her walls. EDWARD. Sirrah ! where I am, mark me, there is but one greater. WALLACE. Thou hast endeavoured to make another, and wilt almost accomplish it. EDWARD. Guards ! away with him.—A traitor's doom awaits thee. WALLACE. Because I would not be one. EDWARD. Laughter, too, and lewd mockery. Carry him back to prison : cord him ! pinion him ! cart him ! WALLACE. Thou followest me to death, less willingly, and slower."

II. MARY AND BOTHWELL

(*Wks.*, ii., 1846 ; *Wks.*, v., 1876.)

MARY. Bothwell ! Bothwell ! what would you have ? I can hardly believe my senses. It was wrong, it was very wrong indeed, to commit such an outrage. You forget my condition, my station, and what you owe me—the allegiance, the duty——

BOTHWELL. Nay, nay, my gracious queen ! I thought of nothing else all our ride. What a sweet fresh colour it has given my royal mistress ! O ! could the ugly Elizabeth but see it ! I should hail you queen of England the next hour.

MARY. How dare you call my cousin ugly ? and to my face ! And do you think she would give the crown of England to look at me ? O you silly man ! But what can you mean ?

BOTHWELL. I mean, she would burst and crack at it, like a dry and gnarly log of mountain-ash on a Christmas hearth.

MARY. At me-! at my colour ! I can not help laughing at your absurdity, most wicked, flattering, deceiving creature !

BOTHWELL. I flatter ! I deceive ! I never try to do what I am likely to fail in : here I must : here all must.

MARY. I wish you had indeed failed altogether.

BOTHWELL. So then, my royal dove ! I did not quite ?

MARY. Impudent man ! go away.

Ah Bothwell ! you are now a traitor after this. They would treat you like one. The laws call it abduction—and God knows what beside.

BOTHWELL. Treat me like a traitor ! me ! the truest man among them. Yea, if I would let them, and this fair hand could sign it.

MARY. O heaven ! Do not talk so ; you make me very sad. I will never be so cruel to you as you have been to me.

BOTHWELL. The laws too ; the laws forsooth ! Neither in our country, nor in any other, do the laws touch anything higher than the collar of the most diminutive thief : and a lawyer is

50

always at hand to change his coat and character with him for a groat.

MARY. With what derision and scorn you speak of laws and lawyers ! You little know how vindictive they are.

BOTHWELL. Faith ! we are not well acquainted ; but I know enough of them to know that.

MARY. Are not you afraid ?

BOTHWELL. I tremble in the presence of majesty and beauty. Where they are, there lies my law. I do confess I am afraid, and hugely ; for I feel hard knockings (there must surely be all the Pandects) where my heart was lately.

MARY. You never had any heart, or you would not have treated me in this manner.

BOTHWELL. You shall want nothing with me : you shall never pine after the past.

MARY. Ah but ! ah but ! indeed, indeed, good Bothwell ! he was very handsome ; and you must acknowledge it—if he had only been less cross and jealous and wayward and childish——

BOTHWELL. Too childish by half for you, fair lady ! and he was all those other little things beside.

MARY. What is over is over ! God forgive you, bad man ! Sinner ! serpent ! it was all you. And you dare smile ! Shame upon you, varlet ! Yes ; now you look as you should do. Nobody ought to be more contrite. You may speak again, if you will only speak to the purpose. Come ; no wicked thoughts ! I mean if you will speak reasonably. But you really are a very, very wicked man indeed.

BOTHWELL. Happy the man who hears those blessed words ! they grow but on soft sweet lips, fresh pouting from ardent pressure.

MARY. If you presume to talk so, I will kill myself. Are you not ashamed ?

BOTHWELL. My blushes quite consume me : I feel my hair crackle on my head : my beard would burn my fingers.

MARY. I will not laugh, sirrah !

BOTHWELL. No, my most gracious lady ! in mercy stop half-way ! that smile is quite sufficient.

MARY. Do you fancy I am capable of smiling ? I am quite serious. You have carried me away, and now you have nothing to do but to take me back again.

BOTHWELL. It would be dangerous : you have too many enemies.

MARY. I do not mind them while you are with me. Am I wild? You have frightened me so I scarcely know what I say.

BOTHWELL. A part of your understanding, most gracious lady! seems at last to have fallen on me.

MARY. Whither now would you carry me? You know it is quite against my will : absolute downright force.

BOTHWELL. Pardon, sweet lady! pardon my excess of zeal and devotion, my unutterable——

MARY. What?

BOTHWELL. Love.

MARY. A subject's is loyalty. Love indeed!

BOTHWELL. Let me perish, but not against an iceberg.

MARY. Ah, bold cruel man! this is scoffing. Does it end *so!*

BOTHWELL. Nay, never let it end *so;* never let it end at all; let one thing under heaven be eternal.

MARY. As if I, so helpless a creature, could order it.

BOTHWELL. What have the Powers above denied you?

MARY. Happiness, innocence, peace. No, they did not deny them. Bothwell! Bothwell! they were mine; were they not?

BOTHWELL. And good things they are, no doubt; but there are other good things beside; all which you possess, and these too. These should not always be shut up in the casket. Where there are peace and happiness, there is sure to be innocence; for what else can anyone wish? but those who can bring them into the hearts of others, and will not, I never will call innocent. I do not remember that any living person has entreated me and met with a refusal.

MARY. Ah! such men may be beloved, but can not love. What is that to me? It is unbecoming in me to reason with a profligate, or to listen any longer. You have often run then into such courses?

BOTHWELL. Alas! from my youth upward I have always been liable to these paroxysms.

MARY. For shame! I do not understand a single word of what you are saying. Again I ask you, and I insist upon an answer, whither are you conducting me?

MARY AND BOTHWELL

BOTHWELL. To freedom, to safety, to the protection of a dutiful subject, to the burning heart of a gallant man.

MARY. I am frightened out of my senses at the mere mention of any such things. What can you possibly mean ? I never knew the like. I will not hear of it, you rebel ! And you dare already——

BOTHWELL. Do you look so sternly on me, when you yourself have reduced me to this extremity ? And now, worse ! worse ! do you deprive me of the last breath, by turning away from me those eyes, the bright unerring stars of my destiny ?

MARY. If they had any power (but they have none !) I would strike you almost dead with them for that audacity. Again ? O madman ! madman ! madman !

BOTHWELL. To mistake the lips for the hand ! hallucination !

MARY. Now if you should (and you must !) be overtaken !

BOTHWELL. You would deliver me up to death and ignominy ?

MARY. Our pure religion teaches us forgiveness.

BOTHWELL.

> Then by my troth is it pure and bright
> As a pewter plate on a Saturday night.

Here is a stave of my own to its honour and glory.

MARY. You sing too ?

BOTHWELL. Yes ; but I am no tenor.

MARY (aside). Ah ! sweet soul ! thou * wert gentle, fond, and faithful !

BOTHWELL (catching the last word). Capital for the faithful : and moreover it is the cleverest and rarest religion in the world. Few, even of the adventurously pious, so far interfere with the attributes of the Almighty as to take pardon into their own hands—unless for offences against others. There indeed they find as little difficulty in practising as in preaching.

MARY. I am quite edified at seeing you grow so serious. I once heard that you had abandoned the religion of your ancestors.

BOTHWELL. I did not abandon it ; it dropped off me unaware. Now to prove my constancy, I never would take another. It is hard that a man like me should be accused of irreligion. They may

* Thinking of Rizzio.—W. S. L.

do anything with me they like, if they will only let me be quiet. I am long-suffering : I never preach again.

MARY. Well ; at least you have not fallen into heresy ? you are not malignant ?

BOTHWELL. By Jupiter ! no ; neither the one nor the other. Sweet gracious lady ! how could you suspect me ?

MARY. Because you men are so violent and so fond of change. You will never hear reason ; you will never do your duty.

BOTHWELL. By the stars above ! I will do mine before I ever presume to pray again.

MARY. And so, you dare to swear and laugh in my presence ! I do really think, Bothwell, you are one of the most impudent men I ever met withal.

BOTHWELL. Ah, my beloved lady !

MARY. Stop, stop ! I shall not let you say that.

BOTHWELL. My most gracious queen and mistress !

MARY. You are now, I believe, within the rules and regulations —that is, if you would not look up to me in such a very odd way. Modest men always look down on the eyelashes, not between them.

BOTHWELL. Happy the modest men, if they do.

MARY. There !˙now you look exactly as you should always.

BOTHWELL. Faint as I am and sinking betwixt fear and love, I feel that, by thus taking my hand, your Highness in part forgives and entirely pities the most unfortunate of your servants. For surely he is the most unfortunate, who, having ventured the most to serve you, has given you thereby the most offence. I do not say I hazarded my freedom ; it was lost when I first beheld you : I do not say I hazarded my life ; I had none until to-day : and who dares touch it on the altar where I devote it. Lady ! vouchsafe to hear me !

MARY. What a rough hand you have, Bothwell ! what a heavy one ! and (holy Virgin !) what a vastly broad one ; it would cover I don't know what ! and what a briary bower of hair over-arching it ! Curious ! it is quite red all over ; everywhere but where there is this long scar ; and these two ugly warts. Do I hurt you ?

BOTHWELL. My heart and every fibre feel it, but can well bear it.

MARY. How much whiter the back of the hand is, for a moment,

54

by just passing two fingers over it! look! But really warts are frightful things; and scars not much better. And yet there are silly girls who, when they have nothing else to think about, could kiss them.

BOTHWELL. Ay, ay; but be girls as silly as they will, I never let them play such idle tricks with me.

MARY. I am glad to hear it: I fancied you had said something very different: you must not joke; it vexes me.

BOTHWELL. The warts will vanish under the royal touch. As for the scar, I would not lose the scar for the crown of Scotland, in defence whereof I fairly won it.

MARY. O! you are a very brave man, but a very bold one.

BOTHWELL. Illiterate and ignorant as I am, I would gladly learn from the best-informed and most intellectual of God's creatures, where lies the difference.

MARY. I don't know, I don't know; I am quite bewildered. Move your hand off my knee. Do not lay your cheek there, sir!

O Bothwell! I am tired to death. Take me back! O take me back! pray do! if you have any pity.

BOTHWELL. Would your Highness be pleased to repose awhile, and remain by yourself in a chamber up-stairs?

MARY. I think it might do me good.

BOTHWELL. May I order the trustiest of the handmaidens to attend your Highness?

MARY. You may. Go, go; I thought I desired you before not to look up at me in that manner. Thank you, gentle Bothwell! I did not speak too harshly, did I? If I did, you may kiss my hand.

BOTHWELL. If this scar and these warts (which are fast disappearing, I perceive) are become less frightful to your Highness, might the humblest of your servitors crave permission to conduct your Highness nigh unto the chamber-door?

MARY. Ah me! where are my own women? where are my ushers?

BOTHWELL. Your Highness, in all your wrongs and straits, has the appointment of one supernumerary.

MARY. Be it so: I can not help myself, as you know; and the blame is all yours.

BOTHWELL. When your Highness is ready to receive the services of the handmaiden, how may it please your Highness that she shall know it ?

MARY. Let her tap twice with her knuckles : I can open the door myself—or she may.

BOTHWELL. My queen's most gracious commands shall be duly executed.

END OF THE SCOTTISH CONVERSATIONS

56

IMAGINARY CONVERSATIONS

IRISH

I. ESSEX AND SPENSER

(With *Citation of William Shakespeare*, 1834; *Wks.*, ii., 1846; v., 1876.)

ESSEX. Instantly on hearing of thy arrival from Ireland, I sent a message to thee, good Edmund, that I might learn from one so judicious and dispassionate as thou art, the real state of things in that distracted country; it having pleased the queen's majesty to think of appointing me her deputy, in order to bring the rebellious to submission.

SPENSER. Wisely and well considered; but more worthily of her judgment than her affection. May your lordship overcome, as you have ever done, the difficulties and dangers you foresee.

ESSEX. We grow weak by striking at random; and knowing that I must strike, and strike heavily, I would fain see exactly where the stroke shall fall.

Some attribute to the Irish all sorts of excesses; others tell us that these are old stories; that there is not a more inoffensive race of merry creatures under heaven, and that their crimes are all hatched for them here in England, by the incubation of printers' boys, and are brought to market at times of distressing dearth in news. From all that I myself have seen of them, I can only say that the civilised (I mean the richer and titled) are as susceptible of heat as iron, and as impenetrable to light as granite. The half-barbarous are probably worse; the utterly barbarous may be somewhat better. Like game-cocks, they must spar when they meet. One fights because he fights an Englishman; another because the fellow he quarrels with comes from a distant county; a third because the next parish is an eyesore to him, and his fist-mate is from it. The only thing in which they all agree as proper law is the tooth-for-tooth act. Luckily we have a bishop who is a native, and we called him before

57

the queen. He represented to her majesty, that everything in Old Ireland tended to re-produce its kind ; crimes among others ; and he declared frankly, that if an honest man is murdered, or what is dearer to an honest man, if his honour is wounded in the person of his wife, it must be expected that he will retaliate. Her majesty delivered it as her opinion, that the latter case of vindictiveness was more likely to take effect than the former. But the bishop replied, that in his conscience he could not answer for either if the man was up. The dean of the same diocese gave us a more favourable report. Being a justice of the peace, he averred most solemnly that no man ever had complained to him of murder, excepting one who had lost so many fore-teeth by a cudgel that his deposition could not be taken exactly ; added to which, his head was a little clouded with drunkenness ; furthermore, that extremely few women had adduced sufficiently clear proofs of violence, excepting those who were wilful, and resisted with tooth and nail. In all which cases it was difficult, nay impossible, to ascertain which violence began first and lasted longest.

There is not a nation upon earth that pretends to be so superlatively generous and high-minded ; and there is not one (I speak from experience) so utterly base and venal. I have positive proof that the nobility, in a mass, are agreed to sell, for a stipulated sum, all their rights and privileges, so much per man ; and the queen is inclined thereunto. But would our parliament consent to pay money for a cargo of rotten pilchards ? And would not our captains be readier to swamp than to import them ? The noisiest rogues in that[1] kingdom, if not quieted by a halter, may be quieted by making them brief-collectors, and by allowing them first to encourage the incendiary, then to denounce and hang him, and lastly to collect all the money they can, running up and down with the whining ferocity of half-starved hyænas, under pretence of repairing the damages their exhausted country hath sustained. Others ask modestly a few thousands a year, and no more, from those whom they represent to us as naked and famished ; and prove clearly to every dispassionate man who hath a single drop of free blood in his veins, that at least this pittance is due to them for abandoning their liberal and lucrative professions, and for endangering their valuable lives on the tempestuous seas, in order that the voice of Truth may sound for once

[1] 1st ed. reads : " our."

upon the shores of England, and Humanity cast her shadow on the council-chamber.

I gave a dinner to a party of these fellows a few weeks ago. I know not how many kings and princes were among them, nor how many poets and prophets and legislators and sages. When they were half-drunk, they coaxed and threatened ; when they had gone somewhat deeper, they joked, and croaked, and hiccupped, and wept over sweet Ireland ; and when they could neither stand nor sit any longer, they fell upon their knees and their noddles, and swore that limbs, life, liberty, Ireland, and God himself, were all at the queen's service. It was only their holy religion, the religion of their forefathers—— here sobs interrupted some, howls others, execrations more, and the liquor they had ingulfed the rest. I looked down on them with stupor and astonishment, seeing faces, forms, dresses, much like ours, and recollecting their ignorance, levity, and ferocity. My pages drew them gently by the heels down the steps ; my grooms set them upright (inasmuch as might be) on their horses ; and the people in the streets, shouting and pelting, sent forward the beasts to their straw.

Various plans have been laid before us for civilising or coercing them. Among the pacific, it was proposed to make an offer to five hundred of the richer Jews in the Hanse-towns and in Poland, who should be raised to the dignity of the Irish peerage, and endowed with four thousand acres of good forfeited land, on condition of each paying two thousand pounds, and of keeping up ten horsemen and twenty foot, Germans or Poles, in readiness for service.

The Catholics bear nowhere such ill-will toward Jews as toward Protestants. Brooks make even worse neighbours than oceans do.

I myself saw no objection to the measure : but our gracious queen declared she had an insuperable one ; *they stank !* We all acknowledged the strength of the argument, and took out our handkerchiefs. Lord Burleigh almost fainted ; and Raleigh wondered how the Emperor Titus could bring up his men against Jerusalem.

" Ah ! " said he, looking reverentially at her majesty, " the star of Berenice shone above him ! and what evil influence could that star not quell ! what malignancy could it not annihilate ! "

Hereupon he touched the earth with his brow until the queen said, " Sir Walter ! lift me up those laurels."

At which manifestation of princely good-will he was advancing to kiss her Majesty's hand, but she waved it, and said sharply,

" Stand there, dog ! "

Now what tale have you for us ?

SPENSER. Interrogate me, my lord, that I may answer each question distinctly, my mind being in sad confusion at what I have seen and undergone.

ESSEX. Give me thy account and opinion of these very affairs as thou leftest them ; for I would rather know one part well, than all imperfectly ; and the violences of which I have heard within the day surpass belief.

Why weepest thou, my gentle Spenser ?   Have the rebels sacked thy house ?

SPENSER. They have plundered and utterly destroyed it.

ESSEX. I grieve for thee, and will see thee righted.

SPENSER. In this they have little harmed me.

ESSEX. How ! I have heard it reported that thy grounds are fertile, and thy mansion * large and pleasant.

SPENSER. If river and lake and meadow-ground and mountain could render any place the abode of pleasantness, pleasant was mine, indeed !

On the lovely banks of Mulla I found deep contentment.   Under the dark alders did I muse and meditate.   Innocent hopes were my gravest cares, and my playfullest fancy was with kindly wishes. Ah ! surely of all cruelties the worst is to extinguish our kindness. Mine is gone : I love the people and the land no longer.   My lord, ask me not about them ; I may speak injuriously.

ESSEX. Think rather then of thy happier hours and busier occupations ; these likewise may instruct me.

SPENSER. The first seeds I sowed in the garden, ere the old castle was made habitable for my lovely bride, were acorns from Penshurst. I planted a little oak before my mansion at the birth of each child. My sons, I said to myself, shall often play in the shade of them when I am gone, and every year shall they take the measure of their growth, as fondly as I take theirs.

* It was purchased by a victualler and banker,[1] the father or grandfather of Lord Riversdale.—W. S. L.

---

[1] Richard Tonson, whose illegitimate son, Colonel William Hull, assumed the name of Tonson, and was created Baron Riversdale.   Mr. Stephen Wheeler provides me with references to Landor's *Commentary*, p. 90, and his poem, " Fæsulan Musings," 1831.

ESSEX AND SPENSER

ESSEX. Well, well; but let not this thought make thee weep so bitterly.

SPENSER. Poison may ooze from beautiful plants; deadly grief from dearest reminiscences.

I *must* grieve, I *must* weep: it seems the law of God, and the only one that men are not disposed to contravene. In the performance of this alone do they effectually aid one another.

ESSEX. Spenser! I wish I had at hand any arguments or persuasions of force sufficient to remove thy sorrow: but really I am not in the habit of seeing men grieve at anything, except the loss of favour at court, or of a hawk, or of a buck-hound. And were I to swear out my condolences to a man of thy discernment, in the same round roll-call phrases we employ with one another upon these occasions, I should be guilty, not of insincerity but of insolence. True grief hath ever something sacred in it; and when it visiteth a wise man and a brave one, is most holy.

Nay, kiss not my hand: he whom God smiteth hath God with him. In his presence what am I?

SPENSER. Never so great, my lord, as at this hour, when you see aright who is greater. May he guide your counsels, and preserve your life and glory!

ESSEX. Where are thy friends? Are they with thee?

SPENSER. Ah, where, indeed! Generous, true-hearted Philip! where art thou? whose presence was unto me peace and safety; whose smile was contentment, and whose praise renown. My lord! I can not but think of him among still heavier losses: he was my earliest friend, and would have taught me wisdom.

ESSEX. Pastoral poetry, my dear Spenser, doth not require tears and lamentations. Dry thine eyes; rebuild thine house: the queen and council, I venture to promise thee, will make ample amends for every evil thou hast sustained. What! does that enforce thee to wail yet louder?

SPENSER. Pardon me, bear with me, most noble heart! I have lost what no council, no queen, no Essex, can restore.

ESSEX. We will see that. There are other swords, and other arms to wield them, beside a Leicester's and a Raleigh's. Others can crush their enemies and serve their friends.

SPENSER. O my sweet child! And of many so powerful, many so wise and so beneficent, was there none to save thee? None! none!

61

Essex. I now perceive that thou lamentest what almost every father is destined to lament. Happiness must be bought, although the payment may be delayed. Consider ; the same calamity might have befallen thee here in London. Neither the houses of ambassadors, nor the palaces of kings, nor the altars of God himself, are asylums against death. How do I know but under this very roof there may sleep some latent calamity, that in an instant shall cover with gloom every inmate of the house, and every far dependant ?

Spenser. God avert it !

Essex. Every day, every hour of the year, do hundreds mourn what thou mournest.

Spenser. Oh, no, no, no ! Calamities there are around us ; calamities there are all over the earth ; calamities there are in all seasons ; but none in any season, none in any place, like mine.

Essex. So say all fathers, so say all husbands. Look at any old mansion-house, and let the sun shine as gloriously as it may on the golden vanes, or the arms recently quartered over the gateway, or the embayed window, and on the happy pair that haply is toying at it ; nevertheless, thou mayest say that of a certainty the same fabric hath seen much sorrow within its chambers, and heard many wailings : and each time this was the heaviest stroke of all. Funerals have passed along through the stout-hearted knights upon the wainscot, and amid the laughing nymphs upon the arras. Old servants have shaken their heads, as if somebody had deceived them, when they found that beauty and nobility could perish.

Edmund ! the things that are too true pass by us as if they were not true at all ; and when they have singled us out, then only do they strike us. Thou and I must go too. Perhaps the next year may blow us away with its fallen leaves.*

Spenser. For you, my lord, many years (I trust) are waiting : I never shall see those fallen leaves. No leaf, no bud, will spring upon the earth before I sink into her breast for ever.

Essex. Thou, who art wiser than most men, shouldst bear with patience, equanimity, and courage, what is common to all.

Spenser. Enough ! enough ! enough ! Have all men seen their infant burned to ashes before their eyes ?

Essex. Gracious God ! Merciful Father ! what is this ?

Spenser. Burned alive ! burned to ashes ! burned to ashes ! The

* It happened so.—W. S. L.

ESSEX AND SPENSER

flames dart their serpent tongues through the nursery-window. I can not quit thee, my Elizabeth ! I can not lay down our Edmund. Oh these flames ! they persecute, they enthrall me, they curl round my temples, they hiss upon my brain, they taunt me with their fierce foul voices, they carp at me, they wither me, they consume me, throwing back to me a little of life, to roll and suffer in, with their fangs upon me. Ask me, my lord, the things you wish to know from me ; I may answer them ; I am now composed again. Command me, my gracious lord ! I would yet serve you ; soon I shall be unable. You have stooped to raise me up ; you have borne with me ; you have pitied me, even like one not powerful ; you have brought comfort, and will leave it with me ; for gratitude is comfort.

Oh ! my memory stands all a tip-toe on one burning point : when it drops from it, then it perishes. Spare me : ask me nothing ; let me weep before you in peace ; the kindest act of greatness.

ESSEX. I should rather have dared to mount into the midst of the conflagration than I now dare entreat thee not to weep. The tears that overflow thy heart, my Spenser, will staunch and heal it in their sacred stream, but not without hope in God.

SPENSER. My hope in God is that I may soon see again what he has taken from me. Amid the myriads of angels there is not one so beautiful : and even he (if there be any) who is appointed my guardian, could never love me so. Ah ! these are idle thoughts, vain wanderings, distempered dreams. If there ever were guardian angels, he who so wanted one, my helpless boy, would not have left these arms upon my knees.

ESSEX. God help and sustain thee, too gentle Spenser ! I never will desert thee. But what am I ? Great they have called me ! Alas, how powerless then and infantile is greatness in the presence of calamity !

Come, give me thy hand : let us walk up and down the gallery. Bravely done ! I will envy no more a Sidney or a Raleigh.

II. ARCHBISHOP BOULTER AND PHILIP SAVAGE *

(*Imag. Convers.*, iv., 1829 ; *Wks.*, i., 1846 ; iii., 1876.)

BOULTER. Heartily glad am I to see you, my brother, if, in these times of calamity and desolation, such a sentiment may be expressed or felt. My wife is impatient to embrace her sister.

SAVAGE. My lord primate, I did not venture to bring her with me from Dublin, wishing to wait until I had explored the road, and had experienced the temper of the people.

BOULTER. I much regret her absence, and yet more the cause of it : let me hope however that nothing unexpectedly unpleasant has occurred to you in your journey hither.

SAVAGE. I came on horseback, attended by one servant. Had I been prudent, he would not have worn his livery ; for hardly any object is more offensive to the poor, in seasons of distress, than a servant in livery, spruce and at his ease. They attach to it the idea of idleness and comfort, which they contrast with their own hard labour and its ill requital.

Two miles from Armagh, we were met by a multitude of work-

* Boulter, primate of Ireland, and president of the council, saved that kingdom from pestilence and famine in the year 1729, by supplying the poor with bread, medicines, attendance, and every possible comfort and accommodation. Again in 1740 and 1741 two hundred and fifty thousands were fed, twice a day, *principally at his expense*, as we find in *La Biographie Universelle* ; an authority the least liable to suspicion. He built hospitals at Drogheda and Armagh, and endowed them richly. No private man, in any age or country, has contributed so largely to relieve the sufferings of his fellow-creatures ; to which object he and his wife devoted their ample fortunes, both during their lives and after their decease.

Boulter was certainly the most disinterested, the most humane, the most beneficent man that ever guided the councils of Ireland. I am not certain that I should have thought of offering this tribute to his memory, if his connection with my family by his marriage had not often reminded me of him : for we do not always bear in mind what is due to others unless there is something at home to stimulate the recollection.

Philip Savage, Chancellor of the Exchequer, was likewise so irreproachable, that even Swift, the reviler of Somers, could find in him no motive for satire and no room for discontent.—W. S. L.

people ; they asked my groom who 1 was ; he told them my name, and, perhaps in the pride of his heart, my office. Happily they never had heard of the one or the other. They then enclosed me, and insisted on knowing whether I came with orders from the castle, to fire upon them ; as had been threatened some days before.

" For what ? my honest friends ! " cried I.

" For wanting bread and asking it," was the answer that ran from mouth to mouth, frequently repeated, and deepening at every repetition, till hoarseness and weakness made it drop and cease. I then assured them that no such orders were given, or would ever be ; and that the king and government were deeply afflicted at their condition, which however was only temporary.

Upon this there came forward one from among them ; and laying his hand upon the mane of my horse, he laughed till he staggered. I looked at him in amaze. When he had recovered himself a little from his transport, he said, " I hope you are honest, my friend ! for you talk like a fool, which in people of your sort is a token of it, though sometimes one no weightier than Will Wood's for a halfpenny. But prythee now, my jewel, how can you in your conscience take upon yourself to say, that the king and his ministers care a flea's rotten tooth, whether or not we crack with emptiness and thirst, so long as our arms fill their bellies, and drive away troublesome neighbours while they are napping afterward ? Deeply afflicted ! is it deeply afflicted ! O' my soul, one would think there was as much pleasure in deep affliction as in deep drinking, or even more : for many have washed away their lands with claret, and have then given over drinking ; but where is the good fellow who has done anything in this quarter by way of raising his head above such a deep affliction ? Has the king or his lord-lieutenant sent us the value of a mangy sow's bristle ? I may be mistaken, but I am apt to think that, shallow as we are bound to believe we are in other things, our affliction is as deep as theirs, or near upon it ; and yet we never said a word about the matter. We only said we were naked and starving, and quitted our cabins that we may leave to our fathers and mothers our own beds to die on, and that we may hear no longer the cries of our wives and little ones, which, let me tell you, are very different in those who are famishing from any we ever heard before. Deeply afflicted ! Now afore God ! what miseries have they suffered, or have they seen ?

I hear of rich people in Dublin with such a relish for deep affliction, they will give eighteen-pence for a book to read of it."

Partly in hopes of proceeding, and partly in commiseration, I slipped a guinea into the fellow's hand. He took it, and did not thank me, but continuing to hold it, together with my horse's mane, he said, " Come along with me." I thought it prudent to comply. At the distance of about a mile, on the right hand, is the cabin to which I was conducted. A wretched horse was standing half within it and half without, and exhibiting in his belly and ribs the clearest signs of famine and weariness. " Let us hear," said my guide, " what is going on."

I dismounted and stood with him. Looking round about the tenement, I found no article of furniture; for the inhabitant was lying on the floor, covered with his clothes only. Against the wall of the doorway was hanging from a nail a broken tin tobacco-box, kept open by a ring, which had formerly been the ornament of a pig's snout. Its more recent service was to make a hole in a piece of paper, on which I read, " Notice to quit."

There was a priest in the cabin, who spoke, as nearly as I can recollect, these words : " You are the only Catholic in the parish, and ought to set an example to the rest of them about you."

" Father ! " said a weak voice, " you told me I might go to the archbishop's when I grew stouter, and get what I could ; it being the spoil of an enemy. Such was my hunger on first recovering from the fever, and the worse perhaps from having had nothing to eat for a couple of days, that, when the servants gave me a basin of broth, I swallowed it. None of them had the charity to warn me that it was a piece of beef which was lying at the bottom, or to tell me that (for what they knew) it might be a turnip ; so, without thinking at all about it, I just let it take its own way ! There was no more of it than the size of a good potato : a healthy man would have made but four bites of it : I had a bitch that would have swallowed it at one, when she had whelps. I have seen a man who would make so little of it, he would let his wife eat it all, at a meal or two : it was next to nothing. In my mind, I have a doubt whether, as there might be some fever left upon me, it was not rather the show of beef rising out of the broth, than real beef. For sure enough I might mistake, as I might in thinking I was well again, when I had still the fever ; which could scarcely come back upon me for eating, when it had come upon me the week before for not eating. Howsoever, I went home and laid myself down and slept, and dreamt of angels with ladles of soup in their hands, some looking ugly enough, and others laughing, and one of them led that very horse of yours into the cabin : I should know him again anywhere : we looked in each other's face for ten minutes—then down he threw himself on me, as though I were no better than ling and fern. There he would have stayed, I warrant, till sunrise, if it had not been Sunday morning."

" How ! " cried the priest. " What then ! all this iniquity was committed upon the Saturday ! " " This day week," answered the sick man, humbled as much, I suspect, by blundering into the confession, as he was by the reproof.

" And now, by my soul ! our Lady calls you to an account, sinner ! " said the priest angrily. " I would not wonder if the arch-heretic, you call archbishop, gave out so many thousand bowls of soup a day, for the sake of drowning that soul of yours, swiller and swine ! Hither have I been riding a matter of thirteen miles, to see that everything is going on as it ought, and not an ounce of oatmeal or a potato in the house."

The poor inhabitant of the cabin sighed aloud. My conductor strode softly toward the priest, and, twitching him by the sleeve, asked him softly what he thought of the man's health. The poor creature heard the question, and much more distinctly the answer, which was, that he could not live out another day. He requested the holy man to hear his confession : the most grievous part of it had been made already : but now the piece of beef had its real size and weight given to it : he had eaten it with pleasure, with knowledge : he had gone to bed upon it : he had tried to sleep : he had slept : he had said no more *ave-maries* than ordinarily. A soul labouring under such a mountain of sin required (God knows how many) masses for its purgation and acquittance.

" Be aisy ! " said my conductor. " He shall sup with our blessed Lord in Paradise by seven o'clock to-morrow night, if masses can mash potatoes, or there is buttermilk above."

On saying this, he pulled open the priest's hand, slapped it with some violence, left the guinea in it, and wished me a pleasant ride. I could not bear to let him quit me so abruptly, glad as I should have been before at his departure. I asked him whether the dying man

67

was his relative. He said, " No." I wished to replace his generosity somewhat more largely.

" Sir ! " said he, " I have enough for several days yet : when it is gone, the archbishop will give me what he gives the rest. As for that massmonger, he shall eat this rasher of bacon with me this blessed night, or I 'll be damned." So saying, he drew a thin slice from his pocket, neither wrapped in paper nor in bread.

BOULTER. I hope soon to find out this worthy man, the warmth of whose heart may well atone for that of his expressions : but, lest he should be too urgent in his invitation, I will immediately send one to my brother clergyman, entreating him to dine with us. We have always fish on Fridays and Saturdays from the lake near us, in case we may be favoured by any Roman Catholic visitor.

This slight displeasure is, I hope, the only one you have met with.

PHILIP SAVAGE. I must confess it grieved me to see the sheriff's officers erecting the gallows at the entrance of the city : it must exasperate the populace. Men in the extremity of suffering lose sooner the sense of fear than the excitability to indignation : the people of Ireland have endured enough already.

BOULTER. Indeed have they. It was thought the excess of hard-heartedness, when man asked for bread, to give a stone ; but better a stone than a halter.

PHILIP SAVAGE. As our country-gentlemen, in this part of Ireland particularly, are rather worse than semi-barbarous, and hear nothing from their cradles but threats and defiance, they may deem it requisite and becoming to erect this formidable signal of regular government against the advances of insurrection.

BOULTER. More are made insurgents by firing on them than by feeding them ; and men are more dangerous in the field than in the kitchen.

PHILIP SAVAGE. In critical times, such as these, some coercion and some intimidation may be necessary. We must be vigilant and resolute against the ill-intentioned.

BOULTER. My dear brother ! would it not be wiser to give other intentions to the ill-intentioned ? Cruelty is no more the cure of crimes than it is the cure of sufferings : compassion, in the first instance, is good for both : I have known it bring compunction when nothing else would. I forbear to enlarge on the enormous inhumanity of inflicting the punishment of death for small offences :

68

yet I must remind you to ask yourself, whether, in your belief, ten years ever elapsed in Ireland, or even in England, without some capital sentence wrongfully pronounced. If this be the case, and most men think it is, does it not occur to you that such a penalty should for ever be expunged from our statute-book? Severe as another may be, reparation of some kind may be made, on the detection of its injustice. But what reparation can reach the dead from the living? What reparation can even reach the judge who condemned him? for he too must be almost as much a sufferer. In vain will the jurymen split and subdivide the responsibility: in vain will they lament that nothing now can mitigate the verdict. Release then the innocent from this long suffering, if you will not release the guilty from a shorter. What can be expected from the humanity of men, habituated to see death inflicted on their fellow-men, for offences which scarcely bring an inconvenience on the prosecutor? And what can be expected from the judgment of those above them, who denounce vengeance to preserve peace, and take away life to show respect for property? More ferocity hath issued from under English scarlet than from under American ochre. Violent resentments are the natural propensities of untamed man: the protection of our property does not require them.

PHILIP SAVAGE. The legislator and judge feel none.

BOULTER. Why then imitate them in voice and action? Is there anything lovely or dignified in such an imitation?

PHILIP SAVAGE. Our judges in these days are not often guilty of the like unseemliness, which was common fifty years ago.

BOULTER. Certainly they are less boisterous and blustering than under the first James and the first Charles, and have wiped away much of that rudeness and effrontery which is chastened in other professions by civiller company and more salutary awe: nevertheless, at the commencement of the disturbances which this famine brought about, many poor wretches were condemned to death, after much intemperate language from the judges, who declined to present petitions on their behalf to the lord-lieutenant, as I told you in my letter. Probably they are little pleased that his flexibility of temper hath yielded to our remonstrances and authority. Painful would be my situation as president of the council, and yours as chancellor of the exchequer, if such people as are usually sent hither for lords-lieutenant were as refractory as they are remiss. I trust it will ever

69

be found convenient to appoint men of clemency to the first station, and that I shall never be forced to exercise on them the powers entrusted to me of coercion and control.

It is well when people can believe that their misfortunes are temporary. How can we apply such a term to pestilence and famine ?

PHILIP SAVAGE. Surely the violence of the evil eats away the substance of it speedily. Pestilence and famine are, and always have been, temporary and brief.

BOULTER. Temporary they are, indeed : brief are they, very brief. But why ? because life is so under them. To the world they are extremely short : but can we say they are short to him who bears them ? And of such there are thousands, tens of thousands, in this most afflicted, most neglected country. The whole of a life, be it what it may be, is not inconsiderable to him who leaves it ; any more than the whole of a property, be it but an acre, is inconsiderable to him who possesses it. Whether want and wretchedness last for a month or for half a century, if they last as long as the sufferer, they are to him of very long duration. Let us try then rather to remove the evils of Ireland, than to persuade those who undergo them that there are none. For, if they could be thus persuaded, we should have brutalised them first to such a degree, as would render them more dangerous than they were in the reigns of Elizabeth or Charles.

There will never be a want of money, or a want of confidence, in any well-governed state that has been long at peace, and without the danger of its interruption. But a want of the necessaries of life, in peasants or artisans, when the seasons have been favourable, is a certain sign of defect in the constitution, or of criminality in the administration. It may not be advisable or safe to tell everyone this truth : yet it is needful to inculcate it on the minds of governors, and to repeat it until they find the remedy : else the people, one day or other, will send those out to look for it who may trample down more in the search than suits good husbandry.

God be praised ! we have no such exclamation to make as that of Ecclesiastes. " Woe to thee, O land ! whose king is a child " : an evil that may afflict a land under the same king, for years indefinite. Our gracious sovereign, ever mindful of his humble origin, and ever grateful to the people who raised him from it to the most exalted throne in the universe, a throne hung round with the trophies of

BOULTER AND SAVAGE

Cressy, Agincourt, Poictiers, and Blenheim, has little inclination to imitate the ruinous pride of Louis the Fourteenth : to expend his revenues, much less those of his people, in the excavation of rivers, the elevation of mountains, and the transplantation of Asia, with all her gauds and vanities, under the gilded domes of faery palaces.

PHILIP SAVAGE. Versailles is a monument, raised by the king of one country for the benefit of kings in all others, warning each in successive generations, not to exhaust the labour and patience of his people, by the indulgence of his profusion and sensuality.

BOULTER. Let us hope, my brother, that the poverty this structure has entailed on the French, may not hereafter serve for the foundation of more extensive evils, and exacerbate a heartless race, ever disposed to wanton cruelties, until they at last strike down the virtuous for standing too near, and for warning them where their blows should fall.   In which case they will become even worse slaves than they are, from the beating they must, sooner or later, undergo.

If I could leave the country in its present state, and if I possessed the same advantage of daily access to the king, as when I attended him from Germany,[1] I should take the liberty of representing to him, that his own moderation of expenditure might well be copied in the public, and that some offices and some pensions in this country might be lopped off, without national dishonour or popular discontent.

PHILIP SAVAGE. There has always been an outcry against places and pensions, whether the country was flourishing or otherwise. We may lop until we cut our fingers and disable ourselves for harder work.   Surely a man of your grace's discernment would look well to it first, and remember that, where the sun is let in, the wind too may let in itself.

BOULTER. A want of caution is not among my defects ; nor is an unsteady deference to the clamours of the multitude.   It is necessary to ask sometimes even well-dressed men, have not the judges places ? is not every office of trust a place ? and can any government be conducted without its functionaries ?   I do not follow the public cry, nor run before it.   Pensions too, occasionally, are just and requisite. What man of either party will deny, that a Marlborough and a Peterborough deserved such a token of esteem, from the country they served so gloriously ? or that the payment of even a large annuity, to such illustrious men, is not in the end the best economy ?   These

---

[1] Boulter in 1719 went to Hanover with George I., as chaplain.

rewards stimulate exertion and create merit. They likewise display to other nations our justice, our generosity, our power, our wealth ; and are the best monuments we can erect to Victory. Do not be alarmed lest the people should insist on too rigorous a defalcation. The British people, and still more the Irish, would resent, as a private wrong, the tearing one leaf from the brow of a brave defender. On the contrary, to say nothing of clerks and commissaries, the grant of pensions to ambassadors and envoys, who can not act from their own judgment, and who only execute the orders of others, without the necessity of genius, of learning, of discernment, or of courage, is superfluous to a nation in its prosperity, and insulting to one in its distress. They are always chosen out of private friendship ; and their stipends, while they act, are only presents made to them by their patrons. To pay them afterward for having taken the trouble to receive these presents, is less needful than to send a Christmas-box to my wig-maker, because I had preferred him already, and had paid him handsomely for making me a wig at Midsummer. Should we not think him a foolish man if he expected it, and an impudent one if he asked it ?

We are so fortunate as to have few pensions to discharge, and little debt : nevertheless, in times disastrous like these, when many thousands, I might say millions, are starving, and when persons once in affluence have neither bread nor work, it behoves us, who wish security and respectability to the government, to deduct from waste and riot that which was not given originally for distinguished merit, and which may now save the lives of generations, and scarcely take the garnish off one dish in the second courses of a few.

At my table you will find only ordinary fare ; and I hardly know whether I am not sinning while I thank my God that it is plentiful.

III. DUKE DE RICHELIEU, SIR FIREBRACE COTES, LADY GLENGRIN, AND MR. NORMANBY

(Imag. Convers., iii., 1828 ; *Wks.*, i., 1846 ; *Wks.*, vi., 1876.)

WHEN the Duke de Richelieu had retired from office,[1] ill health, which is usually the cause of retirement, was the consequence of it. Not that ministers ever care about loss of place ; privation of dignity and emolument is nothing to them ; and if they are excluded from the only area grand enough for the development of their conceptions, those are much to be pitied, although not in the least to be blamed (God forbid !), who gave the key for that purpose to some dark designer, at the instant when such conceptions had arrived at their maturity.

He went to Genoa. The narrowness and obscurity of the streets incommoded him, and eighty stairs, which must always be mounted to reach the best apartments, were too many for an invalid. He went to Nice : the *bise* was troublesome. Here, however, he was amused a little at the sight of well-dressed strangers, and was not insensible of pleasure in being looked at, and in hearing his name perpetually mentioned in the same low tone of voice as he passed.

Do you doubt this weakness ? Call it as you please and doubt it as you may—it was this low tone of voice which the manly hearts of a Marius and a Cromwell panted for. Vanity and agiotage are to a Parisian the oxygen and hydrogen of life. Richelieu, as honest a man as he was an ill-requited minister, had little of the latter ; of the former as much as was requisite.

There were at Nice, at the same time, Sir Firebrace Cotes,[2] an Irish general, and the Countess of Glengrin, an Irish lady inconsolable for her husband. I do not mean the one she had just lost, but the one she feared never to have.

The general thought it his duty to pay his respects to the minister, as none in place was there, and as he had a rich uniform which he

---

[1] Richelieu retired December 1818, and was in power again in February 1820.
[2] 1st ed. reads " Sir Fire Coats " throughout.

73

never could so well show before, and indeed had never put on. Lady Glengrin too left her card.

That is contrary to etiquette.

One among the many reasons why she did it : Confident in her beauty, for she really had been pretty in her youth, and possessing in an eminent degree that facility of reply, which, if delivered with sharpness,[1] is called *repartee*, and claims relationship, by a left-hand connexion, with wit, she never lost an opportunity of passing into the company of distinguished personages. She was of all politics ; so that when rank failed her, nobody was surprised to hear that she had headed a deputation of fishwomen at Paris.[2] Related to one of those who preserve the peace by cocking the pistol, and the gradations of social order by trampling on their equals, she associated and assimilated with the [3] worst in the polar circle of both vulgars.

Her petulance and liveliness amused the duke, and mostly when she talked about her country. He had not been accustomed to Irish society, though he had known some of Irish extraction, and a few born and educated in Ireland. He had found them decorous and graceful, frank, and full of humour, not much addicted to study, but respectful to those who were, until some peculiarity caught them, and they exploded in loud laughter. He considered them particularly delicate in affairs of love and friendship. One of them, suspected (as it appears most wrongfully) of many amorous intrigues, swore he never had and never would have one with a man's wife or daughter. Richelieu admired his primitive chastity. Among his friends, however, was an elderly gentleman, who had meditated long upon the declaration, and felt certain there was some blunder in it. At supper he found it out ; and when they were alone, " Faith ! " said he, " Marcus, your mischief will lie then in a mighty narrow compass." Being locked up in logic, and unable to put his head through the grating, he agreed at last that the expression, to a man not very acute, might require an explanation. " I meant," said he, " a friend's ; at dinner or over a bottle ; for in my mind, whatever others may think, that would be very base."

" You must come among us, duke," said her ladyship.

---

[1] 1st ed. reads : " sharpness and impudence."
[2] 1st ed. reads : " Paris, and had harangued the citizen sans-culottes. Related," etc.
[3] 1st ed. reads : " the very worst."

74

DUKE DE RICHELIEU, ETC.

" I must indeed," answered he.

" Sir Firebrace, you are witness to the promise."

" I am," said Sir Firebrace.

There is no person in the world upon whom idleness hangs so heavily as upon a minister of state dismissed. Reprehended for sighing when he only yawned, and ashamed of being thought to yawn when he really sighed, he accepted the invitation, on condition that he should live privately. " For," said he smiling, " your government would watch me ; and I should be sorry to be under martial law in Ireland, my skin being none of the toughest, and suspicious as my character must be, both as a catholic and a minister out of place. I will be colonel—colonel—I wish I could think of some colonel among my old friends who would consent to lend me his name."

" Oh," said Lady Glengrin, " if you want a name and are resolved to be a colonel, I have one for you, now you are so good and tractable : you shall be Colonel Le Doux."

" On receiving our commissions we kiss hands," said he ; and by the gracefulness of his action, if Madame de Genlis had been present, she would have fancied herself in the Louvre some years before the last century.

They embarked. Of all the coasts in the universe of the same extent, those of France for nearly their totality in three seas, are the least beautiful, and those which the eye tires the worst upon are in the vicinity of Marseilles. When you are at sea, the hills above the town appear like little mounds which some children have been just whitewashing. Here the party was becalmed two days. The regular beating of time by the waves against the sides of the vessel ; the regular creaking as she moved slowly on, heaving and nodding like some bulky churl half-asleep ; the flapping of the sail against the mast ; the monotonous and wearisome song (there was only one) of the sailors, who being Englishmen could neither dance nor fiddle, and had not even a monkey nor a cat among them for the strangers to joke about and play with ; rendered the colonel and his companions sad and silent. Sir Firebrace was flat and smooth as a billiard-table. Lady Glengrin having no object to attack or defend, at least no person known to Le Doux, turned, as we read of scorpions, upon herself, and her features and conversation languished equally. To relieve her listlessness, she sometimes made a spring at some friends of Sir Firebrace : but alas ! she really had lost her elasticity. Le

75

Doux smiled when he should have been serious, and was serious when he should have smiled. " One would think he hardly could have been attentive, though he seemed so," said her ladyship to herself. Sir Firebrace often begged leave to set her ladyship right upon the character of very good fellows, if she knew them thoroughly, and worthy women enough—at least he always believed so. He never went beyond in word or thought ; excepting that, if he was mistaken, as any man might be, he was certain from her goodness of heart that her ladyship would pardon him.

There was not a book belonging to the party : she asked the captain whether he had any interesting one : he brought her the log-book. Tossing it aside, " O that we had a book ! though it were the Bible or the Peerage," said the countess : and observed for the first time a young man whom the duke had noticed before, and whom he had taken for a runaway barber, his beard being always close-shaven, and his linen and face quite clean. He smiled with somewhat of concern and sarcasm. " Well, my friend," said she, " let us hear the joke."

" Really, madam," he replied, " I have no joke worth hearing."

" Favour us, at least," added she maliciously, " with the fruits of your reflection."

Sir Firebrace now began to brighten. " They might not please you, madam," replied the sailor.

" O yes they would : I insist upon having them."

" In that case, madam, there is no denial. I was thinking it strange that, of all the books in the world, you should pitch upon either of those. On the contrary, I wonder that petitions are not laid before parliament to suppress them, and signed by every person of the first distinction."

" Why so ? "

" Because the one shows us their vices, and the other does worse."

" What does the other ? "

" It shows us their ages."

" The fellow would be witty," said Sir Firebrace, " as all ignorant people would."

" All ? " said the man submissively. " I think I have seen some too modest ; but one can not judge of character in a couple of days."

" Sir Firebrace," said the captain, " you would better let that chap alone : he is too much for you and me. I have no power over him ; seaman he is and a right good one ; but though he lends a hand at any time, he takes nothing, not a can of grog. The lemon he puts into his water is to blame. He is the quietest and silentest man in the world, but if an oath escapes, you would fancy it was a leak, so quickly is he upon the plank. He has been a scholar not long ago, I mistrust, though he has dollars and better things in his box. As for madam, clever as she is, I would not have her fish for sting-rays." [1]

From his calmness and self-possession, Le Doux now imagined there was something in the man announcing high birth, and thought him, for an Englishman, well-bred, though satirical. He approached him ; and first expressed his sorrow that a person of an appearance so prepossessing should put forth *so much strength* where homage is best becoming. " The changes in my own country, sir," added he, " make me think it probable that they may have partially occurred in others."

" Sir," said the sailor,[2] " your observation, I perceive, is but a delicate and discreet inquiry. There is nothing romantic in my history : I never was what you call noble : I never was better than a schoolmaster in a small market-town. My education has taught me to reprove any open disrespect to the Bible. If the lady had spoken where only her equals were present, I should have gone away quietly ; but sailors may be corrupted."

" Without doubt there are good things in the Bible," said Le Doux. " Bossuet has quoted it in the place about the white cemetery. Then you read Latin ! "

" No, sir ! "

" How ! O ! I forgot : you have a translation of it—have you not ? A little [3]—it does not quite correspond with the original ? " This he spoke, not so much in his own character as in his country's.

---

[1] 1st ed. reads : " sting-rays. I knew that at the upshot, if she did not look sharp, he would *** in her eye like a dog-fox. I am ashamed at his incivility to a court-lady.' ' Captain, tack and stand out,' growled the mate, with a strong objurgation of the elbow in his ribs. ' You only make bad worse, with your foul dog-fox and his tornado. One would fancy, according to you, that dog-foxes are marines, and are practised in firing at a bottle upon deck. I never will believe till I see it, that the best dog-fox upon earth could hit her eye.' Sir Fire went toward the shaven sailor and said I know not what, which was answered by a bow. Le Doux imagined . . . an Englishman respectful and well-bred . . . sorrow, in very indifferent English, that he could not perhaps make himself understood, and then that a person . . . *strength* (this he spoke low) where," etc.

[2] 1st ed. reads : " sailor, in better french than Le Doux's english, ' your," etc.

[3] 1st ed. reads : " little—I would not say very unfairly—but it does," etc.

One would have supposed that he understood Greek and Hebrew, yet he did not understand a sentence even of Latin. One would have supposed that he had collated the original with the English version, yet it was by an old and obscure report that he knew of its existence.

" I was zealous for my Bible," said the sailor. " I love my country and am proud of my language : the Bible is the best thing in both. Often have I thought of those who translated it, what they were, what their fathers were, what were their friends and teachers. Sir, I would have given my life, when it was a life of hope and happiness, to make by such holy means as this book the English language known through the world. And yet my love of it has done me for a time some harm."

Le Doux was desirous of hearing what it could be : indeed there are few who are not so of hearing any harm : some from sympathy, some from malignity, some from curiosity, the rest from a wish of excitement. Lady Glengrin beckoned him away. " Favour me another time," said he to the sailor ; " I am deeply penetrated."

Lady Glengrin nodded again, and asked him how he could be so ill-natured, when he had a musician with him, as not to call forth his talent. " Oracles are obscure," replied he. " Mac Arthur tells me," she rejoined, " that Michael showed him a flute, made out of a broken cane which he picked up in Genoa." " We will have a dance then, please God ! " cried he. " Life is at stake, general ! You and I must draw lots for the lady, since I dare not leave it to her choice, and she would not make mortal enemies." This he spoke, bowing in turn to each, appealing to her solicitously, and awaiting with deference her determination.

The proposal was sanctioned : the three stood up : the Russian was commanded to bring out his flute : the seal-skin that contained his clothes and his treasure was unstrapped : he ran upon deck with it in his hand : but this and the other too were raised upon his head and tearing his black bear-like hair : tears ran down his cheeks : and now for the first time after many years was heard from his lips the Russian language.

" What is the matter ? " said the Swiss, his comrade, with perfect composure, to the Irish butler Mac Arthur. " The son of a *** is a woman ! " answered the butler. " Did you ever hear such a soft language as she makes of her Russian ? "

He had not finished when his lady, indignant at some word in the sentence, walked toward him fiercely from behind, and seizing him by

78

the collar, gave him a hearty kick in the bull's-eye of the pantaloon, with " I will teach you decency, you reptile ! " He retired and sat down by a sailor, who asked him in the universal silence that had succeeded, " Pat, how do you like the new fashion of sharp-toed shoes ? "

" Sir," answered he, " I would have you to know, my name is not Pat nor anything like it, but Agrippa Mac Arthur."

" No offence, I hope, Mr. Agrippa Mac Arthur. It would have been uncharitable and unchristianlike, if I could have seen such a sad mischance befall a fellow-creature, and hold my tongue upon it. Suppose you try a pickled herring while the hurt is fresh : a rare thing to bring out the fire that flies from a witch's toe-nail ! "

Agrippa was consoled by friendship. " No, thank you," replied he ; " she shall never have the satisfaction of seeing it." And then whispered in the sailor's ear, " What a marksman the vixen is ! " [1]

We must now endure the griefs and tribulations of the poor Russian whose flute was broken.

" Can not you repair it, Michael ? " said Le Doux, humanely.

" Saint Nicolas could not ! " answered he, with a sigh from the bottom of his heart. And he crossed himself as rapidly as possible, that his contrition might be observed by the saint at the first glance after the derogatory words, and before they could well be written down against him.

" What is all this blubbering about ? " said the captain to Le Doux.

" My servant Michael has broken his flute," answered he, " and the poor fellow is inconsolable. Indeed we could have danced if we had it ; the loss is no trifling one to any of us, and heavy to him who made the instrument."

" He made it ! " cried the captain incredulously.

" Yes," said Le Doux, " I saw him cutting the cane, now I remember."

---

[1] 1st ed. reads : " is ! she has fairly figged me ! ' shewing the latter proposition διὰ σημείων, as Cicero did in a letter to Atticus ; but Cicero did it with much greater doubt of being understood. I am fond of leading away my reader from scenes of sorrow ; and of planting in such manner as to break the angles of some prominent objects, not without care, however, that the plants themselves be choice and vigorous no less than apposite. We can now . . . humanely. ' Mr. Nicholas . . . heart ; and his melancholy now grew deeper, for in his despair he had said too much. ' What," etc.

" Why then, sir," replied the captain, " he could make such
another out of this sugar-stick : let him try his hand."

Joy played upon deck like the sun. Even Lady Glengrin grew
calm, and said to Le Doux, " These cursed Irish must be treated like
dogs, colonel. I hope nevertheless you will excuse my anger."

" Madam," said he, dissembling that he had seen the *voie de fait*,
" if you were angry at the accident, I do assure you, your servant
was not in fault. Renault slept upon it (as I saw) last night, and
perhaps cracked it. I would not tell Michael, to make the man more
uneasy, and turn friends into enemies."

" But that fellow's impudence, my butler's."

" He has been sitting among the sailors, and if indeed he laughed
a little, Michael did not see him probably, and I do assure you, if
he had, poor Michael is a good creature. They will live again in
harmony."

Her ladyship was persuaded that the castigation she had given
was unobserved. The flute was made : paniers of grapes and
peaches stood ready for any of the three who might be thirsty from
the dance : and there was a cask containing the wines of Lunel in
bottles, covered over with wet leaves and sail-cloth. In the whole
ship there was but one rueful face. An old seaman, whose arms and
breast had various marks upon them punctured and inlaid with gun-
powder, and whose back too bore sundry transverse white stripes,
probably from his mother having dreamt of a zebra, was very officious
in keeping the leaves and sail-cloth wet. At last he crept away, and
whispered to the messmate in whom he placed the most confidence [1] :
" Things may happen beyond our reckoning. I have known many
such, and have heard of more ; but none like this. The Hecla has
passed us in the night ! Captain Parry has been aboard ! As I am
a Christian, there is ice among the bottles ! " Le Doux had ordered
a small provision of it, enough for a day or two, and this was only
the morning of the second ; and Renault had exerted his utmost
skill in preserving and preparing it below.

The biblical sailor was much amused at seeing the colonel, who
left him an hour before so " deeply penetrated," dance delightfully.[2]

---

[1] 1st ed. reads : " confidence. ' I am not superstitious ; but things," etc.

[2] 1st ed. reads : " delightfully and return to him after a few . . . went to
rest, with a countenance full of interest and concern, just as when he left him, and
as when ' life was at stake,' " etc.

DUKE DE RICHELIEU, ETC.

After a few compliments to his partner, who was incommoded by the sea and went to lie down, he returned with a countenance full of interest, just as when " life was at stake."

" I have always heard the Bible," said he, " called a very dangerous book in the hands of the laity, and I am most anxious to know what was the peculiar harm it did you."

" Thomas Paine," answered the sailor, " had written something against it. I had not read this, nor thought of reading it, when I saw in a gazette which I took weekly the advertisement of an *Apology* for it. *An Apology for the Bible!* and by a *bishop!* [1] The word in Greek, I am informed, does not convey the same idea as with us : but I knew nothing of Greek, and was shocked at what I thought an intimation that the book of life required an excuse. I bought it, together with the strictures which provoked it. The fierceness and effrontery of the one, the smooth insincerity and flat yewberry sweetness of the other, equally disgusted me. I had only a single shelf for my books, in all about forty-five or fifty, and never did I think it necessary to conceal one. A neighbour asked me what I thought of these : I answered that I would rather have Paine's pen than Watson's crosier. He entreated me to lend him the volume. Unwilling to propagate the seeds of scepticism, I said, ' I am sorry I can not ; I have lent it.' This deliberate and cowardly falsehood brought its punishment. I never had refused a book to an acquaintance, or anything else in my house, and until that moment I had always thought myself as incapable of a falsehood as a denial. In most of our towns and villages the system has now commenced of that which you Frenchmen call *espionage :* we had no name for it, and have none yet. Before the war, we were somewhat different from other nations. This convulsion of Europe joined, morally speaking, the island to the continent. We then began to talk a language we had never learnt or heard ; we had *aristocrat* and *democrat ;* and, what is worse, our aristocrats and democrats were just like yours."

Le Doux bowed and smiled.

" I am afraid I have said an uncivil thing," continued the sailor, " and I beg pardon. Injuries in one respect hurt the memory ; that is, by contracting it to the narrow point they spring from."

" My friend," said Le Doux, placing his hand with gentleness

[1] Richard Watson, Bishop of Llandaff.

under the elbow of the apologist, " I have as little reason to be pleased with either of these parties as you have. Continue."

" The story, that my shelf was filled with profane and seditious and indecent books, became current in the parish. My scholars were taken away from me ; even those who came upon the charity, disappeared. Parents who had known me from my childhood, visited me now only to obtain a glance at my library. They found no other work of ill repute than Paine's, which from a sense of honour and openness I had replaced. Nevertheless all who were in business were threatened with the loss of it unless they removed their children from my tuition ; others removed them, as they declared to me, that they might not quarrel with their customers ; ' for they loved,' they said, ' peace and quiet.' Elias Halliday, that friend who had asked me for the *Age of Reason*, went to the Reverend Mr. Chisholm, now curate to his father ; and he, immediately on the intelligence, drew on his boots and came to me.

" ' Mr. Christopher Normanby,' said he, ' I never thought you taught lads blasphemy and sedition.'

" ' Sir,' answered I, quietly, ' you, being our spiritual guide, should have inquired into it ; for the report I have reason to believe is a fortnight old ! '

" ' A damned pretty fellow ! ' said he, striking his spur with a switch. ' Well, I must be back to the glebe.'

" Mr. Chisholm was never my friend, from the strangest of motives ; from possessing what he thought should have been mine. The rectory was presented to his father by Lord Sandyhurst, who resides in another part of the county, and to whom that gentleman was steward. He had been an attorney; but, for some wrong erasure, which he made perhaps by candle-light, he was induced to abandon his profession. My father was educated at the expense of the late lord, for having saved his son from drowning in the Trent, and not only was indebted for his education to that worthy peer, but for a legacy of five hundred pounds, bequeathed to him in his last words almost. Never was there a tenderer heart, a humbler soul, than my father's. At Oxford he had made great progress in the mathematics, which brought him many enemies, that study being in his time much discouraged there. He was suspected to be a good classical scholar, but his shyness would not let it appear : those who knew him best were not certain of it, for they could judge only from what they saw at lecture, and to those who knew him little there appeared to be a proof to the contrary. When he was about to take his degree, in order that he might be inducted to the rectory of Sandyhurst, one of the examining masters was resolved to pluck him."

" A very uncivil interruption ! " said Le Doux. " Are the masters themselves so rude ? "

" You do not understand the term, sir: you do not know perhaps that any single master can prevent a person from taking a degree. A student a year older than my father, and in competition with whom he had carried off a college-prize, discouraged him so at the examination that he lost his degree. He returned into the country, and told his young patron (for the father was lately dead) what had happened.

" ' Pooh, Kit,' cried he, patting him on the shoulder, ' go to Glasgow, man ! Jim Towne, my farrier, was made a doctor there in the twinkling of an eye : the rascal was starving on horse-flesh. At present, by a good intelligence with the resurrection-men, he holds up his head like a heron half-a-wing from the marsh, and looks askance in your face fiercer than a caught polecat, as he passes.'

" ' My lord,' answered my father, ' their church is different from ours.'

" ' Go to Cambridge then. My word for it, with your figures and two little straight lines betwixt, they will send you back nicked and cropped and spruce enough for the deanery of Durham. Remember, the rectory is a good eighty a-year—— by the bye, would you like the perpetual advowson ? At the end of the twelvemonth you have five hundred, you know, and we can sign and seal thereupon—aye, Kit ? '

" ' It would be simoniacal,' answered my father.

" ' Simoniacal ! ' repeated the peer with grave mimicry. ' The word itself in any man's mouth is enough to make him a hypocrite for life. A sand-boy, who does not know the meaning of it, has only to say it, and it turns him into a pickpocket or swindler. Why, thou cursed fool ! simony is everything in form and nothing in fact. Is there a Father in God upon the bench that has not committed it, if you put the thing in place of the letter ? '

" My father's health declined. ' I tell you what, young man ! unless you take a wife it is all over with you,' said the doctor. My father could no more take a wife than he could take a city : he was acquainted with no young woman : he declared it. ' Egad, I thought as much,' cried the doctor : looking at him, nevertheless, as he would have done at an ibis or crocodile just unboxed. ' We will remedy that too : the drug is as easily found as buckthorn.'

" Doctor Broom had been surgeon to a ship in the fleet under Rodney, and was the intimate friend of his captain, who, after being in constant service for fifty years, was made an admiral, and, as they call it, *laid on the shelf*. To kill time, when he had nothing else to kill, he married a bar-maid at Torquay. They both drank hard, and were so affectionate a couple that one did not survive the other above a twelvemonth. They left an infant daughter, ill provided for : the doctor took it, and sent it to school. She was now sixteen : he rode over for her, and told her she must come and help him. His garden joined my father's ; and he thought of hedges as lawyers think of laws. ' I have no notion of a hedge,' said he, ' without a gap in it ' : his boots were thick, he was strong and corpulent, he soon made one. ' Have a care ! ' said he, ' grasp my coat-pocket ! mind the onion-sauce ! ' He arrived at my father's with his ward, holding a dish in her two hands, and cried, ' Kit, my hearty dog, hast any appetite for a young rabbit, clean as a penny, out of my own cub, fed upon bran and sowthistle, and smothered in onions ? '

" My father thanked with much courtesy his kind friend, and really felt a good appetite.

" ' If this young lady and yourself will favour me.'

" ' Not she, nor I either : we have just eaten the fellow to it.'

" ' Miss will at least sit down.'

" ' No, thank you, sir : I must go.'

" ' Who told you that ? ' cried the doctor, glancing his eye athwart the back of his chair. She looked out of the window, and answered ' She did not know.'

" ' Sit down then,' cried her guardian, in the same authoritative tone as before. She was walking toward the only vacant seat, one with a wooden bottom, when my father (an absent man on many occasions) rose hastily, and placed his, which had his pillow upon it, before her.

" ' O no, sir ! '

" ' I beg and entreat you will, miss ! '

" ' O no ! '

" He took her gently by the arm, soft as a flower, and the coolness of it refreshed him to the heart. He seated her : he spoke to her :

only that he might stand near her.   Was he then so feeble that he could not be heard across a chamber of fourteen feet by twelve ?

" When he wanted me to marry, he told me the tale, and added, ' Christopher, there is no such preservative against vice as the recollection of these events.   I do believe that beauty, in its early innocence, has something of what, for want of a better and more definite name, we call etherial ; something pure and rapid, something that stands impassibly between us and evil, and holds our little world from ruin and corruption ; something that unites us here in love and amity, inasmuch as what is mortal can be united, and converts us at last to itself in fulness and perfection.' "

Le Doux heard the sailor with wonder, and looked at his rigid throat, his reddened breast, his hands covered with wiry and inverted hair.

" I am at home again," said he, " I am with my father, and talk freely.   If you are tired of me, leave me."

" My friend," said Le Doux, " I hear you with interest : pray proceed."

" Alice hardly ever would enter the bedchamber again, but she was fond of walking in the garden, steep as it was and short and narrow, and containing but one cherry-tree, some gooseberry-bushes, and a Virginian sumach that darkened the casement of the lower room.   My father must go down and talk to his little maid.

" ' Go,' said the doctor, ' I get fond of reading, and you have a power of books here.'

" Alice had been long below : she must now go and see what her guardian was doing : he might want her.   She tripped up stairs : my father stopped breathless in the middle.   ' Are you coming too, Mr. Normanby ? come then.   What is the matter ? are you tired, you sly romp ? '—for he had thrown a gooseberry at her bonnet.

" ' No, little Alice, the only fault of this house is, that the staircase wants air.'

" ' What ! with the door wide open and the windows too, and only the twenty-fourth of May ?   Indeed, Mr. Normanby, I cannot but think you are a very discontented man : you always want something.'

" ' Who makes that noise there ? ' cried the doctor.   Alice ran down, and found in her turn an inconvenience in the staircase to complain of. If my father had not caught her, who knows what might have happened ! It was providential.

" ' Alice,' said my father a few days afterward, ' I have often seen you eating my gooseberries and cherries, and what is worse, before they are half grown.'

" ' It is very true,' replied she, blushing, ' but I protest it was not in malice, and that whenever I caught myself doing it, I stopped.'

" ' You must pay me.'

" ' How can I ? I have only a sampler.'

" ' I will have that then.'

" She ran like a greyhound through the gap and brought it. It was neatly worked.

" ' Really, Alice, these letters are formed divinely.'

" ' Some of them,' said she, ' are better than others.'

" ' I cannot see that,' said my father.

" ' O yes they are : but what do you men know about work ? '

" ' Come, my little Alice, show me now the best.'

" She looked over them, and sometimes drew one straiter, and sometimes another, across her fore-finger.

" ' They are not much amiss,' said she.

" ' But show me the difference.'

" ' I think the N is rather better than those on each side.'

" ' O you deserve a coronet for such a present,' cried my father, seeing her embarrassment, and, running before her that she might not suspect he saw it, leaped up at a flower on the sumach. She laughed that he had missed it, and leaped at it too ; nor was it at the first attempt that she reached it, nor without help.

" ' Alice,' said the doctor one afternoon, ' you sit working all the day, and work worse than ever ; where is your sampler, child ? What do you colour at ? '

" ' I thought I might give it, sir, to Mr. Normanby ; I took so much of his fruit whenever I went there.'

" ' Alice,' said he, ' you are seventeen the first of October : I cannot treat you with green gooseberries and pale cherries, but the grapes against the kitchen chimney will soon be ripe, and I have such a rarity for you, as you never saw in your life-time.'

" ' O dear, sir, do not think of it ! and you have patients in the fever who care more about grapes.'

86

" ' I have one indeed who has such a fever on him, he would play the devil with the best fruit at table, and have it all to himself.'

" ' Let him have it, my dear sir.'

" ' So I will.'

" Alice ran and kissed the doctor. ' Poor Kit ! ' cried he. Alice, in the act of starting back, had fainted in his arms. ' Why ! how now, girl ! art in love with *me !* 'sblood ? I 'll bring thee to thyself again.' He had no more scruple with her than a child has with a doll, and his remedies were within reach. ' Simpleton ! ' whined he in derision, when she began to recover, ' he has just as much of a fever as you have.'

" Sir, it is time I should stop," said the sailor : " I am relating these things of my mother, just as if she had been an heiress of a thousand a-year, had lived in a turret and run along a corridor from her birth, had married a marquis, and had been presented at court."

" She was a pretty girl, I am persuaded," said Le Doux, " and we will suppose in her favour that she had those advantages. Go on, Mr. Normanby ; there is little to add, I fancy."

" ' If,' said the doctor, ' he should have a small matter of ailment, which by neglect is one that might grow violent, would you sit by him ? '

" ' Willingly.'

" ' All day long ? '

" ' All night too. I have a good deal of courage when nobody frightens me.'

" ' And quite alone ? you timid thing ! Remember how you shrieked when the kitten the other evening purred and rubbed against your legs. Could you stay quite alone ? '

" ' Quite.'

" ' Whether he slept or woke ? '

" ' I would pray God he might sleep, and would make no noise.'

" The doctor at this burst into what he called a horse-laugh. ' Come, now,' said he, ' you are a good girl, and I will show you the curiosity I mentioned.'

" He walked to my father's with her, and found him pruning his cherry-tree : he stepped down joyously and ran toward them. 'Have you done ? ' asked the doctor. On the affirmative, ' Give me the pruning-knife, then : it is a shame to see that thief of a sumach getting in at the window.'

" ' O my dear sir ! ' cried Alice, ' show me the curiosity. Mr. Normanby, I never saw that pruning-knife—do let me see it.'

" My father placed his back against the sumach, looked tenderly and anxiously at Alice, shut the knife, gave it to her, and whispered, ' Don't let him ! '

" ' I will disappoint you, my dear guardian, in your pruning, for frightening me.'

" ' What frightened you, Alice ? ' said my father, looking with great solicitude.

" ' He knows,' said Alice, shaking her head.

" ' And Normanby shall know too, deceitful whisperer ! '

" ' O dear, dear sir, don't let him ! '

" ' A truce with pruning,' said the doctor, ' I have other things to do. And now for the curiosity.'

" ' I know what you mean,' said my father : ' several boys were after it.'

" ' And will be, if I don't secure it,' said the doctor.

" ' It was late, I suppose,' said my father, ' for that sort of butter-fly ; yet it was only a butterfly after all.'

" ' O, foul-mouthed fellow ! ' cried the doctor.

" ' Really, I never troubled my head about such trifles,' replied my father in vindication.

" ' Here is the curiosity ! Come and take it, Alice. A man who can hardly live a day without you, and dares not say he loves you.' "

LE DOUX. And you are the only fruit of this marriage ?

NORMANBY. A rough-flavoured and worthless one ! I had a sister, three years younger than myself, whose birth caused the death of my mother.

LE DOUX. Whom you do not remember then.

NORMANBY. I do, and well. I have before me her clear colourless face, which I have heard was always so ; her quiet blue eyes, which she turned on me when I ran out of my bed the morning before her death, hearing her sigh and ask about me. The infant was born weakly, and my mother being weaklier still, it was recommended to find another nurse for it. " The child is mine," exclaimed she in desperation, " she shall not have two mothers."

" And would you rather she should have none, my blessed Alice ?"

" I know not, my Normanby. God protect her ! "

God did ; and, when the parent could not hear her, took her.

DUKE DE RICHELIEU, ETC.

Soon after the marriage, Lord Sandyhurst pressed my father a second time to enter on the living, which he remarked was holden in trust for him ; " or if you do not like it," said his lordship, before any reply could be given, " you shall have the charity-school instead : it is worth as much within a trifle, and there are no quarrels or trouble about tithes : added to which the house is kept in repair by the trustees." My father thanked him, and accepted the school. Five hundred pounds were paid by his lordship's house-steward, and Mr. Chisholm, the land-steward, became rector improprietor of Sandyhurst, the bishop having ordained him at the recommendation of his patron, and every necessary preliminary having been legally observed. He was soon appointed his lordship's chaplain, and within the year was doctor of laws. People found that they had been much mistaken in his character. He was a pious, humane, and liberal man ; so averse from litigation that no wonder he had not succeeded as a lawyer ! He visited the farmers separately ; told them he would leave all questions to their discretion and goodness ; that they might give him a tenth or a twentieth, as they pleased. Some indeed had pretended, while he was agent, that they from time immemorial had paid a modus or composition : he smiled at that, and said he should be truly sorry to prove the contrary.

" Come," said he to the richest of the tenants, whom he had always favoured most, " what have you paid me ? "

" Don't you remember, doctor, you never took more than forty-two shillings, saying that forty-five was too much."

" We must give and take," said the rector, " like good Christians. You shall pay me forty-eight for fourteen years, or during your residence and your son's, and here are two ten-pound bank-notes."

" A bargain ! " exclaimed the farmer.

The rest sent him chickens and ducks ; and, finding him wary, said plainly, they did not see why one neighbour was more neighbour than another. He declared that he would encourage the civil and industrious ; and he would see who was grateful before he carried his liberality much farther. They brought him their waste paper ; such they called the old receipts ; he altered (it was said) such figures as were changed the easiest, and laid them by. In the new agreements those who had large families paid less, those who had none or smaller paid more. Lord Sandyhurst, at the recommendation of his new steward, went over to the estate. The steward was of opinion that it could be doubled : the tenants were ejected. The good rector received them like a father, and consoled them. They lent him their teams, they sold him the manure, they would rather give it to him than leave it on the ground. The steward and a surveyor recommended an enclosure of the common and the warren. The doctor would not oppose any plan conducive to the public good, and would be contented for his share to accept the worst part of the common and the poor barren warren, rather than have litigations about tithes.[1] He gave notice, however, that for the future he should take them in kind, until the commissioners had made their award. Lord Sandyhurst threatened to litigate : the rector would feel the deepest sorrow at any such thing, and would refer the matter to arbitration : nay, his lordship should appoint both arbiters. Blight and another, who came by accident to visit him, were nominated : Chisholm submitted : he had given his word. On the return of the arbiters they were very melancholic.

" Well, what have you done with him ? " said his lordship : they shook their heads. The commissioners, who were neighbours, had left the tithes as they found them : Dr. Chisholm had consented to exchange a part of his glebe for only half the common, and that nuisance which in its present state brought so many foxes about it, the warren.

" He must have seen your lordship's receipts and other papers."

" Surely : he was my steward you know."

" He should not have taken advantage of his knowledge, if indeed he did ; in other respects nobody could have acted more liberally. His warmest wish was the harmony of the parish."

" A lawyer turned parson," cried Lord Sandyhurst, " has the devil by both horns, and can dance him about as he pleases : however I will eat him up with my game."

" My lord," said one of them, " I am sorry to inform you, he has a right of free warren, which is dependent on the warrener's house. He showed us the document."

---

[1] 1st ed. has a footnote : " The same thing happened in an estate belonging to my mother. Mr. Savage made the rector of his parish his gamekeeper and steward, neglecting all inquiries. The tenants had always paid a modus, a few shillings. The rector showed them many indulgencies in their rents, added a trifle to the tithes, and the estate now pays the rector about two hundred a year : for the church never loses its rights, though acquired by wrongs ; and a part of *Saint Peter's patrimony* lies in England."

" I myself gave him with my own hands that long musty scroll about the warren, to prove the extent and show him his advantages. The rogue said my word was enough, and would hardly throw his eyes over the parchment : I observed that his horse was frightened at it, and went off at full speed."

My father heard these particulars, and thanked God that his lordship had relieved him from such heart-burnings and such imputations.

" A pretty thing to thank God for ! " said Dr. Broom, " you might have netted a third of what Chisholm does, and have been deemed an honest man. You have now only your school and your five hundred."

The school he had : the five hundred he never had. Dr. Broom, of his own accord, went to remind the peer that Mr. Normanby of the school had a small matter left by his lordship's worthy father.

" He did say something about five hundred, but he was light-headed in a manner, as you must remember, Broom ; and besides I gave Normanby the school. If he had not been the greatest booby in the universe, he might have been rector of Sandyhurst, and kept his carriage."

" My lord, it is easier in our days for a man to keep his carriage than his word I find."

" I shall not ask you what you mean, my friend Broom, but you shall presently see what I mean."

He walked away, and returned with a horsewhip. Broom, outrageous at the indignity, forgot that he was by thirty years the older man, and, running at him, knocked him down.

LE DOUX. A peer of parliament ! that is grave !—Normanby did not attend to the observation, but went on. " Such, sir, is the custom of our country, that, a man once down is sacred."

LE DOUX. You are the strangest people in the world ! the very opposite of the rest !

NORMANBY. His lordship rose, and, casting aside the whip, became the pugilist, and, not without a long and doubtful contest, threw his adversary. " Do you know who keeps his word now ? " cried he. " Who is the best man now ? "

" The greatest rascal, I must needs confess it," cried the doctor ; " but every dog has his day."

As the late peer had no other child, and was a widower, he made no will : the bequest was verbal. My father could never be induced to apply for the money, and indeed (what he did not know) Lord

Sandyhurst swore he never would pay it, lest he should seem to have been bullied out of it. Broom, thinking that he by his rashness had been the cause of this resolution, lost his admirable flow of spirits, gave up his gun, sat and mused with my parents, whom, he told them, he had ruined, went late to bed, and some say indulged in mild ale. His health, however, did not visibly decline. What then was the astonishment and consternation of his friends, when Phineas, who had taken his boots to his bedside, found him dead from apoplexy ! No work was done in the town that day. He left the little he possessed to my mother and her children, trusting that she would take care of his two servants, who had lived with him all their lives. It amounted to a few hundred pounds, for the tenement was not his own, and he always had been generous. My mother wept over him as over a father ; she had known no other : my father as over a friend ; no other had he known. They found a better place for their maid, and took his domestics into their house.

My mother followed to the grave her parental guardian before she had completed her twenty-second year. My father lived till I was almost of age. The loss of his companion, of whom he talked to me every day from my sixteenth year, shortened his innocent and useful life. In my earlier boyhood I do not think he ever mentioned her. " Christopher," said he on his death-bed, " I have borne up more manfully than you are aware of. You are now old enough to keep the school ; and see here the kindness of our patron."

Lord Sandyhurst, at the entreaty of the parish, had been prevailed on to appoint me to the place of master, vacant by reason of my father's ill health.

" The day is sultry," said he, " open the casement. I have kept my bed three weeks. Look out, and see whether the sumach is in flower : it ought to be, or near it."

" There is one."

" Go down and cut it, and bring it me.—Stop a moment.—Yes, I must have it, Christopher."

I ran down and brought it to him. " How sweet it is ! " said he, laying it on his face, and smiling as if refreshed by it.

" Father," said I, smiling too ; for he seemed much better ; " I did not know that there was any sweet scent in the sumach " ; and would have taken it to smell. One breath shook its feathery flower. It was his last.

DUKE DE RICHELIEU, ETC.

—The colonel pressed the hand of the mariner; for there are workings of the heart that cast down all distinctions.

LE DOUX. Lord Sandyhurst, I am afraid, can have but a very bad heart.

NORMANBY. I am unwilling to suppose that his heart is a very bad one; which would be a heavy accusation; since every man who has received the rudiments of culture, is in great measure the framer of his own. I am more inclined to believe that there is something in his brain defective or amiss; an evil which no man can remedy or control.

LE DOUX. Why do you think so? What you have related is no proof or sign of it, but shows rather that sort of brain which most people have, and which they call the soundest.

NORMANBY. My reason for thinking as I do, is this. When his maternal uncle died, who was doatingly fond of him, and at whose house he had passed the greater part of his boyhood and his youth, he received the congratulations of his acquaintance on his increase of fortune.

LE DOUX. Surely: ought he then to exclude them?

NORMANBY. I should have said, if it had not seemed malicious, that he received their congratulations with pleasure and satisfaction.

LE DOUX. He inherited as much as he expected, did he not?

NORMANBY. I imagine so; everyone knew that Mr. Edward [1] spent his whole income; but the land was unencumbered by debt, and worth about four thousand a-year.

LE DOUX. Well then! he might fairly rejoice at coming into possession.

NORMANBY. Good God! into what possession did he come which was not his more amply and more delightfully before? He gained nothing: he lost the hand that gave him it, the heart that welcomed him to it, the voice that cheered him in his use of it, the dispenser that kept it for his sake, the friend in whose conviviality and converse he could and did enjoy it. On what account do the wise and frugal, on what account do even the idlest and most unthinking, wish for property?

LE DOUX. To spend it among their friends.

NORMANBY. Are then those who plunder them at the gaming-table, those who sell them an unsound horse or such as they them-

[1] 1st, 2nd, and 3rd eds. misprint the name.

selves are afraid to ride, those who recommend to them a cast mistress
or a cashiered steward, those who, seeing them in sickness, call them
in their tenderest mood *poor devils*, and whose most anxious inquiry
is, *what ! alive still ?*—are those the friends that a rational soul
should prefer to the guardian of his infancy, the director of his
adolescence, the crowner of his energies at the goal of manhood,
whose eye stiffened on his harder features (and did not find them so)
ere it closed in death ! Men have been the richer, but no man,
thinking as he ought, ever inherited a *fortune* from parent or from
friend. What mine produces them ! what labour can acquire them !
what regret can recover them once lost ! and shall the only thing
worthless that they leave behind compensate us !

LE DOUX. My good friend, you did not find any great difference in
your fortune, or else perhaps——

NORMANBY. Go on, sir !—Then let me. I possessed so few
things that every one of them gave me a distinct sensation, and a
painful one, reminding me of him who had left them. In this alone
had I to regret the humbleness of my condition. The regret was,
however, of such a nature that by degrees I placed myself in its way
voluntarily, and even went after it above stairs and below. When
I had nothing else remaining to look at, I looked at the knots in the
deal unpainted door, and conned over one of my early lessons on the
cause of their transparency in the sunshine.

LE DOUX. If we retain these weaknesses too long, we are good
for little.

NORMANBY. True ; and if we never have them, we are good for
nothing. Neither our weaknesses nor our strength should come into
play incessantly. Both were given us wisely ; which I should say,
even if I could think of no other purpose than the necessity of
moderating them.

LE DOUX. I do not think, my honest friend, a man like you could
reasonably be suspected of disloyalty or irreligion.

NORMANBY. And if you did think it, sir, my mind would be the
same. I have opened my heart to you because it is long since I have
seen a countenance I like so well, and because it is a pleasure to be
heard attentively.

LE DOUX. Pity ! that your father did not teach you the languages
he had acquired.

NORMANBY. He taught me gardening and geometry, which, he

94

used to tell me playfully, are the washing and clear-starching of the mind, while other things for the most part he considered as the rags or ruffles. When [1] I had acquired from him the elements of Latin, he said to me that I was now able to teach as much as was enjoined by the statutes; and that if ever I had leisure I might extend my knowledge. After a pause, he added that he had seen some who had gained nothing from the classics but the right (as they imagined) of repining, when they found those who had made no greater progress in them, raised to vicarages and rectories, and even higher; and that he would rather leave to me a moderate sustenance than a defective and fallacious title to one more plentiful.

Le Doux. I am charmed at his just views of society, which many men, less prudent than yourself, might turn away from. I must make you better known to my fellow-passengers.

Normanby. Sir, I beg you will not bring them hither.

Le Doux. Have they offended you past forgiveness?

Normanby. They have never offended me at all; but my heart closes at them; as there are some flowers which, without being delicate, close against insects.

Le Doux. I ought to be much flattered at your reception of me.

Normanby. Flattered! no, sir. That is a phrase of your country, and fit for it: let me hear it again, and we converse no longer.

Le Doux. A phrase has lost many a man a friend: I will be more cautious in future. I have listened with due attention to your father's history, and now am anxious to hear the rest of yours, which you abandoned as soon almost as you began.

Normanby. The ashes were hot underfoot. I flew from myself to my father: my wrongs rose up before me. I have now again lost sight of them, partly by the memory of that saintly man, and partly by your encouragement and compassion. Yes, sir, I am like a child who runs behind its parent, a child little used to be caressed and fondled, when at last a stranger bids it come and sit beside him, and is ready and well-pleased to listen to the idle rill of its discourse.

I was pained excessively at the fathers of my boys refusing to visit or receive me; some because they had been so much mistaken in me, and others because, as they said, it really would hurt them. My grief was intolerable when the boys themselves, who had revered

---

[1] From " When " to " away from " added in 2nd ed.

and loved me, hissed me on my way home from church, calling me atheist,[1] jacobin, and regicide. I had taught them to love their neighbour, and had never seen in them anything cruel or unkind. Several of them, on my father's decease, said anxiously to me, " And what shall we do if we lose *you ?* " awaiting my answer in tears. Mr. Chisholm, who had been present at their altered conduct, came up to me just as I was entering my door, and said he hoped what I had heard would be a warning to me. As I returned no answer, but invited him to walk in, " O your humble servant ! many thanks ; is it come to this ! It is well for you that there are no press-gangs up the country : they would teach you loyalty at the mast."

Never had I thought to receive a hint out of church from Mr. Chisholm, of which I should be likely to make any use in my conduct. Another aided him unconsciously. Phineas Pooley, my old servant, placed the roast veal upon the table, and asked me whether I was satisfied with him and Martha, as my parents and Dr. Broom had been.

" Yes, my good Phineas, perfectly."

" Then, sir," said he, " I shall be sorry (God forgive me !) to leave you, though you are now become an enemy to God and man."

" Leave me ? Phineas ! "

" Both of us. We have places for life in the county hospital : we are fitted for the work, and ready to go when you can spare us."

" Dear honest Phineas ! who persuaded you ? "

" No matter : there are good who were thought bad, and bad who were thought good."

" What evil have you ever seen in me, Phineas ? "

" None, sir ; unhappily."

" How ! "

" We can not see the heart."

" Ah then, Phineas, you are in the right to leave me. If you have not yet been able to see my heart, I am to the full as bad a man as any one would represent me."

" You have been kind to me, as I told them, in sickness and in health, and never said a cross word to either of us. ' *Nor did the Tempter to Eve*,' was the reply for this, ' *nor again on the exceeding high mountain.*' At these words, master, I felt how little I was of a

---

[1] Added in 2nd ed. 1st ed. reads : " me jacobin and regicide."

96

scholar (though I heard them a hundred times) and how entirely in the snares of Sin and Death."

Le Doux. There have been people worse treated than you have been, Mr. Normanby, but none more undeservedly. The civility due to your fair countrywoman does not suspend my interest in your recital, yet it obliges me to make inquiries, and, if she is awake, to receive her commands. You will allow me to join you again : you will acknowledge an old acquaintance ?

Normanby. At any time, and with pleasure.

The colonel found Lady Glengrin just waking. She hoped he would by degrees be fitted for the society it would be his destiny to find in Ireland : and some other such pleasantries passed, which were commented on and explained by Sir Firebrace. They spent together the whole evening. Two of the party never rose before noon : Le Doux was of opinion that the only thing tolerable at sea was the rising sun, and always was prepared to greet it.

Does anyone remember (ah ! who does not remember ?) the first time he ever saw myrtles in blossom on the bleak heath, where they spread the most widely and bloom the most profusely ? Does he remember the jolts and jerks, the sands and sudden stops, among the poor cultivation just before he reached them ? How gladly folded he his arms upon his breast and drew the pure air from amid [1] their starry stillness ! Not unlike his feeling was the feeling of Le Doux. He [2] had noticed for the first time a neglected plant, capable of becoming the ornament (if chance had placed it there) of domestic life in an unthrifty station. He had lived, it is true, among the Russians ; but they present no variety ; there is a Tartar flat along the whole people. Potemkin and Orloff differed from cooks and porters only in strength of limb, the pedestal of their greatness.

Uniforms and diamond rings are useful, since without them I should often have forgotten the personages I conversed with, and have ordered them to bring me a glass of water and a biscuit. Resolute to avoid peculiarity, and to conquer that abstraction which is called *absence*, it hardly ever has been my failing, unless in the company of such people ; and I have usually felt a listlessness to amend, or even to apologise for, my fault.

[1] 1st ed. reads : " amid the starry stillness of these interminable plants."
[2] 1st ed. reads : " He had seen for the first time a wild and neglected one, but sweet and pliant, and the ornament . . . domestic and polished life. He had," etc.

Normanby saw the head of Le Doux mounting from the cabin, and saluted him. The conversation was on various subjects, light and uninteresting. Both felt it. " Come, Mr. Normanby," said Le Doux, " I am still your persecutor ; I hope your last. Let us take our old places, and then to Phineas again and the exceeding high mountain."

Normanby smiled and continued.

" Determined to sell my furniture and leave the country, I gave notice of my intention, and sent for the auctioneer, a civil man. He said he owed me no ill-will, and would do as much by me as by another. Looking over the volumes, of which about eight were Greek authors, and fewer Latin, he found hardly anything else than our old English divines. As you have acquired our language, and as these contain three-fourths of what is excellent in it, you must have read them, and must know thoroughly those I am about to mention."

Le Doux bowed, and left no doubt whatever on the mind of Normanby, who thus reported to him the discourse of Edgeware the auctioneer.

" ' These fetch nothing, Mr. Normanby, I do assure you. Let us see—*Lucas on Holiness, Lucas on Happiness.* Lord help us ! we have newer things on them by years and years, living as we do in an age of discovery.[1] *Leighton's Sermons.* The style seems mighty low and wretched.'

" ' It was once a good one,' I answered, ' and will be again when we are fit for it. But crooked thoughts are to be supported by stiff sentences. Let no writer be solicitous of Fame ; she is more uncertain and more blind than Fortune ; let them do for the best and be prepared for the worst. There are few readers and indeed few critics (we must call men by the names they assume) who [2] tolerate Leighton.'

" ' Why, Mr. Normanby, you talk like your father,' said the auctioneer.

" ' I believe, Mr. Edgeware,' said I, ' they are his very words. He used to call the book his milk and honey, and said that if

---

[1] 1st ed. reads : " discovery. Bishop Patrick's *Parable of a Pilgrim.* The style," etc.

[2] 1st ed. reads : " who doubt that Johnson is wiser than Patrick : I have even heard it said in conversation that his periods are more harmonious.' ' Why," etc.

DUKE DE RICHELIEU, ETC.

Leighton [1] had lived in the time of Christ, he doubted whether John would have been the disciple best beloved.[2] He sighed, I remember, as he added, taking me aside by the sleeve, although we were alone, " We are nothing now but sounding-board and cushion." '

" ' *Taylor . . . Barrow——*'

" ' Stop, Mr. Edgeware,' cried I, ' do not throw those aside so carelessly. My father, who knew the ancients intimately, said, " Kit, that couple are worth all their philosophers put together, and would be though they all were Christians. Plato and Xenophon, as men of thought and wisdom, might walk without brushing their skirts between these two covers," striking his hand on a volume of Barrow.'

" ' May be,' interposed the auctioneer ; ' but this Doctor Hugh Blair, with his noble cassock and five-guinea wig, close, trim, and hard, as the feathers round an owlet's eye, outsells him twenty to one. What did your father say of him ? '

" ' That he was a comely man, a well-conditioned Christian, and fair writer ; but that he was so unfriendly to what he called involutions and parentheses, and so fond of straightness and uniformity, that he would straighten a fish-hook, and prefer a file of pins in smooth stiff blue paper, to a diamond crescent with its knobs and bends, among a set of such riotous curls as it can not keep in order and subjection.'

" ' The expression is nobler,' replied the auctioneer, ' but the matter is not unlike in the main what I heard from Squire Prew, to whom I knocked down a copy last year. " It comes cheap," said he, " and I know who wants one, or I would never have bought it. I have read the doctor once ; and what such a genius says once is quite enough. He is indeed a neat handy sort of a person ; but he washes his butter so, and in such saltless water, that one can not tell whether it is butter or bear grease. First, he would persuade you that verse has nothing to do with poetry ; then that Ossian wrote what M'Pherson fabricated. When you have swallowed this, he thinks you drunk enough to believe it is excellent, carries you across his shoulders to bed, and whispers *Well, God bless you !* that is, if you lie quiet, and believe you have found a treasure worth more than Homer

[1] 1st ed. reads : " Patrick."
[2] 1st ed. has a footnote : " The worthy clergyman, whose character is represented in the elder Normanby, held Patrick in high estimation, unconscious of his resemblance to the prelate in the finer features. The reader is not expected to participate this feeling quite equally."

99

and Milton." I made bold to answer; "then, Mr. Prew, you doubt these battles of the *car-borne*." " Hearkye, honest Edgeware; I believe the stories of few battles; for where there are two that fight there are ten that lie; but I believe that in some way or other they were fought. I will admit that these were fought too, when my coachman drives four in hand along the eaves of the houses in Sandy-hurst : he would do no more than they did, unless he stormed the belfry with 'em." As I knew of Ossian only what I had heard Mrs. Edgeware read in a rainy day, the day before I knocked him down to the Squire, I could make no answer; but I felt hurt at hearing this ridicule at what she distinctly told me was the finest thing in the world, adding that men in those days were men indeed.'

" The conversation about my books might have gone on, if some-one had not tapped gently at the door. It was the servant-maid of Miss Penelope Haynes, the lady of whom my father had rented his cottage. The girl desired to have a word in private with the auctioneer. He returned to me and said, ' I am going to speak against my interest : you may have a guinea for your books.'

" ' No, Edgeware,' said I, ' the three bibles and three prayer-books I never sell, nor this Epictetus.'

" ' You cannot want three bibles and three prayer-books; beside, they are alike, even to the binding.'

" ' And yet,' answered I, ' sometimes I read in one with more pleasure, and sometimes in another.' It was so; for often did I think whose manuals two were, and whose gift the third.

" ' Well,' said the auctioneer, ' I fancied now one was too much.'

" ' Do not let Miss Pen be disappointed,' said I; ' take the list; leave the price to her.'

" He went, and acted faithfully. She looked over the catalogue, and said with peevishness, ' I do not find that bad book which contains such stuff: I wanted to burn it.' Edgeware ran to me with the answer.

" ' Tell her,' said I, ' that I burned it myself; that Martha covered the veal yesterday with the last pages.'

" She sent for Martha, and asked her.

" ' No, Miss Haynes ! ' cried Martha.

" ' See the effect of such publications ! ' ejaculated Miss Haynes. ' Until the present time, Mr. Normanby, I am certain, was incapable of a falsehood.'

" ' Miss,' added Martha, ' I have no grudge against my master, an upright man until now, and never shall it be said that, whether he ordered it or not, I covered a loin of veal for him with a poisonous book. I threw the remnant of it into the kitchen fire ; and even that did the meat no good ; he could hardly touch it at dinner.'

" Miss Haynes sent Martha back to me, in order to confer about the library. I waited upon her. She said she was happy to see me, which she could do without the slightest impropriety in the presence of witnesses. Then she added, she was sorry that she might have been thought uncivil to my father at the decease of his worthy lady, particularly as he had given her a fine magnolia ; but people might talk, and she should think long before she changed her condition.

" ' Madam,' said I, ' few persons have lived so irreproachably as you have done ; and I can not imagine you have to blame yourself in regard to my father. The magnolia was not a present : you admired it, I have heard him say,[1] and he carried it to your house intending to request your acceptance of it, when seeing a sumach on the gravel-walk, he asked Tobias whether you would make an exchange : you did so.'

" ' It was only the stump,' replied she.

" ' I preserve it still, madam, and of all the things I leave in the country I leave it with most regret.'

" Penelope blushed deeply and looked timorously. ' You are then really leaving us ? ' said she.

" ' Yes, madam.'

" ' And what do you do with your furniture, Mr. Normanby ? '

" ' Sell it.'

" On any other day of her life Penelope would have bargained about it ; for she was shrewd, selfish, and the only parishioner of the landholders that did not suffer in some way by the inclosure. She had thirty acres of freehold : four more were stipulated from the waste ; and the rector whispered in her ear, ' I should not wonder if, with the little knoll you set your heart upon, they throw the green lane in. Do you know ! the hollies are worth twenty pounds ! ' The rector prognosticated wonderfully : it turned out exactly so. She enlarged the cottage and garden, and called it Eden-place, in preference to Eden-villa, Eden-lodge, or Eden-house, and would have

---

[1] 1st ed. reads : " say, when you condescended to visit my Mother on her marriage. He," etc.

painted the grey stone brick-colour, if my father had not designedly lent her a treatise which prevented it. ' We may sometimes pick up an idea from a book,' said she.

" To return. ' As to those volumes, I will take care of them for you, if you please, Mr. Normanby, on your giving me your word of honour that there is no indecent print in them, nor blasphemy, nor sedition.' I did so, at each pause, and thanked her warmly.

" ' If you should not be able to dispose of your furniture, I have room in my barn for it.' I accepted this offer too, in favour of an arm-chair covered with white dimity, and a bed of crimson-moreen, with two watch-pockets fancifully embroidered, requesting her in my gratitude to accept any volume she chose : she thanked me and declined it. I took my leave, paid my two servants a year's wages, gave them what clothes and linen I could spare, and left my house an hour before sunrise the next morning. Neither I nor my father had had any acquaintance out of Sandyhurst : I never had been twenty miles from home. When I had walked about that distance, and must be near Nottingham, as I fancied, I found myself in a park, in the midst of old pinasters, trees I had never seen before, and observed a water of vast extent. Even this was to me a strange country. I began to feel a desire of wandering ; I went toward the water, and (was I awake or dreaming ?) I saw before me a monument erected to the memory of Captain Riou—a naval officer of high merit, as we know better than you can : but not better than some of you do. The sun grew hotter, for it was near mid-day, and I went to lie under the pinasters. I was watching the squirrels on them, playing their tricks and leaping from tree to tree, when a prodigious herd of deer gallopped past me. Another strange sight ! although I had remarked the same creature in books of natural history. My eyes were pursuing them, when a gentleman on a pony, seeing me cleanly and well dressed, saluted me very courteously, and asked me if I was looking for the road to the house. I rose, answered in the negative, and told him I had been induced to rest there for the pleasure of observing the squirrels. ' It must be a humane man who suffers them to riot here, seeing the number of holes they have made in these trees.'

" ' They began to make the holes long ago,' said he, ' and the property is now theirs.'

" ' But the trees are every day growing worse and worse, and here are many thousands : are they all bored so by these little animals ? '

" ' I believe every one.'

" ' Ah spare yon emmet.'

" ' I beg your pardon; you were making a remark: have I interrupted ? '

" ' Sir,' answered I, ' if I had not been here, perhaps I never should have remembered two verses which my father taught me, I am afraid on some childish act of cruelty, and which I began to repeat, and checked myself.   They are ill applicable to the occasion.'

" ' What may they be ? ' said he.

> " ' Ah spare yon emmet, rich in hoarded grain ;
>   He lives with pleasure and he dies with pain.'

" ' They are from the Persian,' [1] said he, ' and, if we dropped the hoarded grain, are among the best thoughts in that poetry, which contains few, and those trivial and distorted.   Like the food of the country, they are in themselves the most insipid things in the world, and, to make them palatable, the most highly spiced.'

" ' Our own poets,' said I, ' are more original, I am inclined to think, and more natural.'

" He replied, ' We have two schools of poetry : one is kept at the milliner's, the other at the workhouse.   At the former we find imitations of Turkish carpets in moth-eaten plush, Persian robes and Scotch phillibegs, claymores, and scymitars, the sheaths of good varnished kid-skin, and the blades of the best waved paper, with every sort of dress that janisary and spahi, lowlander and highlander, faery and kelpy, witch and houri, ought to put on in gala.   There is also the most elegant assortment of tombs, and the sweetest poisons one's heart could desire ; with wax-candles of peeled elder, and flambeaux of red hair, and polygraphic transparencies (the oil indeed rather rancid and fishy), to be had for next to nothing.'

" ' I perceive, sir, you are not a patron or trustee of this school.'

" ' Nor of the other,' answered he ; ' I prefer Gray.'

" ' Sir,' replied I, ' the other must at least be acknowledged to be nearer to truth and nature.   Can poets too much avoid the artificial ? We prefer what is past.   Gray in his time was less considered than even our tavern-toasters, crowned with the parsley of the kitchen and sitting on the tripod of the tap-room.   In what manner has the

---

[1] Firdausi, translated by Sir W. Jones.

greatest of critics (to pass over the public) treated the greatest of writers ? '

" It was my custom in my walks to carry an Epictetus in one pocket and a Pascal in the other : on a blank leaf of Pascal had my father written these words, which, not being able to pronounce them correctly, I gave to the gentleman on the pony.   And I now present them to you in the same volume."

LE DOUX (*reads*).

" Paschal est un gentil personnage ; il ecrit bien ; il a fait de si jolies prieres ; il a esté nourry à Genes ; il est conseiller d'estat."

Who wrote this ?

NORMANBY. Joseph Scaliger.

LE DOUX. A German critic, was he not ?

NORMANBY. I rather think, a French.

LE DOUX. He writes then as if he lived a hundred years ago.   I have seen exactly such French in an old treaty.   Now let me hear more about the gentleman : his remarks are admirable.   But you, I imagine, were in the midst of your reply ; pray indulge me with it.

NORMANBY. " I have heard my father say thus," continued I, " when he lent me Potter's *Æschylus* to read.   ' Christopher, I doubt not that Thespis was preferred to him by the graver critics ;   there was something so unaffected in a cart, and so little of deception in wine-dregs ;   and yet, Christopher, the *Prometheus* is the grandest poetical conception that ever entered into the heart of man.   Homer could no more have written this tragedy than Æschylus could have written the *Iliad*.   Mind me, I do not compare them.   An elephant could not beget a lion, nor a lion an elephant.   Critics talk most about the *visible* in sublimity : the Jupiter, the Neptune.   Magnitude and power are sublime but in the second degree, managed as they may be.   Where the heart is not shaken, the Gods thunder and stride in vain.   True sublimity is the perfection of the pathetic, which has other sources than pity ; generosity, for instance, and self-devotion.   When the generous and self-devoted man suffers, there comes Pity : the basis of the sublime is then above the water, and the poet, with or without the Gods, can elevate it above the skies.   Terror is but the relic of a childish feeling : pity is not given to children.'   So said he ; I know not whether rightly.   For the wisest differ on poetry, the knowledge of which, like other most important truths, seems to be reserved for a purer state of sensation and existence. Seldom have I doubted my father's judgment; but as he was not a poet, and as none but the very greatest have a voice on poetry, here I hesitate."

I had paused : the gentleman on the pony looked at me attentively. "If you will take any refreshment," said he, "I shall have great pleasure in accompanying you to the house."

I thanked him, and told him that I was on my road to the sea, hoping to serve my country, and impatient to reach my destination.

"I myself was of that profession," said he. "Have you been fortunate in your promotion ? "

"To say the truth, sir," answered I, "I never was in the profession, and wish chiefly to try whether the service will benefit my spirits."

"Have you any friend who has a command, or whose credit may recommend you ? "

I mentioned my grandfather's name, as the only chance.

"He was a gallant and good creature, I have heard, and must have many friends still living among our older admirals. My recommendation is less weighty, but such as it is you may command it."

I requested to know the name of a person to whose benevolence a stranger was so deeply indebted.

"Not at all," said he. "A few lines are written while you take a sandwich, and Lady Newark will be charmed that I present to her the grandson of so distinguished an officer."

"It is Lord Newark [1] then who has condescended to show me this kindness——"

He bowed. "It can hardly be called so, though you accept it, as I trust you will do."

I thanked him ; but added that, as I did not intend to remain at sea long, and as my studies had not been nautical, I must decline an introduction which might procure for me eventually what could not belong to me. Whether my words, my resolute but respectful manner, a faultering in a voice that seemed little apt to faulter, or the bow, so unlike what I could make again or ever had made, while I placed my right hand upon a breast enlarged with gratitude, whether one of these or all of them interested him, as I walked fast away he sat quietly upon his pony. Soon however he came beside me. "I

[1] 1st ed. has a footnote : "The late Earl Manvers."

perceive, sir," said he, taking off his hat again, " I have done very ill the honours of the place : we have not always the same presence of mind, seamen or landsmen. You will not favour me with your company, nor permit me to make a trial whether I have a friend in the navy who may recollect me "—he paused. I was silent. " If however at any time you should happen to think of our short conversation, allow me to tell you that this place is called Thoresby Park, and that the post town is Ollerton. I wish you a pleasant journey, a prosperous voyage, and a speedy recovery of your health."

Everything I had seen this day, everything I had felt, was new and strange to me. Unkindness had pained me ; kindness, in such swift succession after it, overthrew me. Little did I then imagine how highly I should have gratified the most amiable and friendly man living, by affording him an opportunity of assisting me ! Little did I consider, or know indeed, that I should be the means of enlivening the sweet sense of obligation, in some one among the many whom his care had educated, his bounty had fed, and his interest had promoted.

I was hardly on the public road when I perceived a magnificent coach at the door of a public-house, and a gentleman in scarlet uniform, whom I supposed to be the general of the district, particularly as he was giving some orders to another in uniform, who held a horn. On seeing me, he cried proudly, but invitingly, " Are you for the Opposition ? "

" No, sir," answered I indignantly and sharply, " I do not rejoice in the misfortunes of my country, nor triumph in its misrule, nor exalt its enemies."

He lifted up his eyebrows scornfully, and addressing himself to a lady in the coach, " The merest fool I ever set eyes upon ! " said he aloud. And looking at me again, " What, in the devil's name, has the Opposition to do with politics ? Out with fifteen shillings, man, and you sleep at the Swan with Two Necks to-morrow night. Come, jump up ; we are off." The passengers explained ; I mounted ; I arrived in London. The next morning, on the road to my banker's, I bowed to those who looked at me. One returned my civility by the words " I am surprised at your assurance : I never knew you." In fact, sir, what is a civility in other countries, in England is the reverse : we have a national antipathy to courtesy and politeness.

LE DOUX. I would not have ventured to make that remark. Allow me to congratulate you on your candour : you have given me better occasions to pay my compliment on your originality. I attend you.

NORMANBY. On reaching Lombard-street, a place excessively thronged, I stopped several times, begging the persons to pass. One asked me whether I took him for a pick-pocket ; I could not imagine why. Unfortunately I did the same thing, in a gentler tone of voice, to a young lady of great beauty, who had just alighted from her carriage, and who in some confusion took the arm of her brother. He filliped me under the nose, threw a card at me, which from the spitefulness of his manner I thought might be some combustible, and said " Another time you will know a modest woman."

Finding my banker, I told him my business. He inquired if I wished to go as school-master. I answered " No ; the active life of a sailor is necessary to my health and spirits." He went away, and conversed in almost a whisper with a gentleman who often looked at me in great good-humour, insomuch that I was on the point of making my obeisance to him, in despite of the lessons I had received. The banker came to me, and said if I would return in three days I might hear of something. I requested of him to inform me where I could find a private lodging. After a few moments of reflection, he spoke to an elderly clerk, who replied in a low voice, " You think then, sir, he may be trusted ? " He nodded : the clerk took me two miles off, across the river, stopped at a small house, and speaking to a decent woman, called to me, and said, " Would you like to dine with the family ? "

" Beyond all things," I replied, " for I do not know a soul within a hundred and fifty miles, and would rather go without a meal than look for one."

The mistress said she had only one spare room ; that if I remained a week the price was one guinea ; but that if I disliked the apartment I should pay the proportion, and not be obliged to keep it. She then asked me when I proposed to come. I told her, if she permitted it I would begin from that moment ; for one hour's walk in London had tired me more than four in the country. She consented. Shortly came my clothes : I placed them on the little white tent-bed, with my bibles, prayer-books, and my father's black pocket-book, containing some maxims, some reminiscences, and a sampler. Believe who will that there are no amulets against evil, against the very worst of evil, mad resentments and desires. Never did one of them touch me the day I had but looked upon that sampler. My landlady said that her sitting-room was always at my disposal ; that the bed-room was too dark to read conveniently ; and that she perceived I had some books. She went down stairs again, and shortly afterward the dinner was served. Two young women entered, curtsied, and took their seats ; they were pretty ; silent, but not shy : immediately after dinner they retired. The lady then said, " Those are my daughters, Mr. Normanby. I did not introduce them ; such is my way ; excuse me."

" Madam," said I, " I must blush at my rusticity : I never was much in the society of ladies, and my spirits make me unworthy of theirs. I hope I committed no peculiar act of inattention."

At tea they both spoke to me, and with such gentleness that I was happy. I retired to bed early, and observed over the chest of drawers two little shelves suspended by a green cord, and filled with books. Different were indeed the authors, far different in manner and merit ; but those who read them seldom know that ; and I hail the family where I find them. *Milton, The Spectator, Young, Parnell*, Hervey's *Meditations*, and Thomson's *Seasons*. Translated from the French were *Telemachus* and the *Travels of Cyrus*.

I returned to my banker at the time appointed : he showed me a letter from Edgeware, by which I learned that, after the sale of my furniture, an addition was made to my fortune of nearly eighty pounds. Incredible ! I had in the whole some hundreds ; and yet I went to sea !

" Well," said my banker, " you go down to the Nore and sail with Admiral Gambier." I went down, and sailed. The [1] gentleman I had seen at the banker's was commander of the fleet. We made on this cruise the greatest nautical discovery that ever had been made by our countrymen.

LE DOUX. I never heard it : you were before Brest, surely, and blockading the harbour.

NORMANBY. We were.

LE DOUX. Well then, how make any discovery ?

NORMANBY. We found that we could fight, when occasion was offered us, just as well without the damnation of our eyes, or any limb or faculty about us, as if we had been splitting or blasting the whole day long, and even though we believed that God was with us and helping us. Peace was concluded. The admiral was pleased to say

---

[1] From " The " to " fleet " added in 2nd ed.

that he had been a witness of my coolness and intrepidity on a service of some enterprise, and thanked me. Perhaps [1] I should not have mentioned this, unless it were to illustrate an observation I made at the time ; namely, that a single good word is quite sufficient to compensate for all the bad that were ever cast against us.

We had two Frenchmen aboard our ship : one of them taught me to pronounce the language so as at least to be understood, and I had permission to go ashore with him at Morlaix. He was a fisherman of St. Servan : his father had been shot by the republicans at the attack on Dinan, and he himself was thrown among the dead and wounded, from the summit of those lofty walls. His brother had been the play-fellow of Lazar Hoche, and, ignorant of his father's fate, accompanied that general in his campaigns, and rose to the rank of colonel. This he learned at Morlaix, and that the reigment was at Paris, where Bonaparte was about to be declared consul for life. The [2] two brothers, though always most brotherly, had taken opposite sides in politics. The sailor was devoted to the cause of Louis, from having heard in his boyhood a little fisher-girl, while she was mending a net, sing a stanza in praise of Henri IV. The colonel was a republican, because a thumb and finger quite as active, and belonging to a lace-maker quite as pretty as his brother's brown Siren, had sewed the tricolor in his hat and had bitten off the thread. They who argue and write and fight about politics have seldom such good reasons or such fixed principles.

I accompanied my messmate : the meeting of the brothers was ecstatic, and the colonel swore to me that the next to Lazar Hoche, the truest of republican hearts, he loved his Pierre. I left them, and looked for lodgings, it being agreed that we should dine together. The colonel then begged my address, put it into his pocket, and called on me early the next day. " You have done well," said he ; " one likes one's own countrymen."

Singular ! that my lodgings should, within a few houses, be opposite the very man's whose book had caused my exile. Curious to see so celebrated a character, on the departure of my visitor I went across to the door. An old woman met me at it, and, on my inquiry, said, " Go up, my friend ; the third story ; he will be at breakfast when I return."

---

[1] From " Perhaps " to " us " added in 2nd ed.
[2] From " The " to " principles " added in 2nd ed.

" Oh ! I will call another time then."

" Go in, go in."

Saying this she closed the door. I mounted the steps, and saw in the antechamber a somewhat elderly man brushing a grey coat.

" Friend," said I, " is your master at home ? "

" Whom do you wish to see ? Mr. Paine ? "

" Yes."

" He will be with you shortly : pray sit down."

He put on his coat, and followed, and lifting off some leaves from a plate of mulberries, invited me to partake of them. I took two or three, while he waved a clean folded cravat over them, to drive away the flies. He was robust and fresh-complexioned, but every hair was white : his appearance, I thought, was military. The old woman returned, with half a small roll of bread in her hand, passed us, entered the next room, and, in answer to a question which I did not hear, replied " I know he is—your eyebrows are adjusted in a manner quite different from ours—and he speaks villanous French, like a Low-Breton, otherwise he is a pretty man enough, and does not look so like a fool or an otter as the rest."

Paine entered. His knees were unbuttoned ; he had neither coat nor waistcoat on ; the white was worn off his shirt ; it had recovered the original hue belonging to it before it saw the bleaching-ground, from the flowers of which, if they have any fragrance, it was innocent of stealing any. He was uncombed, unshaven, and unwashed. He looked at me, and returned my salutation not ungracefully.

" Mr. Paine," said I, smiling, " you owe me some reparation."

" If I do and can make it, I will."

I repeated my story, during which he dipped his bread into a glass of brandy, and ate it : his hand and head trembled. It was noon : martial music was heard in the street. He pushed away the better part of his roll and brandy ; his countenance was inflamed ; he looked stedfastly at his friend, and said, " I think, Tate,[1] if I may judge, you have heard military music you like better."

" You judge rightly, Thomas ! " answered General Tate.

" Wonderful it appears to me," said I, " that a nation of late so enthusiastic for liberty, should voluntarily bend to despotism."

" You have not lived among us," answered Paine. " The whole

[1] Tate : an American appointed to command the Legion of criminals that was to be allowed amplest licence in the invasion of England.

nation may be made as enthusiastic about a salad as about a constitution ; about the colour of a cockade as about a consul or a king. This fellow has done advisedly in calling himself consul : it will hold for a couple of years : he will then change the name, and be tribune or emperor—tribune, if prudent, as the more popular, and as the people see emperors in the vilest of their enemies : urchins whipt and promising to be good, very good, for ever good, by Christ and Peter ! but spitting at the flogger on being let loose, and holding out one fist at a distance, while the other draws up the waistband. Bonaparte wants conduct, foresight, knowledge, experience, and (the Council of Five-hundred knows it) courage. He will do harm, but not long. He lives in terror—— What are you smiling at, Tate ? ”

“ My mother had a proverb of her own,” replied he, “ that a frightened cat throws down most pewter.”

“ You will shortly see,” resumed Paine, “ the real strength and figure of Bonaparte. He is wilful, headstrong, proud, morose, presumptuous : he will be guided no longer : he has pulled the pad from his forehead, and will break his nose or bruise his cranium against every table, chair, and brick in the room, until at last he must be sent to the hospital.”

“ He has the finest army upon earth,” said Tate, “ and his enemies are down.”

“ If it were possible,” Paine replied, “ to be hurt by such enemies, he would point at them, nettle them, shout in their ears while they were sleepy, put crumbs in their beds, shorten their sheets, and empty foul water down their throats, till they contrived to break his shins for him by some machination or other. The army, with such means of recruiting it, with Glory for his crimp and Plutus for his paymaster, seems indestructible. If the earth can not do it, he will throw it into crucible after crucible ; he will melt it in water or evaporate it in air. In other words, navies and climates can and will shake and dissolve it.”

“ Thomas,” answered the general, “ I never thought you a visionary ; but now indeed I must think you one. I do not estimate very highly the man’s abilities, and less highly still his prudence ; but he is no fool ; he will not throw away what he has.”

“ I will retract my words,” said Paine, “ at the first wise thing he does. Smile, sir ! it is rarely that the wisest man can do anything better, or anything on some occasions more difficult.

" Let gazetteers and hawkers be dazzled by the emblazoned names they wave about their ears, and hold out to us with fierce vociferations : but let calmer men ask themselves, whether they really think Bonaparte would have surmounted the difficulties and dangers that environed Three-fingered Jack ?   And whether Three-fingered Jack would have thrown away fifty thousand soldiers so inconsiderately and fruitlessly as Bonaparte ?   There is not on record one who has committed so many faults and crimes with so little temptation to commit them.   There [1] is not a leveret three months old that does not shape its course more sagaciously.   Tyrants in general shed blood upon plan or from passion : he seems to have shed it only because he could not be quiet, and from no stronger motive or better reason than he would have had for going to the theatre or the chase.   Depend upon it, this giddy and insensate man, deserter of his armies and of his principles, will finish no better than he has been going on.

" There are few who form their opinions of greatness from the individual.   His sword, his mantle, his strut, his swagger, and even things which constitute no part of him, are his greatness ; such as his porters, his guards, his soldiers, and the gilding on the ceilings of his rooms.   Not those who need the fewest, but those who have the most about them, are the great ; as though people, like bars of iron, could be mended and magnified by adding one to another.   Even in quieter scenes than where such excrescences spring up, if you see a gentleman go out fox-hunting in his scarlet jacket and his velvet cap, on a spirited horse, with merry dogs, and a couple of grooms behind him, you consider him as a personage far more worshipful, than if, ignorant of his condition, you found him catching a rabbit in a hedge-bank with a ferret.   Ovid says, ' The girl is the least part of herself ' : of himself as certainly the man is.   I should not wonder if Bonaparte, by his intemperate use of power and thirst of dominion——"

LE DOUX. I never heard before of this Mr. Paine : he appears to be a staunch royalist, an enemy of usurpation : but his language in

---

[1] From " There " to " sagaciously " taken from a footnote in 1st ed., which reads : " I have been censured by the liberal, I hear, for my attacks, as they are called, on this impostor.   I confess, I do not love him the better, as many do, for having been the enemy of my country ; nor should I love him the less for it, if his enmity had been principled and manly.   At the time when Paine is represented speaking, his blunders had but begun.   Every great step he took after his first accession to power was erroneous.   There is not a leveret three months old, unterrified or terrified, that does not choose its course more wisely."

regard to the emperors is deficient in that decorum with which we are in the habit of treating friendly powers. What were his prophetic words?

NORMANBY. " That the people would wish for their old kings."

LE DOUX. Excellent!

NORMANBY. The words that follow injure them materially.

LE DOUX. Impossible! so clear-sighted a politician!—But let me hear the end.

NORMANBY. " Forgetting what beasts they were."

LE DOUX. The English are much in the practice of using this language, speaking of our kings, and the same bad taste begins to be imitated on the Continent. What did Mr. Tate reply?

NORMANBY. " They may eat their white beans while turkeys and truffles are before them; but they will never run and take down the carrion they have thrown aside and left stinking on the hedge."

LE DOUX. Two fools! Ignorant of French loyalty, of the veneration we bear toward our kings. The Revolution was the work of half-a-dozen philosophers over their coffee; and its enormities were committed by about as many lawyers and literators, followed by thirty or forty miscreants from Marseilles. The nation was not guilty of it.

NORMANBY. Strange! that the good did not put down the bad.

LE DOUX. Panic, panic! We are subject to that and the *migraine*. Mr. Paine and the other might have conversed with you upon subjects they understood better than politics, which require a peculiar tact.

NORMANBY. Indeed they left off where I did. Mr. Paine expressed his regret that he himself was not the only man persecuted for his writings: he offered me brandy. I declined it : " Tate," said he, " you have some flavoured with orange-flowers : bring it."

Tate rose for it. I declared that I never had tasted brandy, nor any other spirit, and could not.

" You are a young man," said he, " and may find perhaps a better remedy for your misfortunes than I could offer you : brandy is mine."

"I wish, Thomas," said the general, "I had been able to persuade you that a glass of claret would have done better. A bottle between us, which is enough, would have given us time for conversation, and warmed us gently and genially as we went on."

" Tate," answered he, " wine is for the indolent and the happy.

Say no more : I am not quite well : that cursed music has hurt me. I might go so far as to complain ; I should then lose your esteem, and my own." He raised his head, which for the first time did not tremble : a short silence ensued : I took my leave, requesting his permission to return. He told me that he should be glad to see me, but that he must claim a privilege which literary men and invalids possess in common, and to which, therefore, he had a double right ; an exemption from the obligation of visiting ; adding, " No man who visits can do much, or anything well."

On the following day (for I was little disposed to look at the strides of a usurper) I went again to Mr. Paine's. " Never mind my face," said he : " water makes it blister : there are blisters enow already : and soap cracks the skin. I needed not have written that book : they tell me the arguments are found in others : I had no money to buy, nor time to read them. Gibbon was pensioned, I was prosecuted, for one and the same thing : but he was a member of parliament, and wore powder."

" And if neither you nor he had written any such things, would you or the world have been the worse ? "

" Certainly," said he, " the world would have been the worse, because the less wise."

" Ah, Mr. Paine ! he is not over-rich in knowledge who can not afford to let the greater part lie fallow, and to bring forward his produce according to the season and the demand. Wisdom is only a good as being an instrument of happiness. There have been great masses of it in the world, collected by experience and approved by experiment ; we only survey the fragments, most of which are pre-served by religion. The ancients had their sacred groves : pirates and philosophers laughed at them as they passed : they were cut down : pestilences followed. Experience had evinced their utility to simpler and calmer men. Whenever people meet——"

A grave decent-looking man now entered, whom the general saluted in silence, giving him his hand, and Mr. Paine said, " Take a seat, Zacharias ! This young man is as religious as you are, and you will hear him with as much pleasure as I do. There are two good things in the world, reason and sincerity : I am convinced he has the one, we will try him on the other—— Go on, go on ; let us lose no time."

I continued : " Wherever people meet and bring with them good intentions, they humanise more and more at the sight of common wants and common sufferings : they warm in sympathy, they strengthen in forbearance. You think no religion good : I think all are, from which cruelty, fraud, lucre, and domination, are excluded. We mortals want supports : some require a crutch iron-cramped, some are contented if it is well-cushioned, others are kept up fearlessly by the weakest walking-stick. If there is only the probability that a man will be the happier or the honester by one belief than by another, would you hesitate to leave him in possession of it ? Wisdom is not to be hazarded with the same levity or indifference as wit. We may acquire the name of deep-thinkers at too high a price, which price, like the interest of money, is limited or illicit, rendering the transaction void, and subjecting us to the forfeit of the little we have been toiling to establish. Shall so acute a reasoner, so clear a writer, rub off his hide and canker his flesh to the bone against a tree, striving to push it down, because some people sit beneath it on a Sunday, and return to their supper the more contented ? "

" That is unfair," said he ; " the motive is misstated."

" The fact remains," replied I, " under the parable : and I thank you for correcting me on the abuse of language. No man ever argued so fairly as he might have done. We pour in more or fewer words, and weaker or stronger, to gratify our organs, according to our warmth and excitement."

" Carry that home with you," said he, seizing my hand, " and tell the twelve judges, and the score or two of bishops, that they never have said anything so just. Eloquence is the varnish of falsehood ; truth has none ! "

" What ! " said I, taking from my pocket and giving to him my Pascal and Epictetus. " Are not these eloquent ? "

" Neither of them," answered he ; " they are only the best-written books in the world, being the plainest and fullest of ratiocination. That is eloquence which moves the reason by working on the passions. Burke is eloquent ; I am not. If I write better than he does, it is because I have seen things more distinctly, and have had the courage to take them up, soft or hard, pretty or ugly, and to turn them on their backs in despite of tooth or claw. Plato would give as noble a description of a rhinoceros as Aristoteles could do ; ninety-nine in a hundred would prefer it. The only difference is this : while the one has been confounding it with the camelopardalis, the other has been measuring its joints, counting its teeth, inspecting its belly, and anatomising the whole animal." [1]

LE DOUX. He spoke of the celebrated Mr. Burke, who wrote that great letter, which excited such a strong sensation ? Did not he ?

NORMANBY. The same.

LE DOUX. A fine noble letter ! full of facts and inferences ! brilliant imagination ! I must read it. I very much approve of your argument in favour of revelation. Mr. Paine can be little short of a Quaker, or Socinian, or Free-thinker.

NORMANBY. I am afraid he remained one.

" O Mr. Paine ! " said I, earnestly, " let me bring you a few good books : let us open the *New Testament* together ! "

" What service will that do ? "

" It is the plantain," cried I, " which the reptile man may creep to and chew with advantage, while the venom is yet fresh in him."

LE DOUX. Mighty smart allusion ! he ought to have been affected : was he ?

NORMANBY. He replied thus.

" Good books, as you call them, make you comfortable : good brandy makes me so. I have the twelve apostles in this bottle, and they never shall complain that I hold them long imprisoned."

LE DOUX. Charlatan !

NORMANBY. I was discouraged.

" At least, Mr. Paine, leave others their habitudes, while they are harmless, and think it equally so to love God as to love brandy."

" Ay, ay," said he, " jog on quietly, and let your neighbour be robbed and plundered by any rogue who may have the impudence to call him my son, or my brother, or my sheep."

" No, sir," answered I indignantly, " there draw the pen and cry, Stand ! For such let there be an *Age of Reason* and *Common Sense*.

---

[1] 1st ed. reads : " animal.' ' Is not Adam Smith eloquent ? ' ' Say elegant —Philosophy does not spurn at elegance—He will open as many eyes, as the other has blinded ; for he has ages to work in ; Edmund's occupation 's gone.' LE DOUX," etc.

[1st ed. in a list of Errata has a note, with erroneous page reference, as follows : " Paine, I have heard, thought Adam Smith the best of Scotch writers : yet I doubt, on reconsideration, whether I am warranted in attributing to him so high an estimate. My own sentiments, in regard to national prosperity, have always been the contrary to those disseminated from Edinburgh ; and altho' I have Archibald Bower and Beattie now before me, I am yet to be instructed that any Scotchman has written in english very elegantly."]

DUKE DE RICHELIEU, ETC.

A branch of a fruit-tree may be so covered with insects, and these insects may have eaten into it so deeply, and have so sucked and blighted it, that the best gardener would cut it off totally."

The general left the room on business ; Mr. Paine seemed as if he grew tired of the conversation ; the gentleman who had entered, and who had taken no part in it, said he would (if I pleased) accompany me. When we were in the street, he thanked me for the defence I had made.

" I wonder," said he, " what motive Mr. Paine can have for his good actions, since he avoids society, and disbelieves (I am afraid) the pleasure God takes in virtue. As for conscience, if that alone were sufficient, and perhaps it might be, he deadens both the bad and the good of it with liquor."

" To speak plainly," answered I, " much as I have heard about him, I never heard of his good actions. That he is strictly honest and just I have reason to believe."

" Sir," said he, " let me tell you what he did for me. My name is Zachariah Wilkes.* I was arrested in Paris, and condemned to die. I had no friend here ; and it was a time when no friend would have served me : Robespierre ruled. ' I am innocent ! ' I cried in desperation. ' I am innocent ; so help me God ! I am condemned for the offence of another.' I wrote a statement of my case with a pencil ; thinking at first of addressing it to my judge, then of directing it to the president of the Convention. The jailer, who had been kind to me, gave me a gazette, and told me not to mind seeing my name, so many were there before it.

" ' O ! ' said I, ' though you would not lend me your ink, do transmit this paper to the president.'

" ' No, my friend ! ' answered he gaily. ' My head is as good as yours, and looks as well between the shoulders, to my liking. Why not send it (if you send it anywhere) to the deputy Paine here ? ' pointing to a column in the paper.

---

* This anecdote was communicated to me at Florence, by Mr. Evans, a painter of merit, who studied under Lawrence, and who knew personally Wilkes and Watt. In religion and politics he differed widely from Paine.—W. S. L.

[In 1st ed. this note continues : " I saw Mr. Paine but once ; it was at General Tate's : he treated me with distrust : I could not blame him. Many ran to see Bonaparte, many to see Mr. Fox : Paine, whose intellectual powers, compared to theirs, were as a myriad to a unit, was unvisited and avoided. Of his virtues I have only one proof : shew me its equal."]

" ' O God ! he must hate and detest the name of Englishman : pelted, insulted, persecuted, plundered——'
" ' I could give it to him,' said the jailer.
" ' Do then ! ' said I wildly. ' One man more shall know my innocence.' He came within the half-hour. I told him my name, that my employers were Watt and Boulton of Birmingham, that I had papers of the greatest consequence, that if I failed to transmit them, not only my life was in question, but my reputation. He replied, ' I know your employers by report only : there are no two men less favourable to the principles I profess, but no two upon earth are honester. You have only one great man among you : it is Watt : for Priestley is gone to America. The church-and-king-men would have japanned him. He left to these philosophers of the rival school his house to try experiments on ; and you may know, better than I do, how much they found in it of carbon and calx, of silex and argilla.'

" He examined me closer than my judge had done : he required my proofs. After a long time I satisfied him. He then said, ' The leaders of the Convention would rather have my life than yours. If by any means I can obtain your release on my own security, will you promise me to return within twenty days ? ' I answered, ' Sir, the security I can at present give you, is trifling—I should say a mere nothing.'

" ' Then you do not give me your word,' said he.
" ' I give it, and will redeem it.'

" He went away, and told me I should see him again when he could inform me whether he had succeeded. He returned in the earlier part of the evening, looking fixedly upon me, and said, ' Zachariah Wilkes ! if you do not return in twenty-four days (four are added) you will be the most unhappy of men ; for had you not been an honest one, you could not be the agent of Watt and Boulton. I do not think I have hazarded much in offering to take your place on your failure : such is the condition.' I was speechless : he was unmoved. Silence was first broken by the jailer. ' He seems to get fond of the spot now he must leave it ! ' I had thrown my arms upon the table toward my liberator, who sat opposite, and I rested my breast and head upon it too, for my temples ached, and tears had not yet relieved them. He said, ' Zachariah ! follow me to the carriage.' The soldiers paid the respect due to his scarf, presenting arms, and drawing up in file as we went along. The jailer called for a glass of wine, gave it me, poured out another, and drank to our next meeting.

118

DUKE DE RICHELIEU, ETC.

" On the fourteenth day I returned to Calais in an American brig. Approaching to Montreuil I saw the girls begin to dance in the meadow; and party after party came tripping down the declivity that leads from the town to the bridge. Some were sitting on the parapet, and communicating a printed paper to many auditors, who however mostly quitted them when they heard of a private letter on the side opposite. Passing the arch and entering the town-gate, I saw the ruined monastery on the left-hand covered with garlands; and men and women were levelling the floor for the reception of several great tables that were standing on the outside. The youths were better dressed than I had ever seen them, although their coats were old-fashioned. The moment my carriage stopped, I cried, ' What festival is this to-day ? ' The answer was from fifty voices, ' The monster is dead ! the constitution for ever ! ' People flocked round a young man, half of whose hair was hidden under his shirt-collar, the other half flowed over the shoulder in long ringlets. It appears he was the poet of the city; and he ran along the streets singing this song, which, before I left the place, was presented to me in print.

> Come, let us dance upon the grass,
>   Ye maidens of Montreuil !
> Sorrows and fears O bid them pass !
>   'Tis better Love should rule.
>
> If you abuse the power you have,
>   If you are cruel, know
> We too may make the light look grave
>   And lay the lofty low.
>
> Frown not, in heedlessness or haste
>   If any step go wrong,
> If too far circled be the waist,
>   Or hand be held too long.
>
> In knees yet tottering from a rod
>   Let failures be forgiven ;
> Slippery with sunshine is the sod,
>   With tufted flowers uneven.
>
> Away ! in bonnet, coif, or cap . . .
>   To fear it is no use ;
> Whene'er you meet with such mishap
>   We 'll make the best excuse.

> I can not dance nor sing alone . . .
>   Haste, haste, my heart Lisette !
> Manon ! what are you at, Manon ?
>   That frill not plaited yet ?
>
> Nay, never mind what people think,
>   Too sorrowful Elise !
> Let the black skirt be trimm'd with pink,
>   Lilac, or what you please,
>
> But put it on and trip away . . .
>   My life ! the violin
> Never was play'd so as to-day,
>   Nor was the mead so green.
>
> Come, let us dance then on the grass,
>   Ye maidens of Montreuil !
> Sorrows and fears O bid them pass !
>   'Tis better Love should rule.

" If in my circumstances I could have been amused at anything, it would have been at the boasts, the resolutions, and the schemes, I witnessed in the groups about me. One swore that, if nobody else had killed Robespierre, he would have done it ; for he had formed a plan impossible to fail. Another said he had inscribed his name among the conspirators against the tyrant, which greatly encouraged them, and that he could exhibit a copy to whoever doubted it. A third declared that nobody alive should hinder him from putting on a clean shirt every fourth morning ; that he would call Sunday *dimanche*, and would bow to the curate the first instant he met him. ' Happy days, good old times are come again,' cried an enthusiast : ' one may exclaim *bon dieu !* on this side the guillotine ; and one may address one's mistress by the title of *angel*, or even *mademoiselle*.' ' What do you think the girls care for that ? ' cried his companion, who still wore the red cap. ' Pretty girls,' answered he, ' are aristocrats, and will be so while there is one upon earth. The Goddess of Liberty herself would smile more graciously if you addressed her *Madame the Goddess of Liberty*.' The republican heard and pondered, and, contrary to my expectation, cried boisterously, ' By Marat ! I believe it—a bitch ! she should be watched.'

" Robespierre had shot himself, was the intelligence brought by the postillions : a few lines to a few families and a few hand-bills announced the same. I hastened to the capital, to the house of my benefactor.

" ' You could not have heard it in England ? '

" ' No,' replied I, ' I heard it at Montreuil : is it true ? ' He did not answer me ; but turning to the general, said ' Tate ! there is yet English blood in England, though it is run and contraband, and found among people who have no right to it. I wish it may do you no harm, Zachariah ! Come, while we are well, let me give you joy.' "

LE DOUX. Did Mr. Paine live to the Restoration ? I am certain his Majesty would have rewarded his services, and have pardoned the indiscretion of his former speeches, the result of inebriety.

NORMANBY. He died before the king's restoration, and was not altogether so good a royalist as one could have wished.

LE DOUX. Pity ! but he might have written some loyal books : nobody asks about opinions. Do you imagine that Soult is a royalist, or Chateaubriand a Christian, or Talleyrand a believer in Providence ? They behave well, and abandon their errors, or, if not abandon, abjure them. This in conscience is all that government and society can exact. You must have been charmed with Paris ?

NORMANBY. Remaining there eleven days, I wrote to the good lady at whose house I had lodged in London, and told her I should be happy to send any models she might desire for her daughters to copy. I had discovered that they gained their livelihood by working in their own house for the first milliners. She returned me a kind letter, containing the substance of a conversation with my banker, to whom it appears she was related. He was surprised he had not heard from me, if living : it was a proof, however, that I wanted no money. Miss Penelope, who had been treated like a princess from her infancy, offended the Chisholms, by telling them that the parishioners began to regret me, and that I had afforded them ample means of judging whether I was disaffected, by becoming a sailor. The curate, now about to marry a woman of distinction, lost common decency in her presence, and told her, his father would no longer take three shillings in composition for his capon ; that capon was the word, and capon he would have, though she herself made him. " O brute beast ! " exclaimed Miss Penelope ; and then shrieked, and would have fainted if there had been anyone else to support her. Soon after she caught an erysipelas, by sitting in a grotto she had constructed just opposite the door of her new farm-house, and between the cow-pen and cart-shed. There was a weeping willow on each side, and there was water in it, preserved by means of a dripping-pan nicely sanded, with a large sea-shell at every corner. She was so delighted at this rural and romantic scene, that, on the day of its completion, she sat an hour or more in it, and did not dream that the coldness of the mortar on the floor could penetrate the moss; but the moss had been wetted to fasten it. When she returned home she shivered : the apothecary said he did not like it : the Chisholms would yet be neighbours if a visit should be agreeable. " No," said she, " and if I die to-morrow I will show them how little I value them." She had no idea of dying, and perhaps, if she had lived, would have made a different will from what she did that evening. She bequeathed her library, plate, and china, her house, furniture, and estate, to me : she willed that the remainder of her property, being in money, should be possessed by her nearest male relative, unless there happened to be in the family a female whose christian name was Penelope. The younger Mr. Chisholm was vexed and confounded. The elder was at first silent : at last he said, " The laws of the land will look to that—the christian name of Penelope ! I hold that there is no such christian name, and that the name is called christian by abuse. This is not a misnomer, or it might be good and valid and got over : misnomer means, when a man's real name is Nicholas, for instance, and you call him Nicodemus, having proven, or proving below, that you intend the man, or child, or adult, so mentioned."

His reasoning, if right, was useless : no Penelope was a claimant. The property, amounting to six or seven thousand pounds, went to a day-labourer, who, by the blessing of God and the mandate of a justice of the peace, had eight children. He swore he would bury Miss Penelope as no queen was ever buried, though it cost him ten pounds.

" Say guineas, Giles ! " cried his wife ; " the charge comes but once."

He drew back, as one who is about to take a leap, admired her high daring, and, rising up from his chair at the decision he was about to pronounce, " Guineas then let it be ! "

I returned and took possession of my cottage and freehold. The first door I opened was the barn-door. My arm-chair stood opposite me : I sat down on it, looking on the crimson bed until its colours were absorbed in my eyes, and the form itself had vanished. I did

not meditate : I had no thoughts : sensation carried them away
half-formed. I did not resist it, nor attempt to alter or direct it. I
felt as if I were in the presence of those I loved, and as if any fresh
motion of the mind or body would deprive me of it.

Few years had elapsed, and yet what changes ! The death of
Penelope and the marriage of Mr. Chisholm occurred in one
week.

There was no turnpike road near Sandyhurst ; and the people
were much surprised, as they were conversing from window to window
one Saturday evening, at the arrival of an elegant chaise and four
post-horses at the public-house, which is a very cleanly and com-
modious one, there being no fewer than six charities the trustees of
which dine there yearly, and the commissioners of two inclosures had
met there daily for eight months. From the carriage alighted a
young lady and her aunt, evidently a woman of fashion, and retaining
the remains of beauty. The innkeeper showed them his apartments ;
they chose two rooms ; the aunt remarking that the delicate state of
her niece's health made her resolve to attend her, whatever might be
the consequence to her own. She desired that her under-butler and
her niece's maid might have a parlour to themselves. The innkeeper,
curious to know the history of his inmates, went backward and forward in the servants' room ; but they paid no attention to him ;
which produced an observation in the passage that servants are
prouder than masters and mistresses. He himself, as he had already
done up-stairs, brought in a pair of candles, and lighted one. The
lady's maid smiled somewhat scornfully, and presumed that the wind
had blowed out the other. " Comfortable or not, Edward, we shall
at least be beyond the reach of that old housekeeper. It is well that
you (instead of the butler) did not drink the Madeira : but the
malicious old creature could not get him discharged. I wish my
young mistress was half as good as yours : good she is, only that she
minds her money. Hardly a gown a month ; and of what use are
silk stockings to me, if I must not wear them ; and shoes, if they
are too big ? "

" I beg pardon for interrupting you, miss," said the innkeeper,
" but really I can not do my duty unless you or this gentleman inform
me of your lady's name."

" You may look for it," said the girl, and continued her discourse.
" No, Mr. Edward, I don't let men put their arms over my chair.

Talk and welcome, but I don't see why you should do in the country what is more than your place is worth if you did it in London."

He begged pardon, and hoped she would say nothing : then turning to the landlord, " Her ladyship is particular : I trust you will not hurt me."

" Not I," said the landlord : " but surely you will have the civility to inform me who the ladies are."

" My mistress," answered he, " is Lady Fosset " ; and whispered in his ear, " She is only the wife of a knight, let the girl say what she will, a proud minx ! "

" And what would you have ? is not a knight enough for you ? Do you think I have no ears in my head ? Had you such a table, I should like to know, at Lord—the Lord knows who's—the one you served last—he whose face is so like a camel's ? "

" I did not complain," said Edward submissively. " Sir Nathaniel kept a better ; but——"

" Go on, go on ; never be satisfied," said the maid. " Say at once he left your mistress a beggar—but hold your tongue upon the score of mine : and now I warn you."

" Miss," replied Edward, " I entreat and beg you not to speak so loud : I am as reasonable as any man, and never said that the same can be done with eighteen hundred a-year as with four thousand."

The landlord, when they were silent, hoped he did not interrupt them, but requested the lady's maid to inform him at her leisure (since the ladies were in their bedroom) when they would like tea.

" Have you not asked them ? " said she, apparently much surprised.

" No, Miss," he answered ; " I have been waiting here."

" God forbid ! you poking, prying creature ! Well ! I said no harm of anybody. And now, Mr. Edward, if you catch it, thank yourself : you have always a bad place, have you ? "

He left the parlour ; the landlord followed. He turned round and whispered in the landlord's ear, " Evil came into the world with the first woman, and will go out with the last, and, by my soul ! I believe against her will. What malice in this little black-and-tan terrier ! always on the watch and alert to catch and snap me."

" She is a pretty little creature to my mind," said the landlord.

" Pretty ! " cried Edward.

" Her complexion by candlelight is the sweetest in the world," said the innkeeper; " and such eyes and eyebrows I never saw in my born days. What teeth and lips! psuh! and that slight shade of down on the upper one."

" Zounds!" cried Edward, " kissing her would be like playing on Pan's pipe. Slight shade of down! Why then a box-coat is a satin slip, and a fox-cover is a grass-plot."

" Do you always ride on the dicky with her, Mr. Edward ?"

" Ah, woe is me!" replied Mr. Edward, and there was an echo to it in the passage—" There is so little room on our dicky!" The innkeeper sighed again—" and such jolting roads! and such light short-legged creatures!" said Edward discontentedly. " It requires all one's patience."

" Egad, does it?" cried the innkeeper, drawing his breath— " and more too!"

After some silence, he invited Mr. Edward to taste the liquors in the tap-room. " If you please, Mr. Edward—— I beg pardon not to know your other name."

" Horton, at command," answered he.

" Mr. Horton, if you please, as I was saying, we will drink to the good health of Miss."

" The poor child!" said Edward. " She is not long for this world."

" I did not mean her," said the landlord; " though methinks her lips and eyes promise to let alone graves and tombstones for the present; I meant the sweet little creature that was so sharp with me."

" Ho! Rosaly Rouse: so the ladies call her: she expects that we should call her Miss Rosaly: the house-keeper and butler may call her Rouse. She has good kin: that must be said for her: but an arm across her chair is a liberty. If you caught her asleep in it— one has a right then, you know—you would sooner dare to kiss a leopard or tiger. Everything would be topside-turvey; you could not rest for her. You would have laughed if you had seen her coming down the hill into the town here: she was frightened at the horses slipping, and, in spite of the ladies behind, threw her arm round my body; and I verily believe it made her hate me worse than ever; for, to do her justice, I never saw her so bad before, never so desperately proud and capricious. She loves her mistress and my lady, and would go through fire for them: drink a little wine in the cellar, and you might as well drink black-strap at the Crown and Anchor."

125

" Really ! " said the innkeeper in great surprise—" then I misunderstood every word about the Madeira."

" Sly creature ! " drawled Mr. Edward. " Faithful she is," added he smartly, " and acute, and prudent : her only fault is, that she never forgives what she calls a liberty, and it puts her out of humour with all the world."

" The very woman ! " cried the host unguardedly ; and, being disconcerted at his own exclamation, desired his companion to help himself and spare not, and went upstairs. He had forgotten to take up the tea, and was much relieved at finding the waiter in the act of removing it, and the ladies at cards, they having thrown a shawl over the table, when the waiter informed them, on their inquiry, that there was no green cloth. He saw several pieces of gold, no silver. His heart was disquieted ; he knew not what to set about ; even his curiosity was enfeebled ; yet he went up again to ask what they would please to have for supper. Lady Fosset desired him to wait a moment ; she then said to her niece, " Come, child, take those five guineas back ; I do not approve of high play, and you could not attend to your game."

" Excuse me, madam," replied the niece, rising from the table, and putting the money in the aunt's reticule.

The landlord was up early the next morning, waited on Dr. Chisholm, and told him and his son the curate all that had passed, adding, as was true, the last thing her ladyship asked was, " At what time begins divine service ? "

" Samuel," said the doctor, " I shall preach."

" Father, if you will, you will," replied he, " but the fairer thing would be to cut for it."

They did : the doctor won. Samuel cried, " By God ! sir, there is no dealing with you. I make no doubt all was fair. What I have to say, is, you have always good luck."

On returning from church, Lady Fosset thanked the doctor for his very admirable sermon, and declared she never had heard the service read so impressively as by the gentleman who assisted him.

" My son, madam."

They both bowed, and attended the ladies to the inn : her lady-ship invited them to tea in the evening, expressing her deep regret that she had no gentleman with her who might do the honours of the table at dinner, if they could have pardoned her so short a notice.

DUKE DE RICHELIEU, ETC.

" Father," said Samuel, just out of the door, " did you ever hear so strange an excuse ? None to do the honours of the table (as she called it) when there are two of us ! You might have had the ducks put down."

On the road to the rectory, " eighteen hundred a-year ! " was the exclamation of both at once. " Well ! father, on this occasion I hope you will not cut."

" Samuel," said the rector, " I soon enter on the grand climacteric ; her ladyship is not five-and-forty."

" True," answered he, " I suspect she has a filly's tooth in her muzzle, and would fain pulp a bean or two yet."

The rector shook his head. " I believe you must have her, Samuel ! I have nothing but the rectory : the money is gone in house and improvements. You were born to less than a hundred a-year, and that from the sweat of my brow ; I shall leave you a thousand. I will nominally make over the living to you, on your giving me such security as can be drawn up between us."

The son thanked him ; was unremitting in his addresses to Lady Fosset ; and at last declared his passion, from the utter impossibility of restraining it. She replied that she was sensible of his merits, but that, if he imagined her fortune to be so considerable as it was represented, he was mistaken : that she had retired, in part for the health of her niece, in part for economy, and was sorry to inform him that her *thirds* (her husband having died intestate) were barely eighteen hundred a-year.

He protested that fortune was the last of his considerations ; that he himself had somewhat less ; that after his worthy father's decease he could not expect many thousands more, beside the rectory.

The rector united them by licence, the third week of her ladyship's residence in Sandyhurst. She condescended to give away, with her own hand, Rosalia Rouse, to Mr. Freeman of the Star and Garter, making her a present of a pearl necklace, the finest and evenest pearls ever seen in Sandyhurst, which Mr. Edward Horton said he did not so much wonder at her doing, now that she had resolved to forget poor Sir Nathaniel. He added, " I remember how nobly her ladyship looked in these pearls when she was in full dress, as persons of quality in London are, stark-naked down to the navel."

" Mercy upon us ! " cried the host. " Are they taken then for pigeons and plovers ! are folks helped only to the nether parts of them ? Why should they neglect themselves ? do not they meet their lovers in this full dress, as you call it ? The men must cry out shame upon them, finding them in good company so slovenly and sluttish. Our ladies here in the country are educated on other principles. When Squire Alvanley of Beachencroft saw Miss Arabella give Captain Barrowdale, who was fain to marry her, a few maidenly kisses, he said not a word about it : but when he observed, another day, that the captain was desperate to lower the tucker, he called her to him off the green bench, pretending all the while to have seen nothing, and kept her a matter of half an hour in lecture. Nobody knows on what he discoursed in the outset ; but Mrs. Snipe, the housekeeper, told me that, hearing some grave words, she looked through the key-hole of the study-door, and saw Miss in tears, and saw the old gentleman, relenting a little, pat her cheek with the back of his fore-finger, and heard him say, partly in comfort, partly in counsel, ' Be liberal of the cherries, girl, but chary of the peaches.' Whereat Miss wiped her eyes, and rose upon tiptoe and kissed her father, and promised to do always as he had bidden her."

" I have her ladyship's commands," said Edward, " to take her your account."

In an instant, " Take it ! " said Mr. Freeman.

" You have written received in full," cried Mr. Edward Horton ; " how is that ? "

" It would be a burning shame to act otherwise," said the publican, " after those pearls ; and look ye what are these ? "

" O ! they are only garnets : nobody would give you five pounds for them, without the gold."

The niece, whose health was surprisingly restored, and whom it was thought indecorous to make the witness of connubial felicity in its first transports, was taken away just before the marriage, by her brother, a young ensign ; and Mr. Edward Horton two days after returned to London, strongly recommended ; for her ladyship would rather reduce her establishment than increase it, accommodating her taste in everything to her dear Chisholm's.

" Samuel ! " said the old rector to the new, " while we think of it, suppose you resign to me that instrument of the advowson."

" Father," said Samuel, " I would gladly do it if my conscience would let me. I repent of having committed one action very like a fraud, and nothing upon earth shall make me commit another. If the bishop heard of it we should be ruined."

The father had seldom lost his temper or composure ; for as other extremes meet in their effects, so do honesty and roguery in this. He felt assured however, in the midst of his resentment, that he had so drawn up the agreement as to make it voidable, although he hardly had thought Lady Fosset was so noble-minded as to accept his son without referring the title-deeds to her solicitor.

There was a young girl in the parish, the daughter of his laundress, whom he condescended to teach the catechism. He often told her in what manner to hold the book, and often said, "Let me see where you are," and sometimes, " Do not be so frightened," when nobody but himself could see that she was frightened in the least. He went to her, and said without prelude or preface, " Sally ! will you marry me ? "

" Lord, sir," cried the mother tremulously, " what do you mean ? "

" Ask me no questions, or I leave the house," said he, more firmly than impetuously. " Will you marry me, child, or will you not ? "

She looked at her mother. " Sally, if the doctor is in earnest, you must not say no."

" Put on your Sunday clothes then ; and, Rebecca ! while she is putting them on, come you with me."

The mother went out with him.

" Step into that carriage."

" With my shoes on, sir ? "

" Step in.[1] Will the girl come or not ? What a quantity of clothes she must be putting on ! "

The mother, holding up two pins, to hint that she could stick them in, if requisite, as they went along, called her thrice, with an admixture of coaxing and reproof. She descended the staircase with timidity, and would have walked by the side of the carriage : but the rector caught her up, and (somewhat asthmatically) lifted her in. He followed ; and, putting his arm partly round her, although on the cushion, that he might not be indecorous, he ordered his coachman to drive to Mr. Gamaliel Shark's at Elvington. Alighting there, leaving the daughter and mother in the chaise, he told Mr. Shark that he came for a license ; and, after the necessary questions, he received it.

---

[1] 1st ed. reads : " in.' He followed her, ordered his coachman," etc.

" And now, sir," said the doctor,[1] " are you ready to unite us ? "

Mr. Shark assented : they were united : they returned home at the moment of dinner-time. The [2] mother was left at her own door very carefully, with an affectionate kiss from the daughter, and not without a generous declaration from the doctor that he would really have made her a present, if he had found in his pocket any less piece than a half-crown. The bridegroom placed Sally by his side quietly. The son was civil, and said, on their arrival, " I suppose, Sally, you have said your catechism better to-day than usual ? "

She looked at her husband. " Yes," answered he placidly, " and read a page more."

After supper he called for his bed-candle, and, wishing Lady Fosset a good-night, conducted Sally upstairs. The elder bride and younger bridegroom at top and bottom looked steadfastly at each other. " Let him go ! " said Mr. Samuel, " let him have his way and will : I did think better of the wench : she had hardly a curtsey for me. Rectory or laundry, barn or stable, what matters it ! it comes to the same thing at last."

" O fie for shame ! " cried her ladyship, looking at him and smiling through her fingers, " I can not sit and hear this." She tripped across the room, opened the door, turned round again, and cried, " Positively I have a great mind to lock you out, you rude creature ! " Mr. Samuel ruminated.

Early the next morning a bailiff entered the rectory, accompanied by two police-officers. The doctor and Sally were fast asleep ; for they had been (backward and forward) eight miles the day before. Mr. Samuel was examining the heel of a horse : he heard the visitors, and, without looking at them, asked them roughly what they wanted. " Margaret Pollock," said one in a clear voice ; another said, " Parson Chisholm."

" What have you to do with me, pray ! " shouted he furiously.

" Nothing, sir, if you pay these trifles. You have married Margaret Pollock."

" Not I : no such woman has been married in my parish."

" Mr. Chisholm, you have taken as your lawful wife Margaret (otherwise called Peg) Pollock."

---

[1] 1st ed. reads : " doctor, ' will you be ready in another hour to," etc.
[2] From " The " to " half-crown " added in 2nd ed.

DUKE DE RICHELIEU, ETC.

" Sirrah ! " said the divine, going up to him with clenched fist, " I would have you to know, I led to the altar Lady Fosset."

" You could not have done better," said the officer, " but she wanted no leading that way. Howsoever we take possession of the rectory."

Mr. Chisholm ran to his father, whom he awakened. Sally still slept ; as being little used to the motion of the carriage ; and I hardly know a rougher road than the road to Elvington, considering it is so flat.

" Father," said Mr. Samuel, " take the resignation "—throwing it on the bed. While the bailiffs were in the house, he mounted his horse, rode into Rutlandshire, and exchanged his curacy with a sporting friend, whom he had known at college. The doctor was surprised to see a neat young clergyman introduce himself the next Friday, and to hear a eulogy on his son's liberality, in giving a curacy of a hundred a-year for one of seventy, when the hounds were at equal distances ; and [1] in return was never so uncivil as to gainsay him until a whole twelvemonth had elapsed, when he complimented him on his horses and sermons, his bold leaps and impressive delivery, and on fifty pounds going farther at Sandyhurst than seventy at Grantham. " I believe, sir, you will find," added he, " that here are five ten-pound Bank of England notes : do me the favour just to cast your eyes over them, and to give me a receipt."

Lady Fosset, by the account of the bailiff and his attendants, had been a street-walker, a kept mistress, and an actress. Her associates at Sandyhurst were of the same strolling company. She escaped by putting on the riding-coat of a groom ; exercising first the functions of a butler, taking care of the plate ; and not forgetting in the performance of this service, that her husband had presented her a brilliant ring and some other ornaments, rich almost as any of those which had devolved on the family of Sir Nathaniel. Seeing her husband gallop off on Blaze, she was contented to mount the horse whose fetlock or hoof had excited such suspicion in her lord, and which he was examining when his guests entered. They obtained nothing from the rector. " My son was my curate," said he ; " of his wife I know nothing. Take him ; take her ; but touch a tin kettle on your peril. This is the rectory-house, and the rectory is mine." They grumbled : they begged a breakfast, as nobody was

---

[1] From " and " to " receipt " added in 2nd ed.

up : the rector held his spread hand before his face, and looked aside.

After the harvest a company of players applied to the magistrates for permission to open a theatre at Sandyhurst, one night only : it was granted. They acted a farce entitled *The Two Rectors*, and were committed to bridewell for an attack on the church.[1]

Not long afterwards, it was discovered that the stratagem introductory to the marriage had been devised by a young gentleman who was fond of theatricals, and no less fond of the young lady who played the niece. The inexperience and giddiness of this prodigal Mr. Chisholm had turned to account at the university, two years before, not without a few sarcasms on his folly, and the inauspicious boast conveyed in the words, " I shall make him remember his rubbers." Hearing that the reverend gentleman was now resident in a village near Grantham, and well surmising that on market-days and fairs he would be bustling about the town, he drove his curricle thither on the great horse-fair, accompanied by his mistress, the niece ; and, meeting Mr. Chisholm in the crowd, he drew up his horses, inquired after the health of Lady Fosset, and expressed an earnest wish to pay her his respects.

" Lookye now, Mr. Randal," said the curate, " if you ar'n't off the ground in a twinkling, I 'll make the place too hot to hold you."

" I don't doubt your interest in a place too hot to hold me, Mr. Chisholm ! but I appeal to the gentlemen here present whether my language was other than civil and friendly." The fashionable young traveller was cheered heartily : he was declared to be an over-match for the parson, and his shrewdness in a minute had drawn the clerical mouth awry. Observing the advantage he had gained, he appealed to every lady who did him the unexpected and unmerited honour of listening to him, and who by such politeness had rendered the present hour the brightest of his life, whether a syllable had escaped his lips which could possibly shock the modesty of the most delicate among them, or could justly wound the feelings of the reverend gentleman, whose sensibility was surely too acute for the occasion.

" Cute ! " cried a farmer with thin yellow whiskers and white eye-

---

[1] 1st ed. reads : " church. The doctor sold the perpetual advowson after his decease for twelve thousand pounds, paying six hundred a year during his life to the lady, who had purchased it for an only son. He did not calculate," etc., p. 133.

brows. " Cute ! 'Sblood ! but you have the parson under the short rib there, master ! You 've doubled him up with that wiper."

" Permit me, gentlemen," said Mr. Randal, " permit me to relate the few facts I have collected on the road concerning Mr. Chisholm's adventure."

" There 's a cross-buttocker for ye ! " cried again the same orator as before. " *Venture* you may well call it. The parson has mettle ; but what a main did he throw on your game ! my eyes ! "

Mr. Chisholm would have returned homeward, but he had promised to meet somebody at the ordinary, to receive a guinea which he had won in a wager, and which he feared he might lose by want of punctuality. At dinner he told the company that, whatever they might think of it, he never in his *born days* was the man to be abashed by anybody, and that he defied any *soul alive* to prove he had been choused of one penny by the old carrion.

" But, parson ! can you marry again ? " was the interrogation of the feeder next him. " Who the devil has the stomach to eat after such a choker ? " squeaked a fat man opposite. " Right ! " said his son. " Nevertheless, the spring physic has sweated you, parson ! " " Damned ungenteel ! " cried Mr. Chisholm, " to talk about physic at dinner-time. I 'll take the sense of the company upon it ; is it not so ? It would cost a young hound his best appetite. And so, gentlemen, I 'm off." At which word he emptied his bottle ; and rising (as the cloth was being removed) stiffly and sorely, whistled, wiped his forehead, and drew up with two smart twitches the buckskin from behind.

Toward the end of the year the doctor sold the perpetual advowson of the rectory. He did not calculate on the grand climacteric or its effects, and died about fourteen months after his marriage, leaving only Porphyrogenitus the fruit of it. He called his infant by that name, declaring that among all the names he knew he never knew one but had many rogues under it, and that he was almost out of humour with his own. He bequeathed his whole property to his children by his last wife, to be equally divided among males and females, reserving a maintenance for his widow of one hundred pounds yearly, on condition that she never married again.

I found his successor an unaffected, quiet, good young man ; rather idle, and therefore he often visited me at my cottage, and was surprised to see how straight I drew the lines for my winter cabbage, and thought the string a most ingenious contrivance. His sister was fond of walking in the green lane, and said to me the second time I found her there, " O, what a mercy it is, Mr. Normanby, that Miss Penelope left the hollies ! they are so covered with woodbine and travellers'-joy ! It seems never to have been a lane ; here are no marks of wheel or horse-shoe ; it is as hollow as an apple-scoop ; and a sheep could not lie crosswise on it comfortably."

LE DOUX. The story would end abruptly if it ended thus.

NORMANBY. Yet thus it must end. She has twelve thousand pounds, like her brother.

LE DOUX. Indeed, my dear sir ; I [1] did not ask about the fortune. I have no designs upon her, and will abstain from mentioning it in the country to which I am going.

NORMANBY. I could not walk but I met her : she has done me as much mischief as an *Age of Reason*. A second time I left my country ; and it was for her.

LE DOUX. And, if I am not greatly mistaken, it is for her you are a second time going back.

NORMANBY. What can be done ? Her brother will have me in the parish.

LE DOUX. I wish Lady Glengrin and Sir Firebrace were ready for breakfast : I am starving now you have concluded.

—The Swiss, having seen the sailor and his master twice in conversation, and unwilling that any but himself should be familiar with so great a personage, whispered to Mr. Normanby the secret of his lord's dignity, and rejoiced at the impression of his whisper. Afterward there always was civility, always frankness, but never confidence, never conversation. Le Doux on his part was just as a man is who has read a novel : he has done with it. Princes and kings are often kind, both from constitution and from fulness of power, in which they usually are without fear and jealousy : but I doubt whether there ever was a minister in the world capable of sincerity and amity, or who, having conversed for years together with anyone, cared if he were drowned or hanged when he no longer could amuse or serve him. The possession and maintenance of power occupy such men totally. If the horse they ride will go on with patting, they will not feed him ; if he cares little for patting and much for provender, they curse him heartily and fill the rack. All cunning men who wish

---

[1] From " I " to " going " added in 2nd ed.

for power may have it : but all cunning men are men of narrow views : and here, when they take possession of power, they must leave some places vacant which are incompatible with it. They are jockeys that sweat themselves to ride light ; and after they have changed their great-coat for a calico jacket, they discover that their heart is too large, and must be swathed and contracted.[1] The habit of haranguing is in itself pernicious : I have known even the conscientious and pious, the humane and liberal, dried up by it, and have watched the mind growing black and rancid in its own smoke.

During the voyage the conversation was usually on Ireland. No people talk so much about their country as the Irish ; not because they are more patriotic (I beg pardon for using a word out of use in that acceptation, and should have said more *national*) than others, but because they are less capable of conversing on literature and science. Le Doux was surprised at exalted eulogies and vehement invective, used by the same persons on the same, as high spirits or low prevailed. Surely, said he to himself, this is the conflict of light and darkness, of the good principle and the evil, of Saint Michael and Satan. On the whole, however, Lady Glengrin and Sir Firebrace agreed on the wretched state of Ireland ; but Sir Firebrace insisted that, although the fact was incontrovertible, no fault whatever *attached* to his majesty's ministers (meaning the king's) or those employed under them, military or civil ; and that the clergy and gentlemen of Ireland, resident and non-resident, had done everything in their power to alleviate the distresses and promote the prosperity of the people. Le Doux was aware, from the roundness and fulness of the period, that the sentence could not be Sir Firebrace's, and attributed it rightly to a minister ; who added that he must also do justice to the *people* of Ireland, in general as orderly and loyal as any in the United Kingdom ; that if a little excess had been committed, it was rather the result of conviviality than of discontent ; and he trusted that what he had risen to state, was a triumphant answer to the malicious and disaffected in England. He then told a story about a mail-coach and a fur-cap, so convincing to the simplest understanding, that the House of Commons voted unanimously any inquiry into the state of Ireland quite unnecessary and useless :

[1] 1st ed. reads : " contracted. Nothing is easier ! astonishing how light they are ! and they still look like other men. The habit," etc.

unfortunately, he added that it might be dangerous at the present juncture; which, *out of doors*, raised some alarm.

" For my soul," after a pause ejaculated Le Doux, " I can not comprehend it : no one is to blame, and the blame is large enough for all." He meditated ; and he found what at first appeared the grossest mismanagement, to be in reality the finest stroke of policy. " What admirable calculations of loss and profit ! None but a commercial people is capable of this precision and exactness ! It costs a great deal of money to keep the Irish in subjection : but to whom does the money go ? To the friends of ministers, to the supporters of government, to the loyal and the rich. Again, if they did not make a very large portion of the people discontented, how would they find soldiers ? Who will leave his family if he can feed it and enjoy it ; unless he has such a sense of honour as a Frenchman, who flies to arms the moment a mayor orders him to be carried off ; and [1] a handcuff unites him to a comrade ? The English are wanted to labour and pay taxes ; the Irish must be kept as they are. Even Cromwell with all his cunning did not see this : his son Henry was the only governor who has made them quiet and contented these six hundred years. The policy now revived is more complex : we can not attribute the glory of the invention to fellows who never learned, from a dictionary and a smuggler, that Walcheren is a pestilential island and Antwerp a fortified town. O my country ! my first wish is that thou mayest have no enemies ; my second is that, having them, they may be men like these : but it would be unfair to deny them the merit of walking firmly and undeviatingly in the footsteps of their predecessors."

It was on the seventh or eighth morning, that Le Doux, rising from the cabin, cried, " Mr. Normanby ! Mr. Normanby ! what vast harbour are we entering ? "

" This is the Strait of Gibraltar," answered he.

" O yes," said Le Doux, " so it is. We are far from the Barbary coast, yet how wild it looks even at this distance ! See the difference between Christian industry and Moorish apathy ! "

" Great indeed, sir," replied Normanby, " but that rock is Gibraltar, and this beautiful country to the left is Barbary. In fact, the Moors are industrious, and always were intelligent on agriculture, even before the Romans, into whose language their books on that

---

[1] From " and " to " comrade " added in 2nd ed.

136

science were translated, and at a time when no original one on the subject had appeared at Rome. The [1] Africans on the coast of Mauritania had a custom, claimed as an invention by the Tuscans, of interring corn for its preservation. The writer * of Cæsar's war in Africa mentions the practice, but mistakes the cause. Spaniards never were cultivators, in modern times or ancient : they [2] only sow in the furrows ploughed for them by the Moors. The southern parts of the Peninsula retain the traces of Moorish enterprise : and the kingdom of the Moors in Spain, if they had been Christians, would have exhibited the most perfect model, ever existing in the world, of industry and civilisation, gallantry and glory. The men were valiant, and the women were chaste ; robberies and murders were unknown ; music was heard from road to road, from castle to castle ; wars were the sports of valour, jousts and tournaments its idle recreations. At last, divided by faction, they were oppressed by numbers, leaving such monuments behind them as the powerfullest of our empires never will erect."

Michael heard this, and whispered to Renault, " I should not be surprised to see our Englishman turn renegade, if the ship draws nearer the coast."

It was then about one mile off : the harvest was gathered, still the country seemed a garden. Several boats approached the vessel with pomegranates of unusual size, undetached from their bright and glossy leaves ; and the late fig ; and grapes of various forms, sizes, and colours ; and live quails and partridges and doves ; and little kids, that leaped back among them from the deck again, and would not leave them. Suddenly the ship tacked, and a fresh breeze blew them into Gibraltar, where they must take in water.

" This long point of land could surely be cultivated," said Le Doux to the captain ; " it is level and not very rocky."

" Sir," answered the captain, " the inhabitants of the city are three-fourths Jews, and most of the rest Spaniards. These people will never work if they can help it. Monopolies and privileges and exemptions furnish the greater part of the governor's emoluments, which are about five hundred guineas a week in time of war, and in

---

[1] From " The " to " cause " is part of the footnote in 1st ed.

* " Est in Africâ consuetudo incolarum, ut in agris et in omnibus fere villis sub terrâ specus, condendi frumenti gratiâ, clam habeant, atque id propter bella maximè hostiumque subitum adventum præparant."—W. S. L.

[2] From " they " to " Moors " added in 2nd ed.

peace little more than fifty a day ; and he would not like to see plantations ; they bring no tariff."

" It is nearly a mile in length," said Le Doux, " and shady walks might be formed upon it, for the convenience and health of the garrison."

" No tariff for the governor from shady walks," replied the captain.

Le Doux and Sir Firebrace went ashore in uniform, in order to leave their cards at the governor's.

" Precede them with flambeaux, for they are persons of distinction," said the governor to his valet.

" My lord, it is mid-day," answered the valet.

" Go down then," said his lordship—" it is time I should think of sleeping." *

For the distance of many miles inland, and many along the shore, there was hardly a sign of cultivation. " How do the people live ? " asked Le Doux.

" By means of the Moors," answered the captain.

Different were the colonel's exclamations all the way from Cape St. Vincent to Cape Finisterre. " Is it possible that sea-coasts can be so beautiful ! O how fine ! O how pretty ! superb ! magnificent ! brilliant ! " There were rocks that were charming, and villages that were minions, and vineyards that were tapestry, and meadows that were carpets. " These countries have very worthy kings," said he, " they only want good ministers." A thousand plans in an instant were ready for the consummation of their happiness.

" O heaven ! this must be France ! " exclaimed he one day in ecstasy.

" No, sir," said the captain, " it is the coast of Asturias."

Le Doux thought the rocks prettier even than those of the Petit Trianon. He expressed a second time his admiration of the coast. " We have passed a better," said the captain, " and you never noticed it. There are no harbours in Asturias like Ferrol and Coruña."

Off the Scilly Isles they found themselves in the midst of fishing-boats. Normanby took leave ; sailed in one of them to Bristol ; two

---

* The sages of antiquity have each left an aphorism on human life ; and there seemed hardly room for another ; but this our sage, if he has not given, causes one : *vita somni breve intervallum.*—W. S. L.

days afterward reached Sandyhurst ; and had the courage to walk directly toward the green lane, just as if he had never met an intruder.

The vessel that conveyed Lady Glengrin, Sir Firebrace, and Le Doux, at length cast anchor in the bay of Dublin, not without another subject of wonder to Le Doux, at seeing a pestilential marsh under one of the finest cities in Europe. " If this had been at Odessa, it would have been converted into docks," said he to himself. He passed the Parliament-house, and lifted up his hands in astonishment. " An Englishman I met at Genoa," said he to the general and the countess, " at an old minister's, fond as he was of extolling the public architecture of his country, and preferring the cathedrals and abbeys to anything antiquity has left us, never said a word about this noble fabric. It was perhaps too modern for him. He was a sort of half-author, a creature so devoted to antiquity, that when he snored he seemed in drawing his breath to say *grec,* and emitting it to say *romain.* I had the personal proof of it ; for whenever he was disposed to sleep he slept, and would have done so had he been called to the levee or to the ministry. I never saw him quite decorous but in church, where he always seemed immersed in the deepest meditation ; and if a person but whispered, even during the music, he fixed his eyes upon him with a stern rebuke."

The society introduced to Le Doux was the most select. The beauty of the women held him breathless. " Am I in Poland, or in Paradise ? " was his soliloquy. He paid his principal attentions to those who put on a clean pair of gloves every day,[1] because he considered it a test of civilisation. Even among these, within the first week, his suspicions were confirmed by his valet that the linen was not always changed so often : but he thought it a scandalous tale when he heard that some of them came to breakfast in a part of the apparel in which they had slept.

" Do not tell me such nonsense, Renault ! Depend upon it, the girl that gave you the information has been discharged : you will see her off soon." " Well, sir," said Renault, sighing, " would you believe it ? a few years ago there was not a bidet in the kingdom of Ireland. The duchess of Rutland, consort of a lord-lieutenant, brought over the first. The duke (some say it was satirically) ordered

---

[1] 1st ed. reads : " day, not because he thought them persons of greater distinction, but because . . . civilization, where the means are ample. Even," etc.

one from London for the lady of the lord chancellor. It was of porcelain, as you may suppose, being the present of a lord-lieutenant; and its inauguration was in the centre of the table, filled with green-pea soup, at a cabinet-dinner given to his grace the lord-lieutenant." " A cabinet-dinner !—and a vengeance—with its green-pea soup, rogue ! " cried Le Doux, laughing immoderately. " Sir," said Renault, gravely, " nobody laughed : everybody admired the contrivance for the ladle, and the maker had made his fortune, if the duchess had mystified as well and reasonably as the duke had done."

Opposite to Le Doux one day at dinner sat a nobleman of high rank, a member of every administration for forty years, placid and pliant, and attentive to nobody but him, into whose history he had been admitted by the countess. " Colonel," said he, " in all countries there are discontented ; there are even in this." " Is it possible ? " answered Le Doux, lifting up his eyebrows with surprise and concern. " But," rejoined the peer, " such is the kindness of Providence,[1] the sounder part of the people is perfectly tranquil, and assured of its being well governed." " His lordship means those that govern," said a worthy major : " none are more open to conviction ; the fact stares them in the face. Every country is rich and flourishing if you look at it through claret."

Politics on this occasion were discussed in few words. The illustrious visitor could collect, however, that most complaints were ill-founded ; that those who complained of any specific grievance were unfair and partial in not considering the whole ; and that those who took a view of the whole, and who proposed an inquiry into it, should state some specific grievance.

In another house, after several glasses were drunk with great cheerfulness, the whole company rose up to a mysterious toast, in silence and sadness. He sipped the wine in doubt, and found that it was the same as he had been drinking from the first, and excellent bordeaux. He could not conceive what had saddened at a single moment so many vacant and rosy faces. The next morning he heard that two of them had been shot by their antagonists, in a quarrel arising from this toast ; the *Immortal Memory* of someone they had

[1] 1st ed. reads : " Providence, a certain part of the people, too, in all countries, and that part the sounder, is assured that it is well governed.' ' His lordship . . .' a worthy major, ' none . . . conviction, but they are not to be run away, neither.' Politics . . . words, which, as he understood but little english, he did not attend to. He could collect," etc.

never seen or thought about. He imagined that silence and sorrow would have come better after ; that wine should make men joyous, and duels serious. On reflection he feared to be ' compromised,' and suspected that the *immortal memory* so religiously observed, and with such awe and taciturnity, might be the memory of Bonaparte. To relieve his suspicions, he joked about it with two of the youngest, whom he found at billiards the succeeding day. They laughed aloud at his mistake. " It was King William," said one. " It was William Pitt," said the other. " It was no more Pitt than it was my pointer," rejoined the first. In fact, the *immortal memory*, in eighteen hours, had as much obscurity and as many thorns about it as the tomb of Archimedes.

Le Doux was walking one day in the streets of Dublin, when the appearance of perfumery in a window reminded him that he wanted a tooth-brush. He went into the shop, and asked for one. The master, a tall, florid, well-dressed, genteel-looking man, took up several, and rubbing them against the extremities of his fingers, recommended one particularly. " Take this : it will keep your teeth clean twenty years at once using. You are a Frenchman, sir, I find by your way of speaking, and I see you have hardly three hairs on a side. In your country they make good pomatum : try mine : but— take the word of a friend—wash your hands well afterward in soap and warm water, or you will have hair upon the palm an inch thick before night. And no razor can touch it."

" What is the price, sir ? " " Ah now ! is it the price ? I never sell for lucre of gain : a half-crown contents me—and, just for the peg-polisher, a thirteen-penny. Recommend me to your friends, if you have any, and I 'll thank you." " Favour me with the number of your shop." " *Magazine,* if you please. The poor beggar of a schoolmaster over the way calls his, *seminary ;* and sure then I might call mine so ; but I would be modest ; *magazine* does for me."

Le Doux was leaving the door, when he was met on the threshold by a young clergyman, who, flapping his lustrous boot with a thin whip, and drawing up his shirt-collar with his left hand, red as a pigeon's claw and broad as an ostrich's, pushed rudely by him into the shop. Le Doux bowed and begged pardon. At the same moment, the hairdresser, for such he was no less than perfumer, caught him by the arm, and taking the clergyman's too, said, " Brother Joe, I must introduce you to this gentleman, who dines with us."

IMAGINARY CONVERSATIONS : IRISH

" A thousand thanks ! excuse me to-day." " To-day or never !
now for your name." " My name is Le Doux, sir : but really——"
" Le Doux ! " said the clergyman, eyeing him suspiciously. " I 'm
damned if it is : that 's a *neger's.* " I would not incommode you, my
kind friend," said Le Doux to the hairdresser : " Have the goodness
to liberate my arm. Another time——"

" Another time I may not have upon the spit a *cock o' the mountain,* ruddy and lusty as any eagle. You shall have him *piping-hot,*
with his best feather through his nose. Lady Clench gave him me,
with a Bologna-sausage, and a note (I would read it you) under.
Hams and double-Gloster are plenty. I could tell you too what
houses these come from, after dinner : and bright whiskey that
widens your nostrils when you smell it, and finds water enough in your
mouth for twenty glasses. Honest folks gave me that ; who might
not like naming. *Cocks o' the mountain* of another breed ; ay, Joe ?
you live among 'em. Come, stay ; we shall dine gloriously. Joe has
a voice, and a song for it. Look at the windows of nine houses on
each side, when he sings ; and you shall see the old women lug the
wenches down, and shall catch many a crimped cap and red wrinkle
over the blinds." " Hold your wild colt's tongue, Matthew ! " said
the clergyman, rebuking him privately ; and then in a lower tone,
" Sure, are not we two enough for a *cock o' the mountain,* ay, and a
sausage as big as a bolster ? "

At the commencement of this pastoral charge, Le Doux, finding
his arm released, made his escape. At which the brothers, much as
one of them had wished his absence, agreed that he was a *blackguard*
and a scamp, and unfit for their society. " Providential ! " Joe
ejaculated. " You would have talked first about your sausages and
cocks o' the mountain and countesses, and then about the whiskey,
letting it out by degrees that I had a trifle in the concern. And now,
Matthew, about these women. Can't you meet with better and
honester ? why then I 'll lend you a guinea. My sacred word for it,
they all make a fool of you ; and with more than their husbands ;
mind that. If you *must* have such sluts, why then have 'em, in God's
name ! but prythee be sober-minded and decent ; for I am sated and
sick of hearing of 'em."

" Only one word, Joe ! " said Matthew mildly, and interlacing his
arm. " Brother Joe, now, my life and love ! who presented you to
that little tight pretty living there of Ennisgalcraig ? and what for ? "

142

" Stuff ! " cried Joseph. " True enough ! " said Matthew. " Are you hungry ? brother Joe ! " " Hungry as a wolf-dog." " Give tongue upon the women then another time, and not when you would eat what they send us."

Invitations to dinner were frequent : among the rest was a long and elaborate one from Captain Phelim O'Mara : it was accepted. Le Doux was placed at his left, and was informed most politely by the captain that he liked foreigners above all things, and that he himself was half a foreigner.

" O no, Captain O'Mara, you are a true Irishman, bred and born," cried Lady Glengrin, " we must not lose our title to you ! "

" I am so by father's side and mother's side, and by uncles and aunts," replied the captain, " but I have travelled of late ; and the ground makes the foreigner, not the—— Pray, if one may make so bold as to ask, what do you see in that to chuckle at, ladies and gentle-men ? And what made you touch my arm, sir, while [1] I was speaking and had not said the word ? "

" Without the slightest idea of offence, I do assure you, Captain O'Mara ! " said Le Doux ; " on the contrary, it was done in my extreme impatience to second you in so just an observation. You were at Paris, I presume : how long did you remain there ? "

" A week," replied the captain : " I had taken my lodgings for a whole week, or I should have gone away directly. Our minister there, would you believe it ? made a difficulty of presenting me to the king. It was explained to me in that way ; although, to do him justice, he only said he should embrace some future opportunity."

" Indeed ! " replied Le Doux from his heart, and with an ex-pression of deep sorrow on his countenance. " His Majesty has borne many misfortunes : I hope no one will tell him of this."

" I will myself, by the Lord, if ever I go over again, and catch his eye," said the captain, striking the table. " I went on to Italy, and at Florence my lord Burghersh knew better what stuff my coat was made of, and what colour this is. The Granduke treated me like his own son, and came behind my chair at supper, and hoped I might find at table something to my taste. I replied to him in Irish ; which I had a better right to do than he to speak in French ; for Irish is my own language, and French is not his. As there was nothing to be seen at Florence but statues and pictures and other such childish

[1] From " while " to " word " added in 2nd ed.

143

things, I proceeded to Rome, in company with a gentleman who said we must have four horses, if we expected clean linen at the inns. ' As for clean linen,' said I, ' let those look to it who are to lie in it ; for my part I sleep all the way in the coach.' Howsoever, to show him that I did not mind my money, I agreed to the four horses."

" Well, captain," said Lady Glengrin, " what do you think of the fair Italians ? " " You smoke me then, my lady, do you ? Who told you about it ? "

She protested she knew nothing of the matter : he continued. " The whole way from Florence to Siena I thought every girl prettier than the last : for which reason I kept the blinds up, not wishing to understand my fellow-traveller, who declared he suffered so violently by the sun, that he was giddy and could see nothing. On some exclamation of mine, he told me that nearer Rome, on this side of the city, I should not find the females so handsome.

" I do not believe in anything supernatural, excepting a ghost or two ; but there are things that puzzle one. I fell asleep from the violent heat, and from the incessant and intolerable noise of a creature they call *grillo*, against which all the carriage-wheels in Christendom would not defend you : and I did not awake until night. This monkey-faced black devil, of an inch or two in length, with his *grill, grill, grill*, makes one hotter than twenty suns could do, bothering and never aisy. We [1] slept at Siena. In the morning, instead of vineyards and corn-fields, a vast barren country, cracked by the heat, lay wide open before me. It looked like some starved monster, from whose powerless bones one still wishes one's-self away. No hedge was there, no tree, nor bird of any kind to inhabit them if there had been. I saw no animal but one long snake, lying in the middle of the road. Then again, instead of well-dressed, smiling, beautiful girls, joking with you innocently or wishing you heartily good day, female devils could not be nakeder nor bonier nor uglier than those wenches who ran before us, begging and screaming, and scratching their heads and blade-bones, and writhing like the damned. I remarked it to my companion, who calmly and indifferently answered me, ' I told you so.' ' Were you ever here before, sir ? ' said I. ' Never,' he replied.

" I trembled—that is—not from fear [2]—but, faith ! it almost

---

[1] From " We " to " Siena " added in 2nd ed.
[2] 1st ed. reads : " fear, but good people that fear tremble just as I did ; for he," etc.

made me say my catechism in the coach : for he threw himself back, as though he had given the order that things should be so, and knew they were so. We entered Rome. He ordered his luggage to remain at the gate, alighted, saluted me ; nobody has met him or heard of him ; the people at the gate are afraid of saying a word about him if you ask them ; never have I seen him from that hour to this, and God forbid I ever should in future."

" You [1] must have been highly gratified, sir, in that city, by the noble specimens of the fine arts," observed the colonel. " O, Lord bless you ! " cried the captain, " they make finer lace, and cambric, and frippery of all sorts, in your own country." " We have indeed some pretensions," answered Le Doux. Lady Glengrin remarked to the captain that his noble guest only meant statues and pictures. He winked at her, and whistled in a low key, and then whispered, " Why, indeed they do dress out their old dolls in the churches with a sight of finery, as for that." " But," added Le Doux, " their pictures in the Capitol, in the Vatican, and also in many private collections, are master-pieces."

" I do think," replied the captain, " they are up to most of us in painting a face or body. But the devil a notion have they of putting the one in good humour or the other in good clothes. They are all old-fashioned : and most of the men are in dressing-gowns : I have seen some half-naked, and some quite, and others that had never been at the barber's. Then what ruins and rubbish about the *demesne !* Scythe and whetstone never thought of ! More gravel than grain, more mountain than clover-field ; and ne'er a potato-plot for love or money. No rich water-meadow ; no hay-stack nor turf-stack ; no tight little cabin, with its window kept nicely in repair with strong substantial paper, and the smoke curling neatly through the doorway over the back of a comfortable pig, black or yellow, blinking at it pleasantly. But I will tell you what there are instead. There are rotten trees, and blighted and blasted ones. There are broken-up roads ; you would swear at first sight that they lead to no magistrate's or grand-juryman's. There are ugly broad weeds just before you ; and farther on there are cranky old towers covered with pantiles ; and there are rivers that are suffered to go undermining them. In all those pictures I never saw a cow fit for the butcher, or a horse that had been groomed, or a sheep with wool

[1] From " You " to " gooseberry bush," p. 146, added in 2nd ed.

about her too good to wipe my boots on. Plenty of goats : but who likes their company? Gentlemen's houses seem quite deserted. Where do you find a hot-house? where do you find a garden-wall? By my soul! I think the best painter in the whole set would fight shy of a gooseberry bush."

Lady Glengrin then asked the captain whether he had been presented to the Pope.

" As soon as I had put on a clean shirt, and got my boots blacked, I went," said he, " to Cardinal Gonsalvi, as the shoeblack told me I should, and desired to be presented to his master : he recommended me to a countryman of mine, Father Taylor, who did it."

" The cardinal is a man of great politeness and extensive information," said Le Doux.

" Politeness enough," replied the captain ; " but information is another thing. The devil a word of English or Irish had he to throw at a dog ; and when I tried him at Latin, by my soul! not a syllable could he put down to it, although it is in the breviary ; which I borrowed on purpose to learn it, from the waiter."

" Did you try the Pope at it, captain? " said Lady Glengrin.

" Madam," after a pause answered he, " I beg your pardon, but it is uncivilish to speak to a lady with a leg of a turkey in limbo between the gullet and grinder. Now then at your service. I told his Holiness I hoped I had the pleasure of seeing him very well, drawing up my pantaloon, and putting my hand at ease in the fob, like a man of fashion. The Pope knows all languages under heaven, they tell me, but he did not hear me at first, and when my words were repeated to him in Italian by my countryman, he replied, with a smile as hearty as mine, that he was always well in the presence of worthy men, and that he suffered as little as could be expected from his age and infirmities. He continued to smile upon me for a moment when he had done, and then said something quite as obliging to another, who had made no inquiries after his health at all. My free noble Milesian manner gave general satisfaction : people were surprised to see how easily and spiritedly I did it : and an English lady was encouraged to ask him for a lock of his hair, not wishing to be outdone by an Irishman."

" Did he give it her? " asked Lady Glengrin.

" He could not well have made any woman jealous ; yet he thought he might ; and said gravely that after his death those who esteemed him might wish for such memorials, but that he could not give them, in the grave or out. He seemed to be much affected at the mention of dying, and went away. The English lady was vexed and angry, and said aloud, ' A stiff old prig ! I would not give a farthing for it.' Nobody applauded her : women and men looked in her face coldly and fixedly. I began to feel for her ; and to show her that I did, I told her, if she drove that way it should go hard with me but I gave her a lock of as good a man's. She [1] stared at me as if she doubted my word. Upon which, to lend her confidence, I said, ' By my soul, Miss, I say only what I mean ; and you shall cut it your own sweet self.' In spite of everything I could think of to pacify her, away she went, with old Holiness sticking in her gizzard : and the last words she uttered were, ' The horrid brute ! ' Now I do not think the offence she received from him warranted so fierce an expression."

Le Doux had offered many little attentions to the lady next him, from whom he sometimes had an answer, but often none. At last she was tired and impatient, and said to a girl on the other side of her, giving her an elbow-kick, " Christ Jesus ! Bess, how this outlandish man does plague and worry me ! Lord Almighty ! will he never let me eat ? "

Le Doux either did not hear or dissembled it : but the captain, who heard it plainly, was not aware of this, and said, " Let her alone, colonel ! old cats will grumble over their meat, and mean nothing. If you intend civility, she is only my sister ; you need not mind her ; ay, Teresa ? "

" I am as much to be minded as another, Phelim. Who soused you that sow's ear ? There 's no bacon where there 's nobody to salt it. Mind that, and munch genteeler."

Universal approbation succeeded, excepting from Lady Glengrin, who neither uttered a word nor changed a feature. Le Doux declared that the lady was in the right ; and that he himself was the only person to blame ; no correction, he added, could make him moderate his attentions to wit, spirit, and beauty.

" Lord ! he speaks as good English as the dean," exclaimed the pacified Teresa to her younger friend, " and when one does not eat, one can listen. Mind him : he is not so old as he seems : he may be forty."

[1] From " She " to " expression " added in 2nd ed.

" A fig for men of forty ! " said the other in her ear ; " and I do not much like him neither ; for his nails are white all the way down, more like a beast's than a Christian's."

The last of these words were interrupted by a violent noise in front of the house ; then at the door ; then within it. Chairs rattled ; imprecations and expostulations clashed, thickened, redoubled.

" Now for fun ! " cried the captain, wiping first his hands with his whiskers, and then rubbing them together in raptures. " But better after our wine—— Moyle, run out and tell them to wait. Lady Glengrin, a thousand to one, among the rebels I find the fellow who stole your peacock, or some of his kin." " I hope, captain, if you do," replied her ladyship, " you will lay the lash on him smartly."

" Have you so many thieves about you, captain ? " said Le Doux. " These, and three hundred thousand more of them," cried he. " We will whip them howsoever, till we find them out."

" What can so many steal ? " asked Le Doux. " Steal ! " replied the captain, " the thieves for the most part steal nothing : but nine in ten of the whole population are rebels ! bloody dogs ! fiery-hot papists as any in hell, enemies to church and king, tithe and orange ! sly Scotch Presbyterians, earthed here ! fellows who cry out so at the sight of a steeple, one would think you had poked it into the hollow tooth. I have flogged them myself until I have a rheumatism in my shoulder that will last me for life, and until there is a dearth of wire and honest hemp in all the midland parts of the country."

" You seem indeed to have been in active service," said Le Doux. " I have flogged this coat upon my back, and five hundred a year into my pocket : I shall be major next Christmas, and die commander of a district. These things are not given for nothing."

" From your enthusiasm in your profession, you must have entered it early in life." " I was in the midst of the rogues at the outset." " You remember then the attempt of the revolutionary French and of Lord Edward Fitz-Gerald."

" O yes ; I was then but a boy though. Often and often has he lifted me above his head, although I was as tall at ten as he was at thirty. He used to say, when people told him to take care of himself, that he had not an enemy that he knew or that knew him. Yet he

148

found one here in Ireland who could do his business.[1] He was such a merry, innocent, ingenuous little devil, he could fidget a man's wife before his face, and no *blood and hounds* upon it, nor spit nor spade nor shillelah. And yet somehow he was the mischiefullest imp of all father Satan's fire-side. Had he lived a couple of years, we should have had barefoot bishops and woollen epaulets ; no army ; all militia ; from bog to parade, from parade to bog ; singing and whistling, as who should care for any ; and it would have been a month's labour to lift a hat. We have *United Irishmen* in every county and township ; and by my soul ! if he had carried his plans into execution, we should have had none at all, at all, but *United Irishmen*. Our people will always be bad when they can be, sir ! "

An Englishman corroborated the observation by the words, " I believe it." At which the captain rose from his chair, and asked him what he meant by speaking ill of Ireland in his presence, which he swore no man should do while he had Irish blood in his veins.

" Nevertheless they are most incorrigible rogues," said Lady Glengrin, remarking the silence and sorrowfulness of Le Doux.

" The vulgar are subject to error," said he, " and in these matters even the wise. Possibly your ladyship may find among them some who aspired to your countenance by participating your opinions on civil liberty."

" Civil liberty ! " cried she indignantly. " What ! among the bogs and mountains ! Beside, these fellows have no more right to my opinions than to my property. Colonel Le Doux, I hardly could have expected in you the champion of robbery and revolt. If it were against a minister or king it might be well enough ; but when one can not keep a favourite peacock on the lawn, matters are carried too far."

There was silence for a moment, the first moment there had been hitherto, and this was violently broken by the obstreperous entrance of the cook, lifting up her ladle, which dropped the grease over the same-coloured kerchief on her ample bosom.

" A dirty pagan ! a dirty pagan ! " cried she. " Because your Honour would not let a scurvy lieutenant come to table among the

---

[1] 1st ed. reads : " business, and another who could trample on his bones, and oust his family ; and one too of his own kin, the nearest of all, but just as the callous is to the foot, never helping but often corning it. People cried, *shame, by Jesus !* and such like, at it, royalist and rebel at once. Lord Edward was such," etc.

quality ! ' What ! forsooth ! ' said the polecat, ' if the daughter of mother Jibbery is become a countess and picks her teeth here, am not I good enough to lift my jacket-flap upon the chair beside her ? ' ' No, you are not,' said I. ' Then,' said he, ' no sucking-pig for countess or captain this blessed day ' ; and,—O the foul fox ! with a devil in him from muzzle to brush—how do you think he began to baste the poor innocent ? "

" Hold hard ! " cried Mr. Roger Moyle. " Have you no decency, Tertulliana Trench ? "

" Decency ! the cockroach ! I could skin him like an eel, out of the Suire, alive alive. No roast pig to-day, by my salvation, as I am true to the Protestant ascendancy, unless your Honour spits the bloody traitor."

" Let me alone for that," said the captain calmly : " I shall see whether his ribs will crackle, and whether he has a handful of thyme and marjoram in his belly."

At this he said grace and would have risen ; but Le Doux took him by the hand, and pressing it between his, submitted to his sounder judgment whether so trifling a matter were worthy of his exalted courage. The captain would have argued in the affirmative.

" Pooh ! pooh ! " said Moyle humanely, " the man was drunk ; and drunken men are up to anything, pretty nearly ; aren't they, Miss ? " She lifted up her shoulder, and said impatiently, " Let Phelim go his way. Sure we shall have a witty song from Tommy Moore upon it, ringing on the piano from Dublin to Belfast."

" Then let the whelp have both pig and fire for his own share ! " exclaimed the captain: " I would rather be in a jail than in a song ; and that witster's are never out of tune or out of fashion. Beside, we had all done with eating ; and as for sucking-pigs, I know where the other seven are. But, right or wrong, I have something to say in Master Ralph's ear another time, for his ill manners, and that won't lie like cotton in it, take my word."

The bottle was then pushed round ; and it was announced to the ladies by the captain that they might sit where they were, as no smutty toasts would be given nor merry songs called for ; and as coffee was fitter for Turks and tea for washerwomen ; and, above all, as good claret was not to be had every day in the best houses. " Mine," added he, " never gets into the head, ladies ! It passes like a guinea : don't be shy. *Church and King*, if you please (what

say you, colonel ?) ; and then *the ladies*, and afterward *the gentlemen*
from their fair lips ; and now afore God, Roger Moyle, I do desire
you will not favour us with any of your explanations."

" Lord help you, O'Mara ! " said Moyle, sneering, " they are no
bigger fools than you and I.   I wave the cap along the ground where
the scent lies fainter round cover."

In despite of invitations and precautions the party broke up early
in the evening.

Lady Glengrin had alike sustained her dignity and her affability,
and told the captain she did not wonder he was such a favourite at
the castle.   Her attendant, Lord Purlingstreamdale, was loftier.
He looked hard, and did not hear Mr. Roger Moyle invite him across
the table to drink a glass of claret.   Mr. Roger Moyle appeared not
to notice it at the time ; but when they rose from table he took him
gently by the sleeve, and reminded him of it plaintively, in almost a
whisper, saying he did not expect it at his hands, having left no less
than eighty pounds for five weeks together in his father's bank, when
his bailiff Sampson Haft sold the bullocks at Crookhaven.   His
lordship looked disdainfully.

" I am sorry you look so strange and modest and red, my lord,"
said Mr. Roger Moyle, " as there is a sort of kin between us."

" How so, Mr. Moyle ? " said his lordship.

" Why sure then," replied Mr. Roger Moyle, " and was not my
father's kitchen-wench, poor Phillis, who died at eighty under my
roof, own sister to Moll Harness, your grandmother, whom your
grandfather, if he had lived, would have made an honest woman ;
for there was not one that scoured better nor harder in those parts,
pewter or brass, though Phillis was never slack—— No drawing up
before me ! no waistcoat-button against mine ! I know your height
without tape.   I have some stray acres, my Lord Purlingstreamdale,
and, if you beat for me, you may know where they lie, and where the
house lies upon 'em ; there 's ne'er a tree hides it ; it looks you in
the face of day, erect and blithe as a bridegroom."   Then, offering
his hand, " Come let us part friends, or we shall not sleep soundly ;
to-morrow every man to his fancy."   He stooped a little, and rubbed
his palms, as men do before a good fire on coming from the cold,
and, in higher spirits than before, ran to the carriage, the steps of
which Lady Glengrin was about to mount, and invited her ladyship
and Colonel Le Doux to Moylestown, where he told them he had

dogs and some dirt for them if the weather should hold. They laughed heartily and drove off.

"Lord Purlingstreamdale, you do not enjoy Moyle's wit," said Lady Glengrin.

"I did not hear the man," replied he.

"Colonel, I should like to take you over," said her ladyship. "Roger Moyle is a man of ancient family. I may say it to you, although when I mentioned it incidentally in the presence of O'Donohough, O'Dono told me that he was only a Saxon, if I called that ancient; and, being informed by a lady that the race was Norman, he scoffed and cried, ' Och ! they are all one ; the same thing top and bottom,' pitying the ignorance of his interrupter. Moyle possesses an estate of twenty miles or more in extent. At the beginning of our disturbances he was a great pacificator, although he commanded a body of cavalry ; and the major of an English regiment told him that by such misconduct he had become suspected. ' I have one reason to be sorry for that ; and only one,' said Roger Moyle. ' What is it, sir ? ' said the major haughtily. ' Because I shall be more so before night,' replied he. ' How ! ' exclaimed the major. ' By contriving a window on English ground that shall never pay tax.' ' I don't understand you, sir,' cried the major. ' Come out then, and bring your best pistols, looking first to flint and priming, and, by the grace of God, I make a loop-hole in that pantry there for a wiser man to look through.'

"They met ; and he took the major by the hand "—here Lord Purlingstreamdale blushed and breathed hard—" and begged and entreated him, as a Christian, to retract his words—in vain—' any word, best or worse ; only retract it,' said Moyle. The major told him to stand off, and not beg and pray there, after his insolent and braggart brogue. They fired ; and the major fell. ' And now, gentlemen,' said Moyle to the seconds, ' as you have each your servant with you, do me the favour to take this uniform to headquarters, and to tell the general, with my best compliments, that it was Roger Moyle's.' And he stripped off his uniform and rode home in his shirt-sleeves, a distance of twenty-five miles, in the beginning of January."

"Captain O'Mara must be very intimate with him," Le Doux remarked. "He desired him at dinner to take a message out of the room."

DUKE DE RICHELIEU, ETC.

" Do you wonder at anything in O'Mara ? " said the countess.
" I never heard of a particular intimacy between them ; but the
maxim of Roger Moyle is, to go wherever he is invited ; for he says
that nobody will invite him who does not like him, and that he has
neither bad heart nor bad stomach. Obliging as he is, he would
have been offended at such a liberty, if there had been a servant in
the room to deliver the message, or if O'Mara could have left the
company. For although his conversation is coarse and clownish,
there are certain points upon which, in common with the Irish in
general, he is delicate and sensitive in the extreme. His moderation
made him as much suspected by some of the insurgents, after he had
laid down his uniform, as by the major. Toward the end of the same
month he had been shooting, and was returning homeward, when
three armed men started up from among the gorse, and one of them
advancing cried, ' Ho ! Moyle ! bring us your gun.'

" ' Gentlemen,' replied he, ' it is easier for you to come and fetch
it than for me to bring it. I have been out all day, with a brace
of hares dangling, as you see, across my shoulder, and fifteen fat
partridges in my pouch, if I counted right.'

" The man came closer, and cried, ' Off with your belt and down
with your fowling-piece, straight forthwith, or——'

" ' Or what ? ' cried Moyle. ' And now you threaten, friend, the
play 's fair.' So saying, he discharged the contents through his body,
and began to load again. The other two at first were astonished, but
after a mutual exhortation, on seeing that the gun was not double-
barrelled, they rushed forward against him. He drew a pistol, and
shot one : the other begged his life until he could confess.

" ' Draw your charge then,' said Moyle ; ' and now give me the
ramrod—and now off my grounds in the twinkling of an eye, or you
sleep in the kennel on raw horse-flesh no sweeter than yourself, and
such whiskey as curs give curs.'

" He broke the ramrod, threw the pieces over the man's head,
and, without looking after him, walked home."

" He appeared to me," said Le Doux, " a very ordinary man ;
begging his pardon, for my opinion was a most unjust one, and I am
happy to correct it. Whatever he says is wrong, and whatever he does
is right. Now of all things in a man's character this is the most
uncommon, the most opposite to what we find or expect. I regret
that I was not near enough to him to lead him into conversation."

IMAGINARY CONVERSATIONS : IRISH

" His conversation," said Lady Glengrin, " has usually a tendency to the indelicate, which produces the effect of wit among the uneducated, and which, I am sorry to say, in this country almost always accompanies it. In France and England the dinner-table is the theatre of decorum : in Ireland there are persons of rank and distinction who forget that the table-cloth is still before them, and that the defilement they suffer to escape them may run down and reach their daughters.

" Moyle entertains that contempt for reading and study which is general, not to say universal, among our gentry. Yet, from the little I have seen of him, I do not think him deficient in understanding or acuteness, although there is a story about him which, if true, goes to prove the contrary. On his return home one morning from some appointment with the justices about a road, to [1] be carried (they told him) directly through his estate, his butler heard him repeat to himself by jerks and twitches some sharp oath-like interjections, as he walked up and down the dining-room ; and took the liberty of saying, ' Master ! what are you angry at ? ' Moyle's answer was, with a smile, ' Because, Nan, I was angry. If a man can't keep his temper, what is he fit to keep ? ' Andrew, who had lived with him from a boy, was satisfied, and only said, he did not think wrath was worth carrying home, though a man rode.

" That Roger Moyle has not much reflection, is proved by an occurrence well known and often related. His mother's uncle was the catholic bishop of the diocese : a learned and pious man. On his death-bed he was frequently visited by Moyle. One evening he said, ' Roger ! you have an excellent heart, sound sense, and great influence in the county. I am sorry, on leaving the world, to think we shall never meet again.'

" ' Don't think about that, uncle Nol,' said Roger. ' I will remain with you, and lie upon a rug in this chamber, if you wish it.' The bishop groaned, ' Poor Roger ! blind still ! kind-hearted nephew ! in another world then we never must meet ! ' and burst into tears. ' Uncle Nol ! ' said Roger, ' tears are good for the tooth-ache, but may do harm in your complaint. Let us be reasonable, and discourse it over.'

" The bishop pressed his hand, and thanked him for the only act of kindness he never had seemed disposed to. ' You will then

---

[1] From " to " to " estate " added in 2nd ed.

hear me, Roger, upon our holy faith?' He brought forward all the arguments in its support, every one of which was irrefragable, and pure from the mouth of the apostles, doctors, and confessors; and at the conclusion he cried, 'I have a cloud more of witnesses.'

" ' The cloud we have had is quite enough, uncle Nol!' 'Now, Roger! can you doubt them?' cried the good man emphatically. 'I can not,' said Roger. 'You hold then these blessed truths?' 'I do.' 'And will stand firmly thereby?' 'I will.' 'You abandon then your own pernicious errors?'

" Roger hesitated; and then said tenderly, 'Uncle Nol, turn upon your back again and lie quiet. Sure I may keep my own errors, and take yours too.'

" ' O nephew Roger! my last hopes are blighted!'

" ' Pooh! pooh! no such thing. I believe all that you have said, uncle Nol; but I may believe other folks as civilly. Men of honour may differ in opinion, and no harm in it, while they don't contradict. If you tell me what you saw and what you know, why then indeed I take your word rather than another's, as being my next of kin, and aware right well what blood is in your veins.' "

" Incapable as I have shown myself," said Le Doux, " of judging the other parts of his character, I will not hazard a word upon his prudence; but it appears wonderful to me that, in the vicinity of those whose relatives he has shot, he rides home alone in the evening, through a country so uninhabited."

" The same thing was remarked to him by Captain O'Mara," said Lady Glengrin, " and he replied that he was mounted on such a horse as no man need be ashamed of : that, if there were few, he would show them his head; and, if the bidders were too many, his tail. Neither expostulation nor experience have altered his custom. Nat Withers, called familiarly from this time forward ' the man of the broken ramrod,' told his story with a few variations, and swore in the presence of several, that he would kill the first soldier he met, private or officer, in service or out. The declaration was made before O'Mara, who, in addition to his other offices, is justice of the peace. He watched his opportunity of surrounding Nat's house, which Nat had been just seen entering, and called aloud ' Nat Withers!' Nat came to the door, and falling on his knees, ' Why sure, captain, your Honour can not want me; you have so many other brave men about you. For the love of Christ ! what are your Worship's commands ? '

" ' Nat Withers ! only just come a step out and be hanged, and hold your tongue upon it. Leave the rest to me : witnesses are sworn : all is ready, just as you could wish it : sentence and service shall be read over you at once : up upon your legs ! be aisy ! '

" Nat sprang up, and attempted to run off, but, turning the corner of the house, was shot. ' There may be more of them within,' said the captain ; ' lose no time, boys ! '

" They were entering the cabin, when the wife met them, and levelled one with her fist, and stabbed another to the heart with a knife. Surrounded and seized by the remainder, she threw it from her, and fixing her eyes upon the captain, ' Och ! bloody hound ! Och ! that it was not thee ! ' ' Ugly witch ! ' cried O'Mara, ' who art thou ? ' ' I am Dinah Shee, Nat Withers's wife these nine years, whose blood be upon thy head ! ' ' Better there than upon this new pantaloon,' said O'Mara, ' where a braver man's is.' ' A lie in your hound's throat a stride across ! ' cried Dinah : ' there was no braver man in all Ireland than Nat Withers, though he was not always brave at the right time.'

" The captain smiled : she struck at him with her fist : he caught her arm, and said calmly : ' Dinah Shee ! thou hast spoken fair, and done well and bravely. If anyone bears false witness against thee on this little matter, I will appear in thy behalf, and swear him down to the devil ! mind that, boys ! '

" At these words she fell upon the ground, and howled tremendously. ' Leave the poor soul in her cabin,' said O'Mara to his men ; ' she can not do less for the dead ; and Nat there won't come again and bother her about it.' "

Le Doux was saddened at the smile on the countenance of Lady Glengrin, who asked him where were his thoughts.

" I would have reserved them entire for Mr. Moyle," replied he, " if your ladyship had not been mistress of them, and given them another direction. Really I should like to see his town."

" Town ! " cried Lady Glengrin with surprise.

" When he did us the honour to invite us, did he not say Moyle's-town ? "

" It was always a lone house ; although once there was another nearer it, which he pulled down, because the tenant had poisoned a

fox ; saying that he who would poison a fox would, in proper time
and place, at last poison a Christian, and, after that, a child. To
explain the subject of your observation ; our houses in the country
we call *towns* and *boroughs ;* we have *castles* and *forts* of one story
high, comfortably thatched, but without wall or ditch, rail or pale,
bolt or shutter, and with green sash-windows, in honour of the
shamrock, down to the ground. Our lodges and cottages are at
the gates of Dublin, in Merion-square, or Stephen's-green, or wings
perhaps to the Custom-house."

During the remainder of their drive homeward, her ladyship
commended the prudence of Le Doux, who fearing that some cruelty
might be committed in the captain's house, on the men arrested, and
before the visitors had left it, requested her ladyship to remember
that the evenings were damp and chilly, that perhaps more of the
disaffected might be abroad, and that, in order to obviate any alarm
to herself on the latter subject, and to him principally on the former,
as her ladyship's health had been delicate, it might be better to
give her commands about the horses. She began to apologise for
introducing him to such a creature ; adding that, as he had been
presented at court, he was a person to be visited, but that still she
did not like it. " However, he keeps the rabble in quietness," said
she : " and we have had only one robbery in the parish, the most
peaceful in Ireland, all the year. Unluckily it was my peacock.
As for murders, there have only been seven or eight in as many
months, chiefly of middlemen and tithemen, beside a cow, which
indeed died rather from hocking, and from having her tongue cut
out unskilfully."

A few days after, Le Doux rode into the country, to the distance
of twelve or fourteen miles. He found the labours of the husband-
man unremitted, his food of the coarsest quality, and proportionally
less plenteous than, from calculation of profit, we give our swine and
calves. He saw the Catholic faith in all its purity, but without its
festivals. On his return he mentioned this, and here both parties,
and every individual, agreed : namely, that the only good thing
among them was the absence of holidays.

" The absence of a thing, a good thing ! " said he, pondering.
" And this absence, *among* them ! That is more like an article of faith
than an article of logic." He had been accustomed to such incon-
sequences ; but never could he persuade himself that incessant labour

157

is a blessing, or that what is individually bad is nationally good.
" Can there be prosperity where there is no happiness ? " said he
within himself : and it was the first time that a statesman ever had
revolved a question the most original and the most important. To be
awake is well ; but to sleep is well also. To work is good ; but to
cease from it is not less. Much is gained to a nation by handicraft
and digging : is nothing gained by joy and gladness, and by
rendering them the immovable Lares of the poor man's hearth ?
The assertion was uncontradicted, that there were in Ireland four
millions of poor or oppressed. " Merciful heaven ! " cried Le Doux,
" four millions ! the remainder of the earth does not contain the half.
Those educated in slavery are willing slaves. The Mahometans have
expeditious, equal, and inexpensive laws, and, for the most part, a
delightful climate ; the two greatest blessings ; and they believe in
fatality—no small one ! The Pagans hear of nothing better than
what they possess and enjoy. The Irish not only hear of it, but are
promised it, and have earned it. Fatalism is the only foolish thing
they do not believe in. And their climate is such that, rather than
bear its inclemency, they eat and drink smoke. What hovels ! what
food ! what beds ! what contests of their children and their swine
for even these ! Shall then their innocent festivals, the best part of
the best religions, and here so requisite as a solace, so acceptable as
a compensation, be forbidden them ? "

O Catholicism ! thou art verily a syphilis among the moral evils,
eating deep into the political, and fatal where unchecked ; but
thou hast thy truckle-couch for thy sores to lie easy on, and something under it to catch thy drivelling. God help thee if these are
removed !

To dance on Sundays, to enjoy the delights of music, the purest of
delights, the greatest, the most humanizing, are things unlawful : the
Catholic and Protestant are covenanters here. They may celebrate
the Lord's-day, but they must be as gloomy as if it were the devil's.
A gauger comes round, and measures every man's smile ; and we may
expect the Society for the Suppression of Vice to offer a reward for a
gelotometre, which Johnson would have defined *a diatonic instrument
whereby the cachinnations of laughter may be mensurated.*

In Ireland, as in England, Sunday is a festival ; but he who pre-
sumes to enjoy the first course, must chew the last in the stocks or
in the house of industry, or acquire an appetite for another such

feast by the wholesome exercise of the tread-mill.[1] If Sundays were holidays, as they should be, and Christmas-day and New-Year's-day were added, the quantity of time devoted to idleness would be sufficient. At present they are days of dead languor, and make the tired labourer wish again for work. To scold is not forbidden on them ; to sing is. He may quarrel with his neighbour ; he must not play with him. Shall the religion then of no nation be free, not only from gross and incoherent, but from restless and insulting absurdities ? Shall kindness be the basis of none ? loudly as Christianity hath proclaimed it, constantly as its divine and ever-blessed Founder hath practised and commanded it ? Intolerant and self-sufficient bigots, the most impudent and crazy of mankind, legislate for churches and gloss for Christ. They do not trouble their heads in what manner the commutative offices of life are executed, the duties of every day, the interests of society in contact with us; and never are quiet on those which they call the *everlasting*, but which in fact are no interests at all, being mere dependencies on belief or unbelief, in matters incapable of demonstration, and inapplicable to practice. Much of fanaticism is seen in England, some in Ireland : but fanaticism here is among the lighter curses.

" It appears to me," said Le Doux, " that in this country the features of evil are harsh, the form indefinite."

" We must acknowledge," said Lady Glengrin, " that none of our statesmen has been capable of improving the condition of the Irish."

" What ! " cried Le Doux, " does the plague rage perennially ? Do the rains of heaven never fall among you ? Have you no roads, no rivers, no harbours ? Have you no herbage, no cattle, no corn ? "

" Of these things," replied she, " we have plenty."

" Bear me witness, heaven ! " exclaimed Le Doux enthusiastically. " To make men happier requires little wisdom, but much will. What was Odessa ? what is it now ? Madam, I do not pretend to greater knowledge than many possess, in every kingdom : I wished to do good, and, being in authority, I did it. The Russians were not advanced in civilisation much farther than the Irish ; but the gentry were more humane, the clergy more tolerant, and in consequence the *serfs* more docile."

The Irish friends of Le Doux began to think him, some a visionary,

---

[1] 1st ed. reads : " tread-mill under the direction and superintendence of Mr. Secretary Peel. If," etc.

some an incendiary : and he, who saw only confusion and contradiction from the first, discovered that the same person was the most polite and the rudest, the most hospitable and the most sordid, the most contentious and the best-natured creature in the world.

" It is time to leave this carnival," said he. " The mask in fashion is half-white and half-black : every man finds its inconvenience, yet every man wears it. There is only one exception, and, strangest of contradictions, it is a minister of state. Let me fly from this scene of enchantment while the bristles are not yet out upon me."

IV. LORD COLERAINE, REV. MR. BLOOMBURY, AND REV. MR. SWAN

(*Imag. Convers.*, iii., 1828 ; *Wks.*, i., 1846 ; *Wks.*, v., 1876.)

SWAN. Whither are you walking so fast, Mr. Bloombury ?

BLOOMBURY. My dear brother in Christ, Mr. Swan, I am truly happy to meet you. A fine fresh pleasant day ! Any news ? I am going to visit Lord Coleraine,[1] who has been attacked by an apoplexy.

SWAN. Such was the report I heard yesterday. Accidents of this kind, when they befall the light and thoughtless, shock us even more than when it pleases God to inflict them on the graver and the better. What is more awful than to confront so unexpectedly the gay in spirit with the king of terrors ? Sincerely as I grieve to hear of this appalling visitation, it is consolatory to think that his lordship has brought himself to such a comfortable and cheering frame of mind.

BLOOMBURY. Has he, Mr. Swan ? Methinks it is rather early, if he has.

SWAN. He must be sensible of his situation, or he would not have required your spiritual aid.

BLOOMBURY. He require it ! no more than a rank heathen or unchristened babe. He shall have it though. I will awaken him ; I will prick him ; I will carry to him the sword of faith ; it shall pierce his heart.

SWAN. Gently with the rowels on a foundered steed.

BLOOMBURY. Mr. Swan, our pulpits should not smell of the horse-cloth. I never heard that text before.

SWAN. You have heard many a worse.

BLOOMBURY. Profane ! there are none but from the Bible.

SWAN. The application and intent make them more or less

---

[1] Lord Coleraine, better known, even after succeeding to the title, as Colonel George Hanger, an associate of the Prince Regent, author of an autobiography containing attacks on Dissenters and much crude, vigorous moralizing.

good. *Smite* is in that book ; *do not smite* is there also. Now which is best ?

BLOOMBURY. Both are excellent if they are there : we can only know which is best by opening the volume of grace, and the text that we open first is for our occasion the best of the two.

SWAN. There is no logic to place against this. Of course you are intimately acquainted with Lord Coleraine. You can remind him of faults which it is still in his power to correct ; of wrongs——

BLOOMBURY. I can, and will. When I was in the Guards, he won a trifle of money from me : I shall bring him to a proper sense of his sinfulness in having done it.

SWAN. In winning your money ?

BLOOMBURY. He may make some reparation to society for his offence.

SWAN. He could not have won your money if you had not played with him.

BLOOMBURY. I was young : he ought to have taught me better.

SWAN. He did, if he won much.

BLOOMBURY. He won fifty guineas.

SWAN. How ? and were you, Mr. Bloombury, ever a gamester ?

BLOOMBURY. At that time I was not under grace.

SWAN. Well, really now I would converse with a dying man on other topics. Comfort him ; prepare him for his long journey.

BLOOMBURY. Ay, sing to him ; read to him Shakespeare and Cervantes and Froissart ! Make him believe that man is better than a worm, lovelier than a toad, wiser than a deaf adder. Mr. Swan, you are a virtuous man (I mean no offence by calling you so), a good neighbour, a cordial friend, but you are not touched.

SWAN. Bloombury, if you are sincere, you will acknowledge that, among your evangelicals, this touching for the most part begins with the pocket, or its environs.

BLOOMBURY. O for shame ! such indecency I never heard ! This comes from your worldly and university view of things, your drinkings and cricketings.

SWAN. Too frequently. We want drilling in our armour of faith from the Horse-guards : we want teaching from those who pay fifty guineas the lesson. I am not so unchristian as to deny that you are adepts in the practice of humility, but it is quite of a new kind. You are humble while you speak, but the reverse when you are spoken to ; and, if it were not for your sanctification, I should call you the most arrogant and self-sufficient of sectarians.

BLOOMBURY. We are of the church ; the true English church.

SWAN. Few sects are not, opposite as they may be. Take the general spirit and practice of it, and tell me what church under heaven is more liberal and forbearing.

BLOOMBURY. Because you forego and forget the most prominent of the thirty-nine articles. There is the sword in them.

SWAN. Let it lie there, in God's name.

BLOOMBURY. There is doctrine.

SWAN. I take what I understand of it, and would not give a pinch of snuff for the rest. Our Saviour has taught me whatever is useful to know in Christianity. If churches, or any members of them, wanted more from his apostles, I hope they enjoyed what they wanted. The coarser Gentiles must needs have cheese and garlic upon their bread of life : my stomach won't digest them. Those who like the same fare may take it ; only let them, when their mouths are full of it, sit quiet, and not open them upon me. We are at the house, I think. Good morning.—A word at parting. May not that musk about you hurt the sick man ?

BLOOMBURY. What musk ? I protest I never have used any.

SWAN. Then the creature that bears it has run between your legs, and rubbed its fur against your dress but lately. Adieu.

BLOOMBURY (to a Servant). Is my Lord Coleraine at home ?

SERVANT. No, sir.

BLOOMBURY. Mark me, young man ; the ways of the world are at an end so near the chamber of death. Tell his lordship that the Reverend—— better tell him that Captain Frederick Bloombury, late of the Guards, has something of great importance to communicate.

SERVANT (returning). My master desires you to walk up, sir.

COLERAINE. I have had the pleasure, I think, of meeting you formerly, Captain Bloombury ; I can not say exactly where ; for we guardsmen meet in strange places. I had sold out : and, as you are not in uniform, I presume that you too have left the service.

BLOOMBURY. On the contrary, I have just entered it.

COLERAINE. Rather late in the day ; is not it ? However, if I can serve you, speak. I feel a difficulty in conversing : this apoplexy has twisted my mouth on one side like a turbot's, and Death and

I seem to be grinning for a wager. What do you lift up your eyebrows at ? My sight is imperfect ; they seem to me to be greyish, and fitter for a lieutenant-general than a captain.

BLOOMBURY. I am ageing—that is, I have a whitish or rather a lighter-coloured hair here and there. Sober thinking brings them.

COLERAINE. Particularly when it comes after the thinking that is not quite so sober—ay, Bloombury ! Excuse me, was it expedient to enter the service so late in life, and in the midst of peace ?

BLOOMBURY. There begins our warfare : these are riotous and bloody times.

COLERAINE. They are getting better, if people will let them. What would they have ? Would they tear a new coat to pieces because the old one will not fit ? How do you like your brother officers ?

BLOOMBURY. Reasonably well.

COLERAINE. And the service at large ?

BLOOMBURY. The sweetest of services is the service of the Lamb.

COLERAINE. They told me so—talking does me harm—yet I did not feel it. Gentlemen, it is of no use to bleed me any more. You need not feel my pulse—I am too weak. I am losing my intellects, such as they are. I seem to see faces and to hear words the strangest in the world.

BLOOMBURY. He shuts his eyes and appears to doze a little. He smiles—a very bad sign in a dying man !

PHYSICIAN. With deference, I think otherwise, sir. He can not live the day through, but he is in full possession of his senses. If you have any secret, anything interesting to his family, any omission to suggest, we will retire. Let me however request of you, not to disturb him on matters of business.

BLOOMBURY. The Lord forbid !

PHYSICIAN. He seems quite tranquil, and may go off so.

BLOOMBURY. In that perilous state ! It is the dimple of a whirlpool, at the bottom whereof is hell. I will arouse him : I will wrestle with Christ for him.

PHYSICIAN. In another ring then : I keep the ground here.

BLOOMBURY. You physicians are materialists.

PHYSICIAN. Undoubtedly, sir, you would desire to be the contrary ?

BLOOMBURY. Undoubtedly, indeed.

COLERAINE, BLOOMBURY, AND SWAN

PHYSICIAN. You methodists then are immaterialists ?

BLOOMBURY. Ho ! ho ! grace and election and sanctification are things immaterial !

PHYSICIAN. Which of you ever has preached gratitude to God ; in another word, contentment ? Which of you has ever told a man that his principal duty is to love his neighbour ?

BLOOMBURY. Who dares lie, in the face of God ? We love the Lamb ; the rest follows.

PHYSICIAN. Unless the rest (as you call it) precedes, the Lamb will never be caught by you, whine to him and pipe to him as you may. Love to God must be conveyed and expressed by a mediator.

BLOOMBURY. There you talk soundly.

PHYSICIAN. You can show your love to him only through the images he has set on every side of you.

BLOOMBURY. Idolater ! When I uplift my eyes to heaven and see Jupiter (so called) and Saturn (name of foolishness) and all the starry host——

PHYSICIAN. You see things less worthy of your attention than a gang of gipsies in a grassy lane. You can not ask Saturn (name of foolishness) nor Jupiter (so called) whether he wants anything, nor could you give it if he did : but one or other of these poor creatures may be befriended in some way, may in short be made better and honester and cleanlier.

BLOOMBURY. What ! no prayers, I suppose, nor thanksgivings ?

PHYSICIAN. Catch the prayer that is rising to God, and act for him ; receive in turn the thanksgiving ; he authorises and commands you. If there is a man in your parish who wants a meal while you eat two in the day, let me advise you neither to sing a psalm nor to bend a knee until you have divided your quartern loaf with him.

I must go in and see my patient : if you follow, step gently.

COLERAINE. I beg your pardon, Captain Bloombury : how long have you been waiting ?

BLOOMBURY. An instant only, my lord. I hope your lordship has benefited by your easy slumber.

COLERAINE. I feel no pain.

BLOOMBURY. Unhappy man !

COLERAINE. Thank you : I am sure you are.*

* Misunderstanding ; and supposing he said " *I am glad to hear it,*" or some such thing.—W. S. L.

BLOOMBURY. The Lord sends hither me, his unworthy servant, O George Viscount Coleraine, to bring you unto him.

COLERAINE. I am obliged to you both.

BLOOMBURY. Well may you be. You have led as wild and wicked a life as one could wish. Repent ! repent !

COLERAINE. Of what ? For, faith ! there are so many things, I cannot see which to take hold on.

BLOOMBURY. If I could suggest any other, I would do it in preference. I know but one.

COLERAINE. Speak out : don't be modest.

BLOOMBURY. You had formerly a strange itch for gaming.

COLERAINE. Not I indeed : but one can game when one can not do the pleasanter thing.

BLOOMBURY. You led me into, or at least you countenanced me in, that vice.

COLERAINE. Which ?

BLOOMBURY. Gaming.

COLERAINE. Pardon me, my worthy friend ; we never were intimate till now. Charmed as I certainly should have been by your acquaintance, it can not be more than once that we met before : for in good society no one forgets names or faces, unless of tradespeople and Jews.

BLOOMBURY. On that one evening I lost fifty guineas to you.

COLERAINE. Express no uneasiness ; do not trouble yourself, Captain Bloombury ; lay it upon the table. If it had escaped your recollection, I assure you it has escaped mine too. Do not, I entreat you, make yourself at all uncomfortable about it. I never said a word upon your leaving town and forgetting me.

BLOOMBURY. Forgetting you, my lord ! I paid the money down in five *rouleaux*. I wish I had kept it for the poor.

COLERAINE. Pooh ! another fifty is just as good as that. What do the poor care whether it is packed in *rouleaux* or not ? It is unpacked, I will answer for it, long before they touch it.

BLOOMBURY. If I had either that or another to give the broken in spirit, the sick and weary——

COLERAINE. O ! I now understand you. Upon my soul, you have a most compassionate and significant eye. Give me your hand, my good fellow ! don't distress yourself. Yes, my dear Bloombury, times have been hard with me heretofore ; but I never was broken in spirit ; and now I want nothing.

BLOOMBURY. Many whom I have visited in their last hours have lent money to the Lord, unasked.

COLERAINE. Impudent dogs !

BLOOMBURY. I part with mine willingly : it is only a snare of Satan. Yet those who have no families have thought of me.

COLERAINE. And those who have families too ; for, I warrant, one of the flock (to say the least) reminded them. You are still a fine stout fellow.

BLOOMBURY. I do not understand your lordship : I am, as the Lord made me, a sinner !

COLERAINE. The deuce you are ! I wish I could be ! Do not groan ; do not be uncomfortable ; I am no worse, though I sighed a little.

BLOOMBURY. Ah my Lord Coleraine ! If you could rightly dispose of your soul and of your superfluities, then might you well exclaim, " O Death ! where is thy sting ? "

COLERAINE. I should not venture : he might show it me.

BLOOMBURY. He could not ; I defy him.

COLERAINE. You are braver : he is one too much for me : he has got me down.

BLOOMBURY. If your lordship would take courage and resolve, it is not even yet too late for the labour of love.

COLERAINE. It would be a labour indeed for me.

BLOOMBURY. Try, strive.

COLERAINE. I am no more up to it than I am to the labours of Hercules. Ah, my dear Captain Bloombury, you are much more capable of such feats : I wish you joy of them : I have bidden them farewell. I begin to think that the world is a very bad world, and that everything goes amiss in it.

BLOOMBURY. Excellent thought ! if it had but come earlier. We should think so all our lives : it would prepare us for heaven. Let us remove from the sick-room all that ever gave you uneasiness by feeding your vices. I would tear off the old man from you.

COLERAINE. The vagabond ! what ! is he here ? Who let him in while I was sleeping ? Tear him off, with a vengeance, the old thief ! Down stairs with him—— I paid the rogue fifteen per cent.

BLOOMBURY. Be tranquillised, my lord ; you misunderstood me.

I would do as much for your lordship, as my brother in Christ, the reverend Christopher Rawbottom, a rooting man, did in regard to your deceased brother.

COLERAINE. What did he?

BLOOMBURY. Being in prison, a sufferer from false witnesses, he begat him, as Paul begat Onesimus, in his chains.

COLERAINE. I don't believe it; I never heard it whispered or hinted. My mother was a very different sort of woman, and would hardly run after a fusty old goat, tied by the leg in a court of the Fleet.

BLOOMBURY. O my lord! how little are you accustomed to the language of the Holy Scriptures! I speak figuratively.

COLERAINE. Egad did you, Bloombury?

BLOOMBURY. I can not bring your lordship to think seriously upon death.

COLERAINE. Excuse me, Captain Bloombury, it is you who think the least seriously. It is you who would ask him where his sting lies, and who would challenge him outright.

BLOOMBURY. My lord, if I am so unfortunate that I can not be of use to your lordship in your interests, should there be remaining any slight matter in the temporal and personal, wherein my humble abilities could be serviceable to you, I entreat you to command me.—He meditates! who knows what he may do yet!—It would be but just.

COLERAINE. Have you a pencil?

BLOOMBURY. Yes, my lord, yes—but pen-and-ink would be better —let me run and find one.

COLERAINE. No, no, no.

BLOOMBURY. O yes, my lord.—Gentlemen, pray walk in again: his lordship is most clear in his intellects—he has a short codicil to add. I carry the ink.—Is this pen a good one? could he write legibly with it?

PHYSICIAN. Perfectly. I wrote with it early in the morning.

BLOOMBURY. My lord, the gentlemen have returned; they are waiting; here are pen, ink, and paper.

COLERAINE. Favour me, Captain Bloombury; write.

BLOOMBURY. It would not do, my lord: if the learned doctor would undertake it, your lordship might sign it—and indeed might sign first.

COLERAINE, BLOOMBURY, AND SWAN

COLERAINE. Well, then, doctor, write [1] ; will you?
PHYSICIAN. I am ready, my lord.
COLERAINE.

> Death ! We don't halt then ! march I must,
> Mortally as I hate the dust.
> I should have been in rare high glee
> To make an April-fool of thee.*

BLOOMBURY. Worldly-minded man ! There are no hopes then !
PHYSICIAN. I told you so, sir ; but although he knew it, you might have spoken lower.

[1] 1st ed. reads : " write, | Death ! We don't halt then," etc.
* He died on the 1st of April, 1824.—W. S. L.

V. CAVALIERE PUNTOMICHINO AND MR. DENIS
EUSEBIUS TALCRANAGH

(*Imag. Convers.*, ii., 1824 ; ii., 1826 ; *Wks.*, i., 1846 ; *Wks.*, vi., 1876.)

THE Cavaliere Puntomichino was the last[1] representative of an ancient family. He was an honest and rich man ; so that, when his intention was understood at Florence of travelling to England, it excited suspicion in some, and surprise in all ; for Italians of that description were seldom known to have crossed the Channel. He went however, and remained there several years, reading our best authors, and wondering (as he informed me) at one thing only, which is, that there could really be in the whole human race so prodigious a diversity, as he found in almost every five men[2] he conversed with in our metropolis. " I have often observed," said he, " more variety in a single household than I believe to exist in all Italy."

He never had about him the slightest taint of affectation ; yet became he singular, and glaringly so, at his first introduction to the academy of La Crusca. For he asserted three paradoxes : first, that no sentence or speech in a comedy should exceed a fair sheet in octavo ; secondly, that no witticism should be followed by an explanation, in the dialogue, of more than two pages ; and thirdly, that Shakespeare had nearly or quite as much[3] genius as Goldoni. Henceforward he was a worthy man, but an oddity. His claim to the literary character I shall forbear to discuss ; although I have many papers, not indeed of his own writing, but addressed to him by others, some of which go so far as to call him a nightingale, some a great doctor, some an eagle, some a phœnix, some a sun, and one both a sun and a phœnix. But this last was written by a rival of him who wrote the preceding ; and therefore its accuracy may be

---

[1] 1st ed. reads : " last male representative."
[2] 1st ed. reads : " men whom he."
[3] 1st ed. reads : " much honour as."

suspected, and it was declared by the academy, after three sittings, to be more ingenious than correct.

His sedentary life had been unfriendly to his health, and he was seized in the beginning of this winter with repeated and severe attacks in the breast. As he had inherited a good property, and had collected many rare books, all the canonics [1] and professors began to write *tributes, monodies, elegies, musæ plangentes, Etruriæ luctus,* and consolations to his heir, no very distant relative, whose brother in the time of the French government had been hanged for a robbery at the age of eighteen.[2] He himself was in the galleys at Pisa for the murder of his father-in-law, who had educated him and had promised to leave him his estate. On the death of the Cavaliere, it was foreseen that he, too late indeed for his happiness and sensibility, would be found innocent of an offence, for which the French laws in their precipitancy had condemned him. The proofs of this innocence were produced, the patron found, the sum stipulated, when the Cavaliere [3] died. On opening the will, it appeared that he had destined his property to the maintenance of soldiers' widows, and the redemption of slaves from Barbary. *Diavoli !* and *cazzo !* and *cappari !* and *Bacco !* tripped up and exploded the Muses and Etruria. Rosini, the Pisan professor, their choregus, who, printer no less than professor and poet, had already struck off his *Lamentation,* spoke more calmly and reasonably than the rest, saying manfully, " Gabriel, take down those sheets in papal quarto, and throw them upon the *Codes* of Napoleon : the thing won't do." The expected and expecting heir was accused of falsifying the evidences ; and fresh severities were added, for his attempts to corrupt justice.

Let me now revert to my first acquaintance with the Cavaliere. I never in my life accepted a letter of introduction, nor ever expressed a wish, whatever I might have felt, for any man's society. By some accident this peculiarity was mentioned to Puntomichino, and he called on me immediately. Returning his visit, I found him in the library : several English books were upon the table, and there was seated at the window a young gentleman of easy manners and fashionable appearance, Mr. Denis Eusebius Talcranagh, of Castle-

---

[1] 1st ed. reads : " canons."
[2] 1st ed. reads : " eighteen, proving as others have done in various ways that misfortune is attendant on early elevation. He," etc.
[3] 1st ed. reads : " Cavaliere, whose decease had been expected daily, died."

IMAGINARY CONVERSATIONS : IRISH

Talcranagh and of Skurrymore-Park, county Down, and first cousin, as he informed me, of Lord Cowslipmead, of Dove's-nest-Hall, county Meath, a great fire-eater. I bowed : on which he fancied that I had known his lordship intimately. On my confessing the contrary, he appeared surprised. " You must however have heard something," continued he, " in your earlier days, of Sir Roderic James O'Rowran, my uncle,[1] who, whenever he entered an inn with his friends, placed himself at the head of the table, and cried, ' Whiskey and pistols for eight ! ' "

It was now my turn to be mortified, and I could only reply that there were many men of merit whom it had never been my fortune to know. " Then, sir," said he, " ten guineas to one you never were in Ireland in your life ; for you must have known him if you had met him, whether you would or not."

There was an infinity of good-humour in Mr. Talcranagh ; and if his ideas were not always perspicuous, they often came forth with somewhat of prismatic brilliancy. He [2] acknowledged a predilection for the writers of his own country, " which," he said, " we authors are not apt to do." I then discovered that I had been conversing with a literary man, who had published an imperial folio of eleven pages on the Irish Wolf-dog.

" I sold my copies," said he, " and bought a tilbury and a leash of setters. And now, sir, if ever you should print anything, take my advice : cuts in wood or cuts in stone, and a black-letter title-page, for your life ! I did it, without a knowledge of printer or publisher —to be sure, I was master of my subject, which goes a great way ; and then indeed I had a pair of extraordinary capital buckskins, which, it is true, began to carry on the surface, as Southey says of Flemish scenery,

A grey and willowy hue,[3]

but I found a fellow in Cockspur-street [4] who procured me a favourable criticism for them. I went no further in expenditure, although

---

[1] 1st ed reads : " great-uncle."

[2] 1st ed reads : " He gave a decided preference to . . . over all others, ' which,' " etc.

[3] *The Poet's Pilgrimage to Waterloo.*

[4] 1st ed. reads : " Cockspur-street who could clean neatly, and these I sent with my best compliments to the prime hand in the *** *Review*, taking care to leave by accident a bran new guinea in the watch pocket. This was good enough. I," etc.

PUNTOMICHINO AND TALCRANAGH

Valpy was constantly at the heels of my groom Honorius, pressing him also to write a criticism on the *Wolf-dog of Erin* for the
Classical Journal; since I from ignorance of custom was too proud
to do it; and assuring him that, look as he might, and shake his
head as he would, he was no Jew, and would do the thing reasonably. Sir," added Mr. Talcranagh smartly, " are you a friend to
dogs ? "

" A thousand thanks to you, Mr. Talcranagh," cried I, " for
asking me a question at last which I can answer in the affirmative.
There is a sort of freemasonry among us, I verily believe ; for no
dog, except a cur, a pug, or a turnspit, ever barks at me ; they and
children love me universally. I have more than divided empire [1] :
these form the best part of the world." " Add the women,"
shouted he aloud, " and here is my hand for you." We saluted
cordially.

" Indeed," said I, " Mr. Talcranagh, you have reason to be proud
of your countrywomen, for their liveliness, their beauty, and their
genius. The book before us, by Miss Edgeworth,[2] which you were
looking into, abounds in philosophy and patriotism ; there is
nothing of commonplace, nothing of sickly sentiment, nothing of
insane enthusiasm. I read warily ; and whenever I find the writings
of a lady, the first thing I do, is to cast my eyes along her pages,
to see whether I am likely to be annoyed by the traps and spring-
guns of interjections, or if any French or Italian is sprinkled on the
surface ; and if I happen to espy them, I do not leap the paling.
In these volumes I see much to admire, and nothing that goads or
worries me into admiration."

" Gentlemen," said the Cavaliere, " I am as warm an admirer of [3]
the Irish ladies in their authorship as either of you, and perhaps if
one of them, lately here in Florence, had consulted me on a few
matters and persons, I could have rendered her some service by
setting her right. Travellers are profuse of praise and censure in
proportion as they have been civilly or indecorously received, not
inquiring nor caring whether the account be quite correct, if the
personages of whom they write be of celebrity : for censure no less

---

[1] 1st ed. reads : " divisum imperium."
[2] Authorship not stated in 1st ed.
[3] 1st ed. reads : " of Lady Morgan as either of you, and if she had consulted,"
etc.

than praise requires a subject of notoriety. Many [1] English and Irish court a stranger of rank * in this city, who did not even put on mourning at the decease of his wife's brother, Napoleon, though he owed to him the highest of his distinctions, and the greater part of his unwieldy fortune. He suffered to die here, imprisoned for debt, a woman once lovely, generous, and confiding ; who had ruined herself to make her house appear worthy of his reception. At the moment when she was breathing her last, in silence, in solitude, in want of sustenance, his palace resounded with music, with dances, with applauses to archducal guests and their magnificent entertainer. The sum expended on that night's revelry would have released her from captivity, and would have rescued her from death. Our fair traveller does not mention this : but did she not know it ? She [2] has spoken of our patriots : what [3] were they doing ? They were contented to act in the character of buffoons before the court.

" Do you wish a little anecdote of the Florentine Russel, as she called the man ? Go half a mile up the road to Bologna, and you will probably see before their cottage a family of thirteen, in tears. Ask them why they weep : they will inform you that our Russel, who administers and manages the estates and affairs of his father, has given them notice to quit their vineyard. Ask them for what reason. They will reply, ' We are thirteen in number ; God has willed it. Some of us are too old, others too young, for work : our family has lived upon this little plot for many generations : many a kind soul, now in Paradise, has drawn water from this well for the thirsty traveller : many a one has given the fig off his bread at noon, to the woman labouring with child, and resting on that stone. We have nothing now to give ! no, not even a bunch of roses to our Protectress over the gate—mercy upon us ! Until this unproductive season we have always paid our rent : we are now thirty crowns in arrears. We went to the good old lady ; she shook her head, and said she would do what she could for us, but that her son managed, and he already knew the case.' On hearing this they will tell you, as they

---

[1] From " Many " to " know it " added in 2nd ed.
* Prince Borghese. — W. S. L. [See Landor's *High and Low Life in Italy*.]
[2] 1st ed. reads : " Lady Morgan has spoken of our patriots, the Russels of our city," etc.
[3] From " what " to " Porta San Gallo " added in 2nd ed.

told me, their courage forsook them, groans burst simultaneously from every breast, desperation seized the adult and vigorous, agony the aged and infirm, and the first articulate sounds they uttered, were, ' O God ! there is none to help us ! ' An Englishman of stern countenance came up at the beginning of the narration : he looked at me with defiance, and seemed to say internally, ' Be off.' As they continued to speak, he closed his lips more strongly ; the muscles of his jaw trembled more and more ; he opened his eyes wider ; I heard every breath of air he drew into his nostrils ; he clenched his fist, stamped with his heel into the turf; cried, ' What can this cursed slave do here ? ' and throwing down a card of address, without a thought of their incapacity to read it, *Venite da me*, cried he, in an accent rather like fury than invitation. He walked away rapidly : the wind was in his face : I saw something white blown over his shoulder at intervals till he reached the Porta San Gallo.

" There may formerly have been a virtuous or a brave citizen in the family so extolled[1], and indeed in what family has there not been, earlier or later ? but if those who now compose it are called Russels, with equal right may the cast horses of a sandcart be called Bucephaluses. Strangers are disposed to consider us the vilest and most contemptible race in Europe ; and they must appear to have reason on their side, if such creatures are taken for the best of us. Not[2] a single one of these flaming patriots ever subscribed a farthing to aid the Spaniards or the Greeks, nor in furtherance of any agricultural or other useful association in their own country. Allowing to the Russel of the Bologna-road all his merits, I insist for the honour of my native place that no inhabitant of it, be his condition what it may, has fewer : I do not depress the one, nor will I suffer the other to be depressed. Patriotism has here a different meaning from what it has in England. A patriot, with us, is a man who is unfriendly to any[3] established government, and who, while he flatters a native prince, courts over an invader. His only grievances are, to pay taxes for the support, and to carry arms for the defence, of his country. He would loosen[4] the laws as impediments to the liberty of action,

---

[1] 1st ed. reads : " extolled by her."
[2] From " Not " to " depressed " added in 2nd ed.
[3] 1st ed. reads : " all."
[4] 1st ed. reads : " loosen all the."

with a reserve of those which secure to him the fruits of rapine and confiscation : those are provident and conservative, and enthroned in light by the philanthropy of the age. Hospitality is the virtue of barbarians——"

" Blood and *hounds !* " cried indignantly my young friend, " I would ask him, whoever he is, whether that was meant for me. If there is barbarism in a bottle of claret, there is as much of it in a corked as in an uncorked one."

" Sir," replied mildly Puntomichino, " I could point out to you a Russel of the Italian school, and it is no other than this, who received unusual civilities in England ; and of all those gentlemen there who treated him with attention and kindness, of all with whom he dined constantly, not a single one, or any relative, was ever invited in his house even to a glass of stale barleywater or sugarless lemonade."

" Cavaliere," said I, " we more willingly give invitations than accept them : I speak of others, not of myself, for I have never been tempted to dine from home these seven [1] years : yet, although I am neither rich nor convivial, and hardly social, I have given at least a hundred dinners in the time, if not superb, at least not sordid : and those who knew me long ago, say, ' Landor is become a miser : his father did otherwise.' "

" *Cappari !* " exclaimed Puntomichino : " this whole family, with thirty thousand crowns of income, has not done a ninetieth part of it within the memory of man."

" Faith ! then," interrupted Talcranagh, " it must have come into the Russels by a forced adoption. The Russels of England are of opinion, right or wrong, that the first thing are good principles, and the next, good cheer. I wish, sir," said he, looking mildly and somewhat mournfully at me, " I had not heard you say what you did about [2] not dining from home. I began to think well of you ; I know not why ; and I doubt not still, God forbid I should, that you are a worthy and conscientious man.[3] As for that other, I thank him for teaching me what I never should have learnt at home, that a fellow may be a good patriot with a very contracted heart, and as much ingratitude as he can carry to market. Why ! you might trust a

---

[1] 1st ed. reads : " last ten."
[2] From " about " to " home " added in 3rd ed.
[3] 1st ed. reads : " man ; but I would fain have thought well of you. As," etc.

PUNTOMICHINO AND TALCRANAGH

Correggio across his kitchen-chimney on Christmas-day ; ay, Signor Puntomichino ? "

" Gentlemen," said our host, " under the least vindictive of Princes we may talk as loudly as we please of liberty, which we could not do without fear and trembling when we were in the full enjoyment of it. What are you pondering so gravely, Mr. Talcranagh ? "

" Woe ! " replied he, " woe to the first family that ever dines yonder ! Let them each take a bottle of *eau de Cologne*,[1] against the explosion of mould from the grand evolution of the tablecloth. Now, concerning your Ministers, there are some things not entirely to my mind, neither : your Prince, I dare to say, knows nothing about them."

Puntomichino looked calmly, and replied, " Our Ministers are liberal, my young friend. They have indeed betrayed in succession all the sovrans who employed them, yet they let every man do his best or his worst : and if you are robbed or insulted, you may insult or rob again. All parties enjoy the same plenitude of power."

" Plenitude ! by my soul, Sir Cavaliere," cried Mr. Talcranagh, " and a trifle, I think, to spare. One of them a few days ago did what a king of Great Britain and Ireland would not dare to do, and which, if the first potentate on earth had done in London, he would have been kicked down the stairs for his impudence. The exhibition of pictures at your Academy was announced as opening to the public at ten. His Excellency entered alone, and remained in the principal apartment until two, the doors of which were locked to others. If it had been possible for him to have acted so among us, he would have been tossed in a blanket till the stars blinked upon him ; the people would have perfumed his frill and ruffles abundantly with home-made essences, would have added new decorations to his waistcoatful of *orders*, and would have treated his eagles with more eggs than they could swallow."

Puntomichino for a time was silent, and then said placidly, " Believe me, sirs, our government, which would be a detestable one for the English, is an excellent one for us. Every day in London brings with it what to a stranger looks like a rebellion, or at best a riot : no mischief is done thereby. Your strength, which causes this irregularity, sustains you : but weak bodies bear little fermentation."

[1] 1st ed. reads : " thieves-vinegar."

" Wisely thought and well expressed," said Mr. Talcranagh. " I am convinced that if we had not a riot now and then in Ireland, we should be mopish and sullen as the English, or insincere and ferocious as the French. And I have observed, Signor Cavaliere, that, strange as it may appear, whenever there has been much of a riot there has been sunshine. Smile as you will, Mr. Landor, I swear to the fact."

To which I answered, " Your assertion, Mr. Talcranagh, is quite sufficient : but is it impossible that the fine weather may have brought together a great concourse of people to the fair or festival, and that whiskey or beauty or politics or religion may have incited them to the exertion of their prowess ? "

" There are causes that we know," replied he, " and there are causes that we know not. Inquiry and reflection are sensible things ; but there is nothing like experience, nothing like seeing with one's own eyes. We must live upon the spot to judge perfectly and to collect evidences. Philosophy ought to lead us, but only to a certain point : there we leave her, and joy go with her. I have seen impudent rogues in Dublin, and have fancied that the world could not match them : now what think you of a set of fellows, with coats without a collar, who take us by the hand, and say with the gravest face upon earth, ' The elements shall be elements no longer,' and strip them one after another of their title-deeds, as easily as Lord *Redwhiskers* stripped a royal Duke of his last curtain and carpet. It is enough to make one grave to think on this abuse of intellect. Do [1] you know, Signor Cavaliere, we have lately had people among us, and learned ones, who doubted the existence of the Trojan war, on which chronicles are founded."

"Sir," remarked Puntomichino, "the doubt is not of recent origin. Eberard Rudolph Roth attempted in 1674 to prove from three ancient coins that Troy was not taken. What, if the *Iliad* should be in great measure a translation ? Many of the names might lead us to suspect it : such as Agamemnon and Sarpedon, which are oriental ones with dignities prefixed : *Aga* and *Sha*, which the Greeks and Romans, not possessing the shiboleth, could pronounce no otherwise. Thus they wrote *Sapor*, the same name (with the title preceding it) as *Porus*. *Aga* seems indeed to have migrated into Greece among the first Pelasgi, and designates in many things what is excellent, as in

[1] From " Do " to " ground nearer us," p. 179, added in 2nd ed.

178

PUNTOMICHINO AND TALCRANAGH

ἀγαθός, ἀγαπητός, and several proper names, as Agamedes, Agasicles, Agatharcides ; but *Memnon* is not hellenic."

" Signor Cavaliere, I cannot keep up with you on your Turkish horse," cried aloud Talcranagh, " which is better for any business than the road. Upon plain ground nearer us, the acutest men may be much mistaken even after long experience. I assure you, I have found grossly inaccurate the first piece of information given me by a very cautious old traveller. He mentions the honesty of the Savoyards and the thievery of the Italians : now here have I been a fortnight, safe and sound, and have not lost a hair. I had not been twenty-four hours in Savoy when they had the meanness to steal my hatband. In future I shall be persuaded how illusory are sketches of national character."

" That [1] a traveller," said the Cavaliere, " may receive a wrong opinion of events and things, after even a deep study of them, and with as much knowledge of the world as happens to most men, I myself have a proof in my late uncle Fontebuoni. On that marriage, the best fruit of which was Peter Leopold, he was sent into France, to announce the event to the Court of Versailles : and after the revolution, when the Directory was established, he resolved to revisit the country of pleasure and politeness. He resided there one month only ; long enough, he protested to me, for any man in his senses. ' I have heard the same thing, uncle,' said I, ' and that not only politeness is swept away, but that the women are become most indecent and wanton.' ' Nephew Puntomichino,' he replied, ' in regard to politeness what you have heard is indeed too true ; but, with all my hatred and abhorrence of the present system, I am obliged in conscience to declare that the women are more correct in their morals than they were formerly. A heart is to be touched only by a diamond pin ; a head is to be turned only by a peruke *à la Lucrèce* worth ten louis. A compliment did formerly : if one knelt it was uncivil not to return the condescension by something as like it as possible.' This he said at dinner, with his tooth-pick in his fingers, wandering and flitting here and there for its quarry, over the wold of his hard smooth gums. He was in his sixty-ninth or seventieth year when he went a second time to Paris, and never found out that women are made continent by our ages more often and more effectually than by their own."

[1] From " That " to " do in general," p. 180, added in 2nd ed.

" Well, that never struck me," said Mr. Talcranagh. I was here startled by some musical accents from a sofa behind me. Puntomichino cried, " What are you about, Magnelli ? " " I must go," replied he, " to the English Minister's. He is composing an opera : he has every note ready and only wants my assistance just to put them in order ; which I shall have accomplished in three weeks, by going daily, and taking my dinner and supper with him."

On this he left the room. " These musicians," said Puntomichino, " are people of no ceremony. He entered, as usual, without a word, threw himself upon the sofa, sate half an hour, and the first we heard of him was the hum of a dozen notes. His observation on parting is very similar to one from a gentleman at my next-door, a worthy creature, and fond of chess. ' Why so much embarrassment, Signor Gozzi ? ' ' It is not embarrassment,' answered he calmly, ' but reflection : I can move my man in a moment : I am only thinking where I may put him.' ' Ah ! Signor Gozzi ! ' said a friend of mine who was present, ' if Ministers of State would think about the same thing as long, they would dispose of places more wisely than they do in general.' "

"As for systems," said Mr. Talcranagh, " come, Signor Cavaliere, you have weighed them all. I have not patience to talk about them. Conclusions are drawn even from skin and bones ; eyes, noses, teeth ; they will soon come (saving your presence)."

" I know not what they will come to," was the timely reply of the Cavaliere ; " but I can mention as wonderful a fact as the sunshine elicited by shillelahs. My father was a physiognomist, and when Lavater first published his work, ' Now,' cried he, rubbing the palms of his hands together, ' men begin to write again as they should do.' He insisted that a man's countenance, in all its changes, indicated his virtues or vices, his capacities or defects. The teeth, among other parts, were infallible indexes ; they were in the human visage what consonants are in the alphabet, the great guides, the plain simple narrators. Amid his apophthegms was, ' Never trust a man with a twisted tooth.' In fact, of all I had ever seen and of all I have ever seen since under that description, not one has proved worthy of trust. I inquired of my father with submission, whether age or accident might not alter the indications. ' By no means,' exclaimed he emphatically ; ' if the indications are changed, the character is changed. God, before he removed the mark, removed the taint.' He observed that where the teeth turn inward, there is wariness, selfishness, avarice, inhumanity ; where they turn outward, there is lasciviousness, prodigality, gaming, gluttony. I then doubted these indications, and imagined that a part of the latter was taken up against a priest, not indeed in high reputation for sobriety or continence, who had offended my father in a tender quarter. My father had erected a stile for the convenience of his peasants ; but the inscription was so prolix * he was forced to engrave the conclusion of it upon the church-porch. The Latin, as the priest acknowledged, was classical ; yet he requested it might be removed to our dove-cote, which was farther off, and not by the side of any road. The exoteric teeth of the reverend gentleman by some unknown accident received a blow, which adjusted them between the extremes ; and my father was asked in joke, whether he had a better opinion of his spiritual guide since his improvement in dentition. ' Indeed I have,' he answered gravely ; ' for so sudden and so great a change, whether brought about by the organic mutations of the frame, or by an irresistible stress, with which certain sentiments or sensations may bear upon it, must be accompanied by new powers, greater or smaller, and by new qualities and propensities. Some internal struggle may in length of time have produced an effect not only on the fibres, but through them on the harder part of the extremities.' The favourable opinion of my father was carried to the priest ; who lamented (he said) no dispensation of Providence by which he conciliated the better sentiments of so enlightened and charitable a man. He was soon a daily visitor at the house ; entered into the studies of his Excellency, meditated on his observations, praised them highly, and by degrees had the courage to submit to so experienced a master a few remarks of his own. He pursued them farther : and I should blush to relate, if all Florence did not know it, that my stepmother,

* Lest an inscription on a stile should surpass the reader's faith, here is one *On a prince changing horses at a Villa*, to the intent, as it says expressly, that *all men and nations and ages* should know it : " Honori Ferdinandi III. Aust. : qui ad veterem Etruriæ dominationem redux in hoc Capponianæ gentis prætorio xv. Kal. Octob. MDCCCXIV. tantisper substitit, dum rhedæ itinerariæ regalis substitueretur, qua urbem principem inter communes plausus et gaudii lacrimas introiret ; herisque ob faustitatem eventûs dignitatemque sibi locoque ab hospite magno impertitam lætitiâ elatis pristinam benevolentiam comitate alloquii gratique animi significatione declaravit ; Marchio Petrus Robertus Capponius ad memoriam facti postgenitis *omnibus* tradendam."—W. S. L.

a young lady of twenty-four, aided him too deeply in his investigations, and confirmed my father, although not exactly by working the problem as he would have recommended, that an internal struggle may produce an effect not only on the fibres, but through them on the harder part of the extremities. Then too became it public, that another husband had been the holy man's dentist, in consequence of too close an application to similar studies in his house."

At [1] the end of which calm narration, up started Mr. Talcranagh, and several times pushing his fingers rapidly through the hair over his forehead, exclaimed ; " Why ! how ! what ! do you talk in this tone and manner ?   Did not you nor your father flay the devil alive ? Did not you spigot him nor singe him ? "

" I was at school : my father," said the Cavaliere, " took his wife to Siena ; proof enough that he resented the injury.   In our country, as you know, every lady of quality has her *cavaliere serviente*. It serves to distinguish the superior order from the lower,[2] and belongs to none, legitimately, excepting those who by wealth or services have obtained the liberty to stick their knee-buckles on their coats with a tag of scarlet.   My father, as you may suppose, was indignant that a priest out of the gates, neither a *canonico* nor a *maestro di casa*, should beget his children, and aspire, as he would have done by degrees (for impudence is never retrogressive), to conduct his lady to her carriage.   I have many books in which is the text written with his own hand, ' Never trust a man with a twisted tooth ' ; but I have searched in vain for any such sentence as, ' Trust a man with an untwisted one.'   His enthusiasm seems to have cooled from the time that he found a scholar so capable of his place.   Another [3] of my father's maxims was, ' Open a man's mouth and look whether his under-jaw be uneven, with a curvature like a swine's, which curvature is necessarily followed by the teeth, and, discovering these, you will infallibly find him swinish in one way or other : you will find him, take my word for it, slothful, or gluttonous, or selfish.   I have observed few such who were not slothful, and never one who was not both selfish and gluttonous.'   ' In the latter case, father,' said I, ' it will not be necessary to open his mouth for him.   I may

---

[1] From " At " to " exclaimed " added in 3rd ed.
[2] 1st ed. reads : " lower who aspire to nothing better than the liberty," etc.
[3] From " Another " to " shall be Antonino," p. 185, added in 2nd ed.

philosophise across the table, finding there all the instruments adapted to the process of investigation.'

" 'It would not demonstrate to you,' added my father, ' how incorrigible is the nature of such men. Goffrido Piccoluomini is of the conformation I have described; and his parents, who themselves love good living, and who are liberal to excess, attempted to divert at a riper age the tendency they were unable to conquer in his childhood. Many means were resorted to, and failed. He had a cousin at Perugia, an heiress, rich, playful, beautiful, and accomplished. Several families were at variance, because the elder son of one had been preferred to the elder of another, this in the morning, that in the evening ; and there were only two things in which they agreed : first, that she was an angel of Paradise ; secondly, that she was very wrong in not fixing her choice. To quiet these animosities, her father, whose health was declining, resolved to join his brother Guido, the father of Goffrido, at the baths of Lucca. Goffrido was beckoning to a boy who carried a basket of trout upon his head, when the carriage drove up to the door. He stood before it, his eye this moment on the trout, that moment on his cousin. The boy had retreated a step or two, when he caught him with his right hand by the coat, and opened with the left the coach-door. He had not seen Leopoldina since she was a chubby ruddy child. There are blossoms in field and garden, which first are pink, and which whiten as they expand : Leopoldina was like one of these. Her face alone had retained its plumpness : she was rather pale and slender. At sight of Goffrido, who still held the boy's skirt, she not merely smiled but laughed ; she would however have put her hand before her face, for she had been educated by a French lady of high rank, when she recollected that she must give it to her cousin, who now held out his. Never had he felt the force of admiration to such a degree : his mouth was open : his teeth, white as ivory, but unlucky in their curvature, looked like a broken portcullis which would not come down. He actually loosed the fisher-boy's coat, and almost had forgotten, in the midst of his compliment, to desire he would go into the house ; which he did, the first of the party.

" ' I am incapable of giving such descriptions as would suit a novel or romance, and must therefore do injustice to the young people. Goffrido is really a fine young man, blooming in health, and addicted to no pleasures but those of the table, which he thinks the most solid of all, and takes especial care shall not be the least durable. These however by degrees he divided awhile with more visionary and exalted. He failed in no kind of attention to his fair cousin, and, when her appetite seemed to flag a little, looked out for whatever was choicest at table, presented it to her with grace and disinterestedness, and pressed it on her attention with recommendations the most anxious, and with solicitude the most pathetic. Spring had passed away, long as it lingers in this delightful region, when some moral reflections, I know not from which first, induced the fathers to devise a union : and never were two children more obedient. *If my father wishes it, his will is mine,* said Goffrido. *Dear sir, you have instructed me in my duty : dispose of your Leopoldina,* was the answer of his cousin. They agreed to remain together at the baths until the vintage, at which time they must be at Perugia, and the ceremony should be performed. It rarely happened now that either had a bad appetite ; and if either had, the other did not observe it : for security had taken place of solicitude, and tenderness had made room for good-humour. The more delicate fruits are seldom conveyed in perfection up these mountains : they are generally bruised and broken. Goffrido, observing this, and corroborated in his observation by Leopoldina, rode manfully to Marlia, bought a basketful of the most lovely peaches, rolled up each separately in several fig-leaves, and returned for dinner. Surely some evil Genius watches the Anti-Vestal fire of our lowest concupiscence, and renders it inextinguishable. Goffrido presented the peaches to Leopoldina, and she took, whether by choice or accident, the finest. Her lover, seeing it in her plate, fixed his heart upon it, and saying, *You have taken a bruised one,* transferred it to his, and gave her two others. His mother said, laughing, *Goffrido, I see no bruise, let me look.* He blushed deeply ; he lost his presence of mind ; he could not support the glance of surprise which his change of countenance alone had excited in his cousin, nor the idea of yielding to so light a temptation : he left the room. The old people sat silent : Leopoldina was afflicted, for she loved him. She too retired soon after ; and, being alone, began to revolve in her memory her whole acquaintance with him ; and this revolving of hers cast up many similar things against him. Finally, her thoughts wandered as far as Perugia, and dwelt for a moment, in the chain of ideas, on a little boy who, a few years before, had

184

fought a battle with a stouter for having taken a pear from her and bitten it before she could catch him. She remembered that, when she would have taken it back and eaten it, her champion cried, *No, Signora Leopoldina, the thief has bitten it ; I will bring you another instead.* Poor Antonino ! sighed she, *what made me think of thee again ?*

" ' He had not been one of her lovers : how could he have been ; she was scarcely eleven years old, he only fourteen ; beside, he was the son of the parish priest, and what is more scandalous, the acknowledged son. The father had been reproved by his bishop, and threatened with suspension unless he denied it publicly. *My Lord !* answered the priest, *my passions on this one occasion overcame my reason. The mother of the child, cruelly treated by her family for my transgression, sank under the double weight of shame and sorrow. Take my poor infant, cried she : teach him, O unhappy man, to love God—as well as I thought I did ! and she expired in my arms. I have educated the child to virtue ; the best reparation of my fault ; falsehood, my lord, would be none.*

" ' Leopoldina, on her return to Perugia, walked often on the field of battle—a more important one not only to her but to us, if I may judge by the interest I seem to have excited, than that other in the vicinity where Hannibal vanquished the Romans. Antonino, she thought, avoided her : she had sometimes seen him, and fancied he had seen her. At last she was certain he had ; for while she was talking with an old woman, she perceived the old woman's eyes to wander from her toward the parsonage, and heard a window-blind close. She turned round. *Another time will do,* said the old woman. *I must say he had patience enough : he has little to give me, but he brings it me himself when I can not walk, or when it rains ; and he comforts me as much by smiling and laughing as another could do by praying.*

" ' I should like to look a little at Leopoldina's teeth,' added my father, ' for she is a most singular girl. Would you believe it ? she is grown at last as decisive as any in the city : she has declined the visits of all her lovers, and has declared to her parents that if she ever marries it shall be Antonino.' "

This Conversation is reported in a manner differing from the rest. The meaner of us have spoken but seldom. A conversation with a young Irishman of good natural abilities, and among no race of men are those abilities more general, is like a forest walk, in which, while you are delighted with the healthy fresh air and the green unbroken turf, you must stop at every twentieth step to extricate yourself from a briar. You acknowledge that you have been amused, but that you rest willingly, and that you would rather take a walk in another direction on the morrow.

END OF THE IRISH CONVERSATIONS

IMAGINARY CONVERSATIONS

AMERICAN

I. WILLIAM PENN AND LORD PETERBOROUGH *

(*Imag. Convers.*, v., 1829 ; *Wks.*, i., 1846 ; *Wks.*, iii., 1876.)

PENN. Friend Mordaunt, thou hast been silent the whole course of our ride hither ; and I should not even now interrupt thy cogitations, if the wood before us were not equally uncivil.

PETERBOROUGH. Cannot we push straight through it ?

PENN. Verily the thing may be done, after a time : but at present we have no direct business with the Pacific Ocean ; and I doubt whether this woodland terminates till these waters bid it.

PETERBOROUGH. And, in this manner, for the sake of liberty you run into a prison. I would not live in a country that does not open to me in all directions, and that I could not go through when I wish.

PENN. Where is such a country on earth ?

PETERBOROUGH. England or France.

PENN. Property lays those restrictions there which here are laid by Nature. Now it is right and proper to bow before each of them ; but Nature is the more worthy of obedience, as being the elder, the more beauteous, the more powerful, and the more kindly. Thou couldst no sooner ride through thy neighbour's park, unless he permitted it, than through this forest ; and even a raspberry-bush in some ten feet border at Southampton would be an impediment for a time to thy free-will.

* Charles Mordaunt, son of John Lord Mordaunt, was born in 1658, succeeded to the paternal honours in 1675 and to those of his uncle, the Earl of Peterborough, in 1697. In Spencer's Anecdotes he says : " I took a trip once with Penn to his colony of Pennsylvania. The laws there are contained in a small volume, and are so extremely good that there has been no alteration wanted in any one of them. There are no lawyers ; everyone is to tell his own case, or some friend for him. There are four persons as judges on the bench ; and after the case has been fairly laid down on both sides, all the four draw lots, and he on whom the lot falls decides the question."—W. S. L.

PETERBOROUGH. I should like rather more elbow-room than this, having gone so far for it.

PENN. Here we are stopped *before* we are tired ; and in thy *rather more elbow-room* we should be stopped *when* we are : a mighty advantage truly ! We run, thou sayest, into a prison, for the sake of liberty. Alas, my friend ! such hath ever been the shortsightedness of mortals. The liberty they have pursued is indeed the very worst of thraldom. But neither am I disposed to preach nor thou to hear a preacher.

Here at least we are liberated from the habitudes and injunctions of semi-barbarous society. We may cultivate, we may manipulate, we may manufacture, what we choose. Industry and thought, and the produce of both, are unrestricted. We may open our hearts to God without offence to man : our brothers we may call our brothers, and without a mockery. If we are studious of wisdom we may procure it at the maker's, and at prime cost : if we are ambitious of learning we may gather it fresh and sound, slowly indeed, but surely and richly, and without holding out our beavers for it, in a beaten and dusty road, to some half-dozen old chatterers and dotards, who, by their quarrelsomeness and pertinacity, testify that they have little of a good quality to impart.

PETERBOROUGH. All this is very well ; but we can not enlighten men if we shock their prejudices too violently.

PENN. The shock comes first, the light follows.

PETERBOROUGH. Most people will run away from both. Children are afraid of being left in the dark : men are afraid of *not* being left in it.

PENN. Well then, let them stay where they are. We will go forward, and hope to find the road of life easier and better. In which hope, if we are disappointed, we will at least contribute our share of materials for mending it, and of labour in laying them where they are most wanted.

Prythee now, setting aside thy prepossessions,what thinkest thou, in regard to appearance and aspect, of our Pennsylvania ?

PETERBOROUGH. Even in this country, like everyone I have visited, there are some places where I fancy I could fix myself for life. True, such a fancy lasts but for a moment : the wonder is that it should ever have arisen in me.

PENN. Certainly in thee it is less to be expected than in another ;

but, as in the earth there is (we have lately been informed) both a centrifugal and a centripetal motion, so in man there is at once a desire of wandering and a tendency to repose.

PETERBOROUGH. The scenery does not altogether please me, I acknowledge, quite so well as Bevis-Mount and its vicinity. I love variety in everything : hill and dale, woodland and pasture, even hedge-rows please me, if they are old.

PENN. Why the rather for being old ? they must be the less perfect in their kind, the less neat in appearance.

PETERBOROUGH. You give two reasons why new hedges should please rather than older ; one derived from vision, the other from judgment. The neatness is produced by regularity and symmetry, which are becoming and desirable in our habiliments, in our furniture, and in our houses, but which little accord with external Nature. At home and about ourselves we wish for propriety, as we call it : out of doors we desire to leave and to forget the idea of what is within ; and there is something in the open air which renders us abhorrent from the very name of this propriety. Your argument, that old hedges are less perfect, and should therefore please us less, is very good, since pleasure comes from fitness : but surely a higher pleasure may arise and meet us in a higher region of the mind. Instead of arguing that a stout young hedge is the best to keep a calf or a galloway within it ; we may imagine, on seeing an ancient one, composed of its variety of plants, differing in size, form, and colour, that these were collected from the unserviceable wild which they deformed, and, after overrunning it for ages, were obliged by a just dispensation to protect it. We may imagine the many happy generations that have enjoyed the beautiful seasons there, under the elder and hawthorn and hickory and maple, under the hazel and dogrose, clematis and honeysuckle, and other flowering shrubs, sur-passing their knowledge and mine. It gives us also the idea, though a vague and incorrect one, of the stability and antiquity of property and possession, and of that negligence which we are fond of consider-ing as akin to liberality. The waving and irregular line in itself is beautiful; and perhaps I like it the better, as varying from the column and platoon, and everything else connected with my profession.

PENN. Yet thou pursuest thy wicked profession with enthusiasm.

PETERBOROUGH. I pursue it, because it leads to distinction and glory.

PENN. Soldiers,[1] it is said in ancient mythology, sprang from dragons' teeth, sown by Cadmus, who introduced letters : and when I consider to what purposes these also have latterly been applied, it would appear that they surely came from the same sack as the soldiers, and were only the rottenest of the fangs kept till the last.

Art thou not contented with the distinction of the peerage ?

PETERBOROUGH. The peerage hides its little men under the robes of its greater. I do confess to you plainly, I am not contented with it : I will stand alone while I stand at all ; and it is only by my profession that I can expect it.

Why groan so ?

PENN. Because millions groan, and millions must groan still : because Crime and Genius, like the wild swans in their wintry course, accommodate one another, preceding and following by turns, and changing their line, but never losing it. In printing and writing the mask of admiration and of horror is the same : oftentimes in life, what we abhor we should admire, and what we admire, abhor. The signs are identified, the things confounded.

I do not wonder that light and trivial minds should look for honour in the army : and indeed if armies were constituted as they were among the ancients, of citizens for the defence of citizens, then indeed, although one might lament their existence, there would be something at least to mitigate the lamentation. But when I hear one gentleman ask another, " how long have you served ? " or, " how do you like the service ? " and when I discover glee lighted up on both sides at the name of *servitude*, the least painful of my thoughts is a very painful one ; that names and things lose their enormity by habit.

If the wiser and better of every country were its governors, there would be few wars, few wants, few vices, few miseries : and this would certainly be the case were people well instructed, which they easily might be, in their rights and duties. These are plain and simple, easy and pleasant : men would learn them one from another by daily conversation, had they not been seized upon from the moment when they begin to speak, and had no pains been taken to amaze them with marvels, and to bend into one circle their infancy and decrepitude. Nothing can enter this enchanted circle ; nor can anyone straighten it ; so hard is the temper it hath acquired

---

[1] From " Soldiers " to " last " occurs also in the Conversation of Peter the Great and Alexis.

PENN AND PETERBOROUGH

from the dust and bellowing fires in which it sweltered, and from the cyclopean anvil on which it was turned and hammered.

Thy vanity prompts and excites in thee the idlest and the foolishest of desires, namely, to be looked at and admired by the idle and the foolish ; while, with less effort and anxiety, thou mightest be esteemed and respected by the considerate and the wise.

PETERBOROUGH. I have almost every fault a man can have, excepting vanity.

PENN. That thou hast many I do verily believe, and that thou art unaware of this lying at the bottom of them ; as a feather will sink below the surface of the water when it is bemired. A sick man knoweth well enough that he is sick, but he knoweth not by what proper name to call his ailment, or whence it originated. If thou art wiser than the many, do that which thou thyself approvest, rather than what they may look for ; and be assured that, when they admire thee most, thou hast done something wrong. For, if they are ignorant, as we know they are, it were superfluous and redundant to say that their judgments are incorrect. Thy own heart is the standard which thy intellect should follow, under the command of God. Vanity bears nothing : what wouldst thou from it ? a public path of flinty materials, trodden on backward and forward from morning to night, and holding no particle of the dews of heaven. Thou knowest what poor sordid creatures direct and control the counsels, of those who proclaim to us aloud and confidently that they act under God, and God only.

PETERBOROUGH. And, some time ago, in the glorious reign of our late gracious king's father, if you did not give ear to them, they took it.

PENN. Whence but from the vapours of the earth appears there to be, to the uninformed vision, a tremulous motion in the stars ? and whence but from the cloudiness and fluctuation of their intellects, do they believe themselves the primary movers of those events, which the Almighty from the beginning willeth and disposeth, and of which they are the weakest instruments, though perhaps the only ones in sight. Pardon me, Mordaunt ! either a wilderness like this, or a man like thee, would be sufficient to awaken in me the most serious thoughts, and the desire of giving them utterance. Common minds and common localities have no such influence over me. Among them, not to speak is best, and not to think is happiest. One older and

191

more experienced than thyself, will be surety for this ; that, if thou lovest true glory, thou must trust her truth ; that, like the Eurydice of the poet, she followeth him invariably who doth not turn and gaze after her ; and slippeth irrecoverably from his embrace who, amid shadows and hellish sights, would seize her and enjoy her upon earth.

PETERBOROUGH. The oil runs to that part of a lamp where there is heat to use it; the animal spirits in like manner to the occupation that can absorb them.   I could easily give you my peculiar reasons for following the military profession, if this general one appears vague and idle : but I am certain you can no more wonder at it in me, than to see a larch in the upper part of a mountain : you must acknowledge it befits the place, rather than a lilac or a weeping-willow.[1]   Men are little better than a row of pins if you stick them close together : but, if you set one upright on a gate-post, the folks below stare, scratch their heads, and cry " The squire ! " or " His honour ! " Set another in cap and plumes on the upper step of a portico, and he suddenly hears from beneath him an appellation which you serious men refuse to anyone but God. The stars themselves are not bright by any brightness of their own. Probably they are merely dull masses, like what our horses are treading on : but, from that light vapour which surrounds them, and from that vast distance at which men see them, they derive and diffuse their splendour.

PENN. Some philosopher hath said, " All 's well that ends well." Pithy, but unsound. For thy words end well, but thy pins do not stick in their paper, friend Mordaunt. People who act perversely, are always in readiness to defend themselves with reasons yet more distorted. When I was a youth at Oxford——

PETERBOROUGH. Ay, Oxford is the arsenal of examples. Come draw out one for me, and throw the sack down again.

PENN. There was a poacher ; and happy is it for his soul if he never was employed by the luxurious and wanton in quest of worse game than partridges : he was named Daniel Fogram. So ready was he to engage his services in any ill scheme or device, that one young collegian laid a wager with another, on his promptitude to assist in the murder of his father. He requested, then, Daniel to meet him at dusk in the middle of a plain, called Port-meadow. Daniel was there before the time, and, on the approach of his employer, sprang up from the turf on which, dewy as it was, he had been lying. The

[1] 1st ed. reads : " willow. PENN. People who act," etc.

PENN AND PETERBOROUGH

young gentleman took his hand in silence, and affected to look behind him, and even behind the man Daniel. At length said he, " Dan ! I hope nobody can hear us. I have an affair," added he slowly and in a whisper, and then broke off.

" Out with it, master ! " said Daniel, partly in a tone of impatience and partly of encouragement.

" My dear friend, Dan ! " rejoined the youth, " I have a project which, if you will help me, will bring you five guineas."

" Anything for your honour's service," cried promptly the courtly thief Daniel ; " speak out ingenuously and boldly, my good young master ! "

" I have then, since the truth must be spoken, a father who is avaricious and rich : if I were not so much in debt, or if tradespeople would trust me any longer, I would not apply to you."

" No, on my conscience," cried Daniel, abruptly. " I have trusted half the gentlemen in Christchurch : and there are grave dons too, in more than one college, who think they are grown again as young and spunky as undergraduates, when they can turn a round oath upon the catching of a poacher. I find no money forthcoming. My pheasants, o' my faith ! are no golden ones. I am sorry, master, your five guineas are spent between us here in Port-meadow, and neither of us the better." Thus spake the man Daniel, as men report of him, whose worldly words (mind ye) are none of mine.

The youth laid his hand upon Daniel's shoulder, and with the other drew forth a purse, with many pieces in it, and said calmly, " You have misunderstood me, you see : I must be rid of him."

" Naturally enough ! if the old dog tugs so hard with his rotten teeth, and won't let go the pudding-bag though he can't get down the pudding. But, master, five guineas for a father out of the way— methinks—you say he is very rich ; and indeed I have heard as much ; very rich indeed—another guinea could do nobody any hurt."

" Well, Dan, you must contrive the means."

" Six guineas, sir ? "

" If it must be, we will say six guineas."

" Lay him, master, in one of my eel-trunks : the eels are running just now, and there are big ones about, and many of 'em ; the old gentleman will give them a dinner, though he would not give you and me one."

" True, Dan, but he must be dead first."

" That is awkward. I don't like blood ; though there is always some about my jacket—and nobody can swear whose ; badger's, hare's, otter's ; a young pig's now and then, if he cries after me piteously on the road, to take up a poor passenger without a fare."

" Seriously, Dan, you can surely have no objection to kill the old curmudgeon in good company."

" Hold, master ; you must do that yourself."

" Why are you so shy, honest Dan ? "

" Nay, nay, master, kill him I will not."

" But why now ? "

" Why ? in the name o' God ! why ? the man is no father of mine."

Now, Mordaunt, thy reasons, I reckon, are about as reasonable as Daniel's. Prythee be sober-minded. Wilt thou always be laughing and hiccupping and hooting at mild and sidelong reproofs ? Off again ! screaming like a boarding-school girl when her bed-fellow tickleth her. Fie upon thee ! fie upon thee ! See there now ! Hold ! hold ! thou makest my mare kick and caper and neigh. Hath Legion entered thee ? trot, creature, slower. Comeliness ! comeliness ! Mordaunt ! Hear me ! There are unruly horses in the pasture : they will surely come up, and perhaps unseat me.

PETERBOROUGH. Friend Penn, prepare yourself to accept the Chiltern Hundreds, and to make room for one or other of 'em.

PENN. Of a truth now this is unseemly.

PETERBOROUGH. By my soul, if you had told the story to the late king, he would have given you the rest of America. Come ; we are out of danger ; I will be grave again.

PENN. God mend thee, madcap! Wilt thou come and live with us?

PETERBOROUGH. I confess I should be reluctant to exchange my native country for any other.

PENN. Are there many parts of England thou hast never seen ?

PETERBOROUGH. Several : I was never in Yorkshire or Lancashire, never in Monmouthshire or Nottinghamshire, never in Lincolnshire or Rutland.

PENN. Hast thou at no time felt a strong desire to visit them ?

PETERBOROUGH. Not I indeed.

PENN. Yet thy earnestness to come over into America was great : so that America had attractions for thee, in its least memorable parts, powerfuller than England in those that are the most. York and Lancaster have stirring sounds about them, particularly for minds easily set in motion at the fluttering of banners. Is the whole island of Britain thy native country, or only a section of it ? If all Britain is, all Ireland must be too ; for both are under the same crown, though not under the same laws. Perhaps not a river nor a channel, but a religion, makes the difference : then I, among millions more of English, am not thy countryman. Consider a little, what portion or parcel of soil is our native land.

PETERBOROUGH. Just as much of it as our friends stand upon.

PENN. I would say more : I would say, just as much as supports our vanity in our shire.

PETERBOROUGH. I confess, the sort of patriotism which attaches most men to their country, is neither a wiser nor a better feeling than the feeling of recluses and cats. Scourges and starvation do not cure them of their stupid love for localities. Mine is different : I like to see the desperate rides I have taken in the forest, and the places where nobody dared follow me. I like to feel and to make felt my superiority, not over tradespeople and farmers in their dull debates, but over lords and archbishops, over chancellors and kings. I would no more live where they are not, than have a mansion-house without a stable, or a paddock without a leaping-bar.

PENN. Superiority in wealth is communicated to many and par-taken by thousands, and therefore men pardon it : while superiority of rank is invidious, and the right to it is questioned in most instances. I would not for the world raise so many evil passions every time I walk in the street.

PETERBOROUGH. It would amuse me. I care not how much people hate me, nor how many, provided their hatred feed upon itself, without a blow at me, or privation or hindrance. Great dogs fondle little dogs : but little dogs hate them mortally, and lift up their ears and tails and spinal [1] hairs, to make themselves as high. Some people are unhappy unless they can display their superiority ; others are satisfied with a consciousness of it : the latter are incontestably the better ; the former are infinitely the more numerous, and, I will venture to say, the more useful. Their vanity, call it nothing else, sets in motion all the activity of less men, and nearly all of greater.

PENN. Prove this activity to be beneficial, prove it only to be

[1] 1st ed. reads : " spiral."

neutral, and we meet almost near enough for discussion ; not quite : for vanity, which is called idle, is never inoperative : when it can not by its position ramble far afield, it chokes the plant that nurtures it. Consciousness of superiority, kept at home and quiet, is the nurse of innocent meditations and of sound content.

Canst not thou feel and exhibit the same superiority at any distance ?

PETERBOROUGH. I can not make *them* feel it nor see it. What is it to be anything, unless we enjoy the faculty of impressing our image at full length on the breast of others, and strongly too and deeply and (when we wish it) painfully : but mostly on those who, because their rank in court-calendars is the same or higher, imagine they are like me, equal to me, over me ! I thank God that there are kings and princes : remove them, and you may leave me alone with swine and sheep.

PENN. I would not draw thee aside from bad company into worse : if indeed that may reasonably be called so, which allows thee greater room and more leisure for reflection, and which imparts to thee purer innocence and engages thee in usefuller occupations. That such is the case is evident. The poets, to whom thou often appealest for sound philosophy and right feeling, never lead shepherds into courts, but often lead the great among shepherds. If it were allowable for me to disdain or despise even the wickedest and vilest of God's creatures, in which condition a king peradventure, as easily as any other, may be, I think I could, without much perplexity or inquiry, find something in the multitude of his blessings quite as reasonable and proper to thank him for. With all thy contemptuousness, thou placest thy fortune and the means of thy advancement in the hands of such persons ; and they may ruin thee.

PETERBOROUGH. You place your money in the hands of bankers ; and they may ruin you. The difference is, your ruiner may gain a good deal by it, and may run off : mine has no such temptation, and should not run far. All titulars else must be produced by others ; a knight by a knight, a peer by a king, while a gentleman is self-existent. Our country exhibits in every part of it what none in the world beside can do, men at once of elegant manners, ripe and sound learning, unostentatious honour, unprofessional courage, confiding hospitality, courteous independence. If a Frenchman saw, as he might do any week in the winter, a hundred or two of our

PENN AND PETERBOROUGH

fox-hunters in velvet caps and scarlet coats, he would imagine he saw only a company of the rich and idle.

PENN. He would think rightly. Such gentlemen ought, willing or loth, to serve an apprenticeship of seven years to a ratcatcher.

PETERBOROUGH. It would be no unwise thing to teach, if not gentlemen, at least the poor, in what manner to catch and exterminate every kind of noxious animal. In our island it is not enough to have exterminated the wolves : we are liable to the censure of idleness and ill husbandry, while an otter, a weazel, a rat, or a snake is upon it. Zoologists [1] may affirm that these and other vermin were created for some peculiar use. Voracious and venomous animals may be highly respectable in their own society : and whenever it is proved that their service to the community is greater than the disadvantage, I will propose in parliament to import them again duty-free.

PENN. Rats come among us with almost every vessel : and nothing is easier than to entice them to a particular spot, either for the purpose of conservation or destruction, as may seem fittest.

PETERBOROUGH. Release me from the traps, and permit me to follow the hounds again ; but previously to remark that probably a third of these fox-hunters is composed of well-educated men. Joining in the amusements of others is, in our social state, the next thing to sympathy in their distresses : and even the slenderest bond that holds society together should rather be strengthened than snapped. I feel no horror at seeing the young clergyman in the field, by the side of his patron the squire and his parishioner the yeoman. Interests, falsely calculated, would keep men and classes separate, if amusements and recreations did not insensibly bring them close.[2] If conviviality (which by your leave I call a virtue) is promoted by fox-hunting, I will drink to its success, whatever word in the formulary may follow or go before it. Nations have fallen by wanting, not unanimity in the hour of danger, so much as union in

---

[1] 1st ed. reads : " upon it. Divines may teach us that . . . some use. I have had such deference for divines that I never argue with them. Voracious . . . duty-free. Rats . . . destruction. PENN. Something of tenderness and consideration is due to them by the heads of parties ; to whom with the consent of Majesty they have given their name and we in compliance with so high authority, say they have *ratted*. PETERBOROUGH. You must allow me to join the hounds again," etc.

[2] 1st ed. reads : " close. There is somewhat of squeamishness in that humanity which appoints the functionaries for the obsequies of a fox, limiting the number of them, and forbidding the use of velvet or broadcloth. If," etc.

the hours preceding it. Our national feelings are healthy and strong by the closeness of their intertexture. What touches one rank is felt by another : it sounds on the rim of the glass, the hall rings with it, and it is well (you will say) if the drum and the trumpet do not catch it. Feelings are more easily communicated among us than manners. Everyone disdains to imitate another : a grace is a peculiarity. Yet in a ride no longer than what we have been taking, how many objects excite our interest ! By how many old mansion-houses should we have passed, within which there are lodged those virtues that constitute the power, stability, and dignity of a people. We never see a flight of rooks or wood-pigeons without the certainty that in a few minutes they will alight on some grove where a brave man has been at his walk or a wise man at his meditations. North America may one day be very rich and powerful ; she can not be otherwise : but she never will gratify the imagination as Europe does. Her history will interest her inhabitants ; but there never will be another page in it so interesting as that which you yourself have left open for unadorned and simple narrative. The poet, the painter, the statuary, will awaken no enthusiasm in it : not a ballad can be written on a *bale of goods :* and not only no artist, but no gentleman is it likely that America will produce in many generations.

PENN. She does not feel the need of them : she can do without 'em.

PETERBOROUGH. Those who have corn may not care for roses ; and those who have dogroses may not care for double ones. I have a buttonhole that wants a posy.

PENN. I do not conceal from thee my opinion of thy abilities, which probably is not a more favourable one than thy own : since however the vices that accompany them, rather than the virtues, thy ambition rather than thy honesty, thy violence rather than thy prudence, may push thee forward to the first station ; it is my duty as a friend to forewarn thee that such promotion will render thee, and probably thy countrymen, less happy.

PETERBOROUGH. I will not permit anything to produce that effect on me : the moment it begins the operation, I resign it. Happiness would overflow my heart, to see reduced to the condition of my lackeys the proudest of our priesthood and our peerage. I should only have to regret that, my condition being equal to theirs, I could not so much enjoy their humiliation, as if my family and my connections were inferior. When I discover men of high birth

PENN AND PETERBOROUGH

condescending to perform the petty tricks of party, for the sake of obtaining a favour at court, I wish it were possible, by the usages of our country and the feelings of Englishmen, to elevate to the rank of prime minister [1] some wrangling barrister, some impudent buffoon, some lampooner from the cockpit, some zany from the theatre, that their backs might serve for his footstool.

PENN. Was there ever in a Christian land a wish more irrational or more impious ?

PETERBOROUGH. The very kind of wish that we oftenest see accomplished.

PENN. Never wilt thou see this.

PETERBOROUGH. Be not over-certain.

PENN. Charles, whose pleasures were low and vulgar, whose parliaments were corrupt and traitorous, chose ministers of some authority. The mob itself, that is amused by dancing dogs, is loth to be ridden by them. The hand that writeth songs on our street-walls, ought never to subscribe to the signature of our kings.

PETERBOROUGH. I speak of parliament.

PENN. Thou speakest then worse still. A king wears its livery and eats its bread. Without a parliament he is but as the slough of a snake, hanging in a hedge : it retains the form and colours, but it wants the force of the creature ; it waves idly in the wind, and is fit only to frighten wrens and mice.

Thy opinions are aristocratical : yet never did I behold a man who despised the body and members of the aristocracy more haughtily and scornfully than thou dost.

PETERBOROUGH. Few have had better opportunities of knowing its composition.

PENN. Those who are older must have had better.

PETERBOROUGH. Say rather, may have had more : yet I have omitted few, unless the lady's choice lay below the chaplain ; for I was always select in my rivals. How many do you imagine of our nobility are not bastards or sons or grandsons of bastards ? If you believe there are a few, I will send the titheman into the enclosure, and he shall levy his proportion in spite of you.

Aristocracy is not contemptible as a system of government ; in fact, it is the only one a true gentleman can acquiesce in. Give me anything rather than the cauldron, eternally bubbling and hissing,

[1] The reference is to Canning.

in which the scum of the sugar-baker has nought at the bottom of it, but the poison of the lawyer's tongue, and the bones of the poor reptiles he hath starved.

Enough for aristocracy ; now for aristocrats. Let me hold my hat before my face and look demurely, while I say, and apply the saying to myself, that, to him whose survey is from any great elevation, all men below are of an equal size. Aristocrats and democrats, kings and scullions, present one form, one stature, one colour, and one gait. I see but two classes of men : those whose names are immortal, and those whose names are perishable. Of the immortal there is but one body : all in it are so high as to seem on an equality, inasmuch as immortality admits of no degree : of the perishable there are several sets and classes ; kings and chamberlains, trumpeters and heralds, take up half their time in cutting them out and sticking them on blank paper. If I by fighting or writing could throw myself forward and gain futurity, I should think myself as much superior to our sovereign lord the king, as our sovereign lord the king is to any bell-wether in his park at Windsor.

PENN. Strange ! that men should toil for earthly glory, when the only difference between the lowest and highest is comprised in two letters : the one *in* a thousand and the one *of* a thousand : an atom in the midst of atoms, take which thou wilt. For the sake of peace and quiet, I would avoid in public too nice inquiries into those dignities, as they are called, which arise fortuitously or spring from favour. Ever since the abolition of the Commonwealth, we have been deafened by exclamations of *Church and King*, and stupified by homilies on *throne and altar*, by which latter the more pious and more intelligent mean *buttery-hatch and cellar*. They indeed declare that by " *throne* " they would signify the *will of one*, and by " *altar*," the *word of the Lord*. Now if the will of one is the degradation of millions ; if the will of one is for strumpets and gamesters and ruinous expenditure in idle recreations ; if the altar is the market-place whereto every man is forced to bring a tenth of his corn and cattle, and must be taught by a hireling and extortioner what Jesus and his disciples and apostles, by commanding and preaching and writing, could not teach him, then indeed must I be confirmed in my opinion, formed after many years from all I have experienced and seen, from the honester part of the reasoners I have heard, and from the wiser of the books I have perused, that, until these

PENN AND PETERBOROUGH

incumbrances and curses, this throne and altar,[1] are removed from the earth, man never can attain, and unworthily will aspire to, the happiness and dignity of his destination.

PETERBOROUGH. I know not to what books you refer. Learned men may be mistaken in their reasonings, and are likely to be : they start with more prejudices than the unlearned, and throw them off with more difficulty. I may differ from Cicero and Sydney——

PENN. Thou mayest ; but if they are wiser than thou art, might we not surmise that they think more rightly on what hath more fully occupied their thoughts ?

PETERBOROUGH. That follows necessarily.

PENN. When a man on any occasion saith " I do not think so," we might ask him, if civility allowed it, " Hast thou thought enough upon it ? or in truth hast thou thought at all ? " In our case, we need not run back to Cicero, we need not invoke the name of Sydney, if in the heaviness of our hearts at the violence of his separation from us it were audible on our lips ; it suffices to look into our farm-yards in the morning, and at midnight to mingle with the groom-porters at the palace. The matter of religion is quite indifferent to thee, as far as the heart is concerned ; and in my opinion it is here that the heart alone is in question. I am grieved to find it insisted on that the *Word of God* requires more explanation than the *Statutes at Large ;* that men are appointed and paid to expound it ; that we must give them money for words, and finally must take their words at their own price. We may know the very thing they do, we may know it better, we may have learned it before they learned it ; there is no appeal ; we must take it after their chewing, and keep it in our mouths and swallow it just as we received it out of theirs. No man whatever is salaried for teaching the laws of the land to the simple, which laws are mostly dark and intricate, although by ignorance or mistake of them a poor creature may be hanged : yet thousands are salaried for teaching what Christ taught better, what is plain to every-one, and what the divine and merciful lawgiver would certainly not hang us for misinterpreting. Indeed he left us no power of doing so : he found a tablet on our bosoms fit for the reception of his precepts, and there is nothing in them which we can erase without a violence to our conscience, nothing which we can neglect without a detriment

[1] Note in 1st ed. : " He speaks of the throne and altar as they stood in the times of Charles and James."

to our interests. If none traded in the expounding of his laws, none would be called heretics, none would be burned alive, none persecuted. Toleration is in itself the essence of Christianity, and the very point which the founder of it most peculiarly enjoined. It is for God to regard our motives; it is for man to regard our acts: and when an act is proved to be against the law, then, and then only, is it our business to inquire into the motive, and whether it aggravates or extenuates the offence.

PETERBOROUGH. Now answer me: would you permit any, whatsoever body of men, to act systematically against the laws?

PENN. If the laws were iniquitous, or forced upon them, there [1] are some who might.

PETERBOROUGH. What, if equitable; what, if conservative of peace?

PENN. Thou knowest my mind on this.

PETERBOROUGH. The popish priesthood must always be opposed to the civil magistrate.

PENN. In what must it, and by what necessity?

PETERBOROUGH. By its institution, by its interests and its vows. Laymen are commanded, by the statutes of every nation in Europe, to denounce a murderer, or whoever is guilty of a capital crime. The popish priest, in quality of confessor, is commanded by other edicts, by edicts issued from without the country, not to denounce any such: so that, by the institutions even of Catholic states, he becomes a partaker of the crime.

PENN. There are contradictory laws that protect them.

PETERBOROUGH. Surely that country can not be well governed, which has one body of laws for one body of men, another for another; which says, " this crime shall make those amends," and yet allows a priest or friar, a thousand miles off, to whisper by proxy in another's ear, " if you hear of it in confession, oblige the criminal to eat a pound of stale sprats and a bundle of stiff radishes; and, when you three divine agents have touched his entrails, take out your whittle and cut the halter." Nevertheless the papists have a strong argument in favour of their religion, disobedient as it is to the command of Jesus Christ, in rising up against the civil magistrate, and claiming a superiority of power.

PENN. What argument?

---

[1] From " there " to " might " added in 2nd ed.

PENN AND PETERBOROUGH

PETERBOROUGH. Its duration.

PENN. I never knew anything good remain so long : and other paganisms may boast the same advantage as this. Whatever is equally well contrived to flatter the vices of men, will exist while the vices themselves do. The little there was of learning in the world, and the much there was of craft and violence, were employed for many centuries in the construction of this vast fabric, where, as is reported of a temple in Babylon, every comer was invited to the mysteries of prostitution. But in Babylon we do not read that people were slain for abstaining therefrom, or for preferring fresh water to salt, and cleanliness to perfumes.

PETERBOROUGH.[1] Perhaps the greatest harm of the religion does not consist in the domination, in the fallacy, in the fraud, in the cruelty it exercises, but in rendering man selfish and ungrateful. The worst ingratitude lies not in the ossified heart of him who commits it ; but we find it in the effect it produces on him against whom it is committed. As water containing stony particles encrusts with them the ferns and mosses it drops on, so the human breast hardens under ingratitude, in proportion to its openness, its softness, and its aptitude to receive impressions. Envy and revenge and lust and tyranny befall the ill-disposed in common with the better ; but ingratitude befalls the better only, and curdles the sweetest drop in the gentlest heart. Almsgiving, that is the giving of money to the idle hangers-on of popery, is among the private duties she inculcates, we know for what ends : let us consider with what arguments and incentives. She assures the alms-giver that he will be richly repaid, and indeed that he can nowhere else find such interest for his money. When he hath given it, he not only is quit of old sins in an exact ratio to the sum deposited, but he may run up a fresh account, and always stand on the creditor side. And here I come to the point of gratitude, at the mention of which you looked on me interrogatively. The ragged receiver knows the motive, counts the coin, thanks the Virgin, rubs his shoulder against the angle of some pedestal, or the fret-work of some shrine, consults his confessor what number is most lucky in the lottery, tries his fortune, loses, blasphemes, crosses his bosom, and returns to mass.

PENN. Poor benighted soul ! The old serpent putteth out his tongue to belime and catch thee.

---

[1] From " PETERBOROUGH " to " sought humanity," p. 204, added in 2nd ed.

IMAGINARY CONVERSATIONS : AMERICAN

PETERBOROUGH. Whoever has given the value of a few shillings, carries back with him a ticket for Paradise, delivered at the counter, and the promise of recommendation to the servants of a garden, where every bush is hung with coronals, and every alley rings with hallelujahs ; but no signification that he might possibly have been actuated by compassion, by a spirit of benevolence, or by a sense of duty. It would be thought unchristian and ungentlemanly, to make inquiries into the causes of a poor man's sufferings : you have no business with sympathy, none with expostulation, none with admonition, none with advice : you must give because you are commanded by the Church : you must abstain from interference because the Church has already appointed to that office. Open your purse to the idle, and you may kiss the first woman you fancy, and stab the first man that interrupts you.

PENN. Wilt thou not stay thee, Mordaunt ! What slough art thou sinking into ?

PETERBOROUGH. I ought to have qualified the expression, by adding so as not to give scandal, but sagely and discreetly. Well may you groan, friend Penn, if ever you dreamt that a religion like this could be eradicated. It needs not the word of God to assure us of its perpetuity ; it needs but the vices of man ; in other words, man's nature. Here couches the serpent that hath swallowed up all the rest : here stands the Temple, with its spacious dome and innumerable pinnacles, where Crime, shaking off Despondency, sits side by side with Virtue.

PENN. Where nothing is divine but mystery, and nothing is damnable but doubt. Nevertheless, the sun of righteousness shall arise——

PETERBOROUGH. To show the vapour, not to scatter it. Wisdom and Folly, Patience and Violence, have alike and equally lent a hand to this resplendent and indestructible pantheon.

PENN. Have Justice and Truth ever ordered it ? Hath Religion, through the clouds of incense that are wafted under her, ever seen there or sought Humanity ? Nowhere in turning over the leaves of the *New Testament* do I find the ordinance of cutting and searing in conversions ; which therefore I must attribute to some holy father, whose notion of bringing up his children makes me wish he had fewer ; or to some pastor who would rather superintend the gelding of his flock than the washing.

204

PENN AND PETERBOROUGH

PETERBOROUGH. Your popish friends in England will be very angry at you if they ever hear you speak in this manner.

PENN. They are the persons who ought to thank me, if any ought. I do not cry at the portcullis of a castle that a fox is under it : I cry at the cottage-door that I saw him steal into the hen-roost. Men hate us worse for trying to set them right than for trying to set them wrong, and have no more fondness for plain truths than for plain clothes. The popish priest hath grounds for disliking me : the popish gentleman hath no better reason for it than for disliking the man who has liberated him from a madhouse, has cured him of a malady caught by seeing others in it, has allowed him to order his own dinner, has kept his daughters from the defilement of foul questions and suggestions, and his wife's tongue from betraying the secrets of the family. These are only a few of the benefits I should confer on him, if he would be warned by me against that worst of falsehood and impiety, which persuades him that any mortal can stand between God and himself, or aid him in his salvation by other means than good counsel. He may swallow a goatskin of the richest *tinta de Rota* through the channel of his teacher, and his forehead may be smeared with Provence oil till it shines like a brazen warming-pan : 'twill be in vain.

PETERBOROUGH. Really, to speak my mind, a religion to be sound and wholesome must be home-brewed. In running across the way with it, you lose almost all but the froth. To force men into public houses of worship, is as unjust and unreasonable as to force them into public houses of carousal. If you will insist upon it, the least you can do is to pay the reckoning.

PENN. This varieth from thy former fantasies.

PETERBOROUGH. It is my custom to say and do whatever occurs to me at the moment. I may be called inconsistent for it, but I can not be called unfair.

PENN. Fairness and consistency are not indeed always the same. Nothing[1] is more consistent with an honest character than to acknowledge a corrected inconsistency.

PETERBOROUGH. If I give several sets of opinions while another gives one opinion only, I give what may be received and what may be rejected, which he does not : and the choice between two things is often as good as either.

[1] From " Nothing " to " inconsistency " added in 2nd ed.

PENN. And the escape from both of them is often as good as the choice.

PETERBOROUGH. In any set speech, in addressing the parliament or the soldiers, you never will find me contradictory or wavering ; whereas among my friends I throw out what comes uppermost, and find a pleasure not only in my versatility, but in the watchfulness it excites among those who purchase from me, at an easy price, the titles of wariness and acuteness. Nothing is so agreeable both to children and men, as to let them catch you tripping, and particularly if you are strong and usually walk upright and with stateliness: and to connive at them is the most economical of pleasures.

PENN. It may hinder thy rise in the state ; which would fret thee.

PETERBOROUGH. What man ever rose in it by his intellects, until he had perverted or contracted or covered them ? The wide and abundant and impetuous stream bears pleasure and wonder on its bosom : wealth rises from the narrow and factitious. What is that to me ? Let us spur on.

You have already proved that what we call patriotism is very different from what rhetoricians and orators represent it. A man's own glory rests well upon the glory of his country : but how few can claim any for their own ! Great generals, great writers : have we in existence or on record, half a dozen of either ? We are apt, I know not with what reason, to ridicule the French for their proneness to servitude and their adulation to princes : yet is there another man in the world so proud of his country as a Frenchman is of France ? We consider no part of God's creation so cringing, so insatiable, so ungrateful, as the Scotch : nevertheless we see them hang together by the claws like bats ; and they bite and scratch you to the bone if you attempt to put an Englishman in the midst of them. Although they tell you they are the most loyal of mankind, yet they are ready at any time to sell their king and abjure their principles, and will haggle less with you about the price of them, than about a bale of linen or a barrel of haddock.

PENN. How is this ? We never gained so much by Charles as we paid for him.

PETERBOROUGH. That bargain was driven hard with us : but if *we* could make little of him, what could *they* do ?

A story comes into my mind, which I heard at Portsmouth just before I left England. It exhibits no unfavourable specimen of a

PENN AND PETERBOROUGH

Scot : and it proves to us that there is a certain Patriotism loth to let Truth stand in her way, or Nature herself do anything disagreeable to her. The Lord Halifax, you may have heard perhaps, is the chief patron of our poets. A Scotchman one day came before him, bowing to the earth, and holding out a piece of rumpled paper. His lordship smiled with his usual affability, thanked him, and told him that, being a disciple of Mr. Locke's, he had no occasion for such an offering so long after breakfast. " Hauld ! hauld ! it 's poesy, it 's poesy, my laird ! written on the scaith of a maiden in Dundalk, and ane of very guid connaxions."

" Well, then, my dear sir, let me see it."

The rhymes are in a kind of step like that of Catiline as described by Sallust : *modo citus modo tardus incessus :* the best invention that poetry ever made : never was there one so serviceable to the memory, for you must read them several times over before you can find out whether there are any verses in them. I should not be surprised if they shortly come supported by such a powerful host of partisans, on our side of the Tweed, as to rout the united forces of Milton and Shakespeare. Listen.

> The southern blast was so bitter cold,
> It almost sheared the sheep in our fold,
> And made the young maiden look like the old,
> Blue as baboon is, where he is bluest—
> Mind thy steps, Meggie ! mind, or thou ruest.

" How ! " cried Lord Halifax, " can Scotchmen then come so near the English border in their phraseology ? " Nevertheless he suspected a mistake, and soon apprehended it. " The southern blast ! you must mean the northern."

" Faith and troth ! and I did mean the northern, and did e'en write it, my laird ! but I thought i' my conscience it ill beseemed me to leave an immortal reflaxion on my ain maither country."

Halifax gave him a guinea, ordered his groom to bring him a sack of oats from the stable, and told him at parting, he ought to be made a doctor of laws for his poetry, and a knight-banneret for his patriotism. The Scotchman looked at his guinea, and said, in the despondency of ambition, " 'T wou'd tak anither to bring 't aboot."

PENN. Yet perhaps this very man, so zealous for the honour of his

207

country that he would lie for her all day long, would be heartily glad
to abandon her, might he thereby be made an officer of excise in
Muscovy or Poland. By my removal from England to America, I do
not think I any more change my country, than my father did when
he left Bristol for London. We relinquish her when we relinquish
her purer habits, her juster laws, her wiser conversations ; not when
we abandon the dissidence and dishonesty of her parties, her political
craft, her theological intolerance. That is properly the land of our
fathers in which we may venerate the image of their virtues ; in
which we may follow their steps, and leave our own not unworthy
to be followed. We want animation, ye tell us ; we want liberality.
O Mordaunt ! in the eyes of men those want everything who want
imposture. How many are there in high places who cry aloud
to clear the way for the conscience ! who shout " Give the poor
creatures corn, give the poor creatures liberty " ; yet who blink
their eyes upon Christian blood flowing forth under the sword of
persecution. Cromwell, at whose frown their rotten hearts would
have melted away, is now a subject of derision to them. He
stretched out his hand over the Alps, and cried, " Defend thy
brother ! preserve the creature that God made ; loose the bondman that Christ redeemed ! " Can I think it the most rational of
happiness, the most obligatory of duties, to reside in a country at
the head of whose councils are the silent associates of thieves and
murderers ? Doubtless I must lose sight of them in it, I must
cherish it, I must love it, because it is the country where I broke my
head seven years ago by forcing my horse over a gate ! Is it anything for such as thou art, or (I would say it with humility) for such
as I am, to be greater in soul and intellect than a king or chancellor
or archbishop ? Have we the same temptation as they have, for
violence, disingenuousness, and falsehood ? Let us praise God that
we have not, and let us keep where we never may catch it.

PETERBOROUGH. Then let us think of the country, the only true
comforter ; or, if you dispute this point, the only general one. Could
not you have left standing in these meadows a few of the shadier
and larger trees ? It appears to me, friend Penn, that you are like
a father who strips two or three of his infants stark-naked, and
encourages his elder son to wear several great-coats.

PENN. Why, perhaps it might have been as well to leave here and
there a tree, for the sake of the cattle.

PENN AND PETERBOROUGH

PETERBOROUGH. And for the sake of ornament.

PENN. I can not see any great ornament in trees, until the carpenter hath had them under his hand. They are dull in summer and ragged in winter, the very best of them, trim them and contrive them as you will. The ornament of a country is the sight of creatures enjoying their existence.

PETERBOROUGH. And yet you would not let people dance.

PENN. I would not call them together for that purpose : but when countryfolks have done the business of the day, I might not reprove them for an innocent relaxation.

PETERBOROUGH. Really I fancied that even the sound of a fiddle was an abomination to you.

PENN. I was never given to capering : but there is something in a violin, if played discreetly, that appeareth to make hot weather cool, and cold weather warm and temperate : not however when its chords have young maidens tied invisibly to the end of them, jerking them up and down in a strange fashion before one's eyes, and, unless one taketh due caution, wafting their hair upon one's face and bosom, and their very breath too between one's lips, if peradventure one omitteth to shut them bitterly and hold tight.

PETERBOROUGH. Egad, friend William, I have talked with dancing-masters in my day who knew less about their business than you do.

PENN. If they knew but half of it, they would change it for a better. They do not see where it finishes.

PETERBOROUGH. Impudent dogs, they would see that too, if they could.

PENN. We must accommodate things and practices to their country. Hot-beds do not want stoves, and stoves do not want furnaces, and furnaces do not want blow-pipes. In cities the youth has pastime enough, without incentives to frowardness and lust : but the labourer of the fields may perhaps dance in the evening with the young woman he has worked with in the noon, and do it irreproachably. His truly is a kind of labour that will not whet his appetite for wanton things : and the motion of the limbs, being different from that wherein they had been exercised many hours, would rather tend to refresh than to weary him. Among the idle, by the presence of what is pleasant to the senses, thoughts swell into wishes, and wishes ripen into deeds.

PETERBOROUGH. Why should not they ?

PENN. Because our destination is higher, if we consent to it ; and because we can do good in as little time and with as little trouble as we can do evil. As [1] all parts of the world are equally nigh to the heavens, so by their primary position are all men equally nigh to God ; but many rational creatures, as we call them, do by their vices draw back from the Creator, while brute matter stands consistently where he placed it.

PETERBOROUGH. I would rather hear a sermon from you than from anybody else : you pluck me for the sake of cooling and cleansing me : the old women who have laid hands on me from the pulpit, plucked me only to get something by my feathers.

PENN. Nobody can lie easily upon such feathers as thine ; and the housewife doth well who singes them all round. The powers bestowed on thee by thy Maker are perverted by thy passions, and, instead of serving thee, bear against thee ; as guns on shipboard, loosened by foul weather, run ruinously back against those who were appointed to direct them. The trees, the blades of grass, the weakest herbs, assume by degrees the consistency they ought to have, and grow to the uttermost height the climate and soil allow to them : we alone droop when our strength should be at its full ; and the strongest man in England sees no reason why we should not. Mordaunt, it would afflict thee to blush at thee : against that fire thou couldst not stand : beware then.

Many in every age have been the hypocrites of Virtue ; ours is the only one, I imagine, that ever saw the hypocrites of Vice. Persons of your condition found a difficulty in becoming profligate to their heart's content. It was a point of conscience with them (when every other point of it was blunted or broken) to seem worse than they really were, and to make their intimates worse, if possible, than themselves. This in great measure was done from a spirit of obstinacy and contradiction : for although on the opposite side there were numbers of strict and holy men, there were certainly more of those who were only so in appearance. Thousands were, heart and soul, devoted to the cause of liberty ; tens of thousands pretended a love of it, merely to obtain a portion of fines and confiscations. Would you wish to have before you any objects more odious ?

PETERBOROUGH. The wish would be fruitless.

PENN. And yet there were those who tried whether they could

_____
[1] From " As " to " direct them " added in 2nd ed.

PENN AND PETERBOROUGH

not become so : and as they had opposed real licentiousness to false religion, so they carried what they called loyalty to such a degree of subserviency as would disgrace a troop of Asiatic slaves, and adored the most reprehensible of kings, not only in the language but with the rites of their church-worship, drinking to his health in the same posture as when they celebrate the most awful event in the ministry of their Redeemer, and devoting their lives to him with the same formality.

PETERBOROUGH. And the same faith.

Every man would rather eat a good dinner than a bad one ; and when it is easier to get it by kneeling and drinking than by labouring and thirsting, I can not call them fools for it.

PENN. Verily I did not designate them by that name, although some of them have seen reason to bestow it on themselves.

PETERBOROUGH. Poverty gives a man of family great privileges : I do not make use of mine, and care little about those who have stolen a march of me, and rest in oblivion. Yet I am poor enough for any pretensions, and am likely to remain so in spite of contingencies ; for I have rather a large family of vices, and am resolved, as becomes a good parent, to cherish and maintain them.

PENN. Inconsiderate young man ! Know, for thy comfort and encouragement, it is less easy in youth to extinguish vices than to convert them into virtues. Afterward we lose the power of doing either, and fancy that to whine and promise serves as well. Fit thyself to become the head and ornament of a family : love someone.

PETERBOROUGH. Easy enough that !

PENN. Perhaps not so easy as at first it appeareth to thee. To desire is not to love : the passions are moderated by tenderness.

PETERBOROUGH. Faith ! I am afraid they are among us men. Love, like canine madness, may be fairly stifled in a feather-bed, with proper assistance. Your advice reminds me of a recitative, I know not in what opera.

> Amare una, e dall' una esser amato,
> È' il sommo ben che possa l' uom godere ;
> Due mi amano ; amo tré ; sono infelice.

PENN. Which being Englished, what may be the import ?

PETERBOROUGH.

> To love one, and to be beloved by one,
> Is the greatest good a mortal can enjoy :
> Two love me ; I love three ; I am unhappy.

PENN. And he deserved it, whoever he was : for truth had opened his eyes, and he would not see. The sentiment [1] is worthy of a pagan in red boots.

PETERBOROUGH. An idle friend of mine spent an autumn and winter in Italy. Soon after his arrival in that country, he took a residence at the lake of Como, and was particularly fond of a shady walk beside the rivulet which runs near the city. Here he saw in the old hedge of a little wood, about a mile from the Milan gate, a very beautiful green lizard. The animal looked at him as steadfastly as he looked at the animal; and, it being the first he had ever seen of that large kind, he continued to admire it for almost half an hour. On the morrow, at the same time of day, he repeated his visit to the place, and found in a few minutes the same inhabitant : and their interview was again the same. Curiosity led him a third time to the spot; but somewhat later; and he really felt a disappointment at not finding his lizard. He sat down and began to read, and after a time was about to change his posture (for the short grass hardly covered the gravel, and he had not under him such a cushion as you have), when the lizard's eyes met his, between him and the bank. It stopped and gazed at him, and then walked slowly into the hedge, and gazed again from the very place in which it was first discovered. Confidence was now established between the parties. One day my friend was tempted to take his lizard home with him, and tried to catch it. The creature, equally swift and quicksighted, sprang away, looked once more at him from its first position, and was never seen afterward. This is the recital of my friend; a friend as foolish as any I have : but I suspect his folly will save me from a greater; and, if idleness should attract me to the side of marriage, I shall think of him and his lizard. He was not contented with all the pleasure it ever could have given him : he must forsooth catch it and keep it : had he succeeded, he would soon have been as tired of the creature as the creature would have been of him. Marriage is the first step to Repentance : and there are not many to climb.

PENN.[2] I have better hopes of thee than thou appearest to enter-

---

[1] Note in 1st ed. : " It may be suspected that the sentiment and the verses too are Peterborough's."

[2] An anecdote related by Penn in 1st ed. is reserved for the Appendix to the final volume of the Conversations.

tain of thyself. A conversion was produced in my own family through means extremely slight, and (if there be any such) upon a fortuitous occasion. My good father had once a waiting-man, whom, among other services, he employed in the pouring out of wine at the sideboard from black bottles into white, of which white there being some lack, he bade the man buy two more. The man went forthwith, and bought them; but ere dinner-time they were broken. Whereupon my father said to him, " Hast thou broken the two bottles ? "

" Yea," said he.

" How? thou fool! " cried my father; for he was quick and choleric.

His waiting-man then answered, and said, " I brake them by striking one against the other, to try if they were good for anything."

The patience of my beloved parent did not hold out against this, and, rising from his seat, he would have smitten the waiting-man : but I arose also, and caught him by the sleeve, and said to him, " Father ! thou art angered. I would speak to thee with all dutifulness, as becometh a young man and thy son. Bethink thee now, my good father, if thou, being a man of war, hast not done to men what thy servant hath done to bottles ; if thou hast not been fain to try, whether, in thy estimation, being a man of war, they were good for anything, and by the same experiment and proof, namely, by making one of them strike the other. Pardon then this thy servant, for that he hath confessed he did it, when it may be that such confession is not yet made by thee, my honoured parent, nor deemed requisite."

PETERBOROUGH. And what said the old admiral to this ?

PENN. I need not tell thee; since it aideth in nothing my discourse.

PETERBOROUGH. But do tell me.

PENN. I will, then, inasmuch as it evinceth his compliancy of temper.

" Son William," said he, " for one sally of such good sense and good nature, I could bear thy sanctification and grimaces seven years. Give me thy hand, my lad ! we are friends again for life."

Now I had angered him, by hoping and resolving to live in future more regularly and religiously than we had been accustomed to do among his nautical companions.

PETERBOROUGH. If joy, which is much less ingenious, much less argumentative, than grief, had allowed him a few moments of reflection, he might have told you that men are well tried whether they are *good for anything*, by this process. For not only do they prove their courage, without which, as the world is constituted, there is neither peace nor equity, the two best things of good things, as you above all people will admit ; but they promote one another's self-esteem, and superadd the delicacy of good manners to those higher and purer attributes of sound morality.

Another thing, my friend, or rather, if you will bear it, two, I must object against your system. You prohibit not dancing only, but singing and drawing. As you will perhaps make the better defence for yourself on singing, I shall speak first upon drawing, and then attack you mainly.

One would imagine that so contemplative a race of people as you are, would cultivate an art of which the early shoots require shade and seclusion, and the first efforts are made in privacy. Others are *chaperons* to society and dissipation. In dancing I concede to you, the figure of the dance is the last figure that is thought of ; and in music, there never was a young person of either sex who, in the softest parts, did not sigh a note higher than the flute. Drawing has no such inconvenience or aberration. This creative faculty is silent and meditative : it leads to a temperate love of Nature, to a selection of what is beautiful, and to a habit of what is correct.

In poetry, the most tender and the least tender emotions are excited. He who draws tears from me, would draw his sword against me, if I tried as a poet to draw any tears from him : so fixedly is jealousy the associate of poetry. And when a woman takes up the art, as some have done among us, I would whisper in her ear, if I dared, that there never was a Sappho who would not plunge over-head for a Phaon.

Drawing here too is widely different. If it raises any aspirations after Fame, they are solitary and sober, and after Fame in her calmest and most quiescent hour.

PENN. Friend, we can do without both Fame and her aspirations, and what we *can* do without, we *should*, or we must forfeit the name of temperate men.

PETERBOROUGH. Surrender then to me this province of Pennsylvania.

PENN. Nay, nay ; I do not play at forfeits with thee : and beside, the gift would harm thee. My prudence is greater (discreetly be it spoken) than thine.

214

PENN AND PETERBOROUGH

PETERBOROUGH. Faith is it !

PENN. And thou wouldst never erect such an asylum for peace
and industry, as, by the blessing of God, I hope to erect herein for
future generations.

PETERBOROUGH. I must attack you then on the side of singing,
and argue upon it as a moralist might do.

PENN. Then verily, friend Mordaunt, thou wilt display much
originality : I yearn to behold thee in that character.

PETERBOROUGH. Have you never heard soldiers and apprentices
sing lewd songs ?

PENN. Why, songs under that description and from those
quarters have reached mine ear : and, if report speak truly, the
breath of such hath tarnished the nearest gold lace on each side
of them.

PETERBOROUGH. If patriotic or tender ones had been written well
among us, and set to good music, they would have gained access to
those persons who, for want of them, amuse their idleness and indulge
their fancies with ribaldry. Nay, had they been awakened early by
them, such idleness and such fancies never would have existed : for
music of this nature is a strengthener both of the mind and of the
heart. I am persuaded that even the highest national character
might be raised still higher, by inspiring boys with a timely love of it,
and by supplying them with lofty and generous sentiments in graceful
and well-composed songs. The Lacedemonians were the rudest
people in Greece : I doubt whether the admirable order that sub-
sisted long among them, as citizens and as soldiers, is more owing
to the laws of Lycurgus than to the elegies of Tyrtæus. The
Athenians were the softest and most effeminate : yet they dashed
down tyranny and strode over valour, singing the praises of
Harmodius and Aristogiton.

PENN. We have no tyranny to dash down and no valour to stride
over : our voice is, " God is among us : he commands us peace."
Thy observations, as applicable to the turbid state wherein it is (as
thou fanciest) the interest of such as thou art to keep thy country,
are not incorrect.

PETERBOROUGH. This avowal is very liberal : keep up with it in
practice. Why cannot you take men as you find them ? You might
make a great deal of them, and spare yourselves the trouble of turning
them inside-out. You resemble the puritans too much for me.

PENN. Are we cruel then, and intolerant, and arrogant ? are we without mercy, without forbearance, without patience ? do we look for God everywhere but where he is to be found ? and are we desirous of setting up before him such another figure as ourselves ?

PETERBOROUGH. No, certainly not, at present : but, if religions were not sideling in their infancy and retrograde in their maturity, one might fear it. Calmness and quietude are your darlings.

PENN. They are the things that men want most.

PETERBOROUGH. You undervalue, or rather you despise and contemn, what exalts us in the arts and sciences, and hence inhibit the growth and tendency of intellect, which surely, to speak in your own manner, God bestowed upon us for our improvement. What is worse, you allow no compromise between Vice and Virtue : by which system, if universal, men, finding the impracticability of perfection, and experiencing the loss of esteem for not bringing what you exact from them, would relapse without a struggle or an effort from the eminence they had obtained. In the large heart, the habitation of generosity and beneficence, I would leave a cell or two vacant for less worthy guests, and pass without peeping in.

PENN. But prythee shut the door, if thou findest it wide open, with the intruders at their tricks.

PETERBOROUGH. It is the privilege of man to do irrational things.

PENN. Do you people who talk of privileges, and (such is the phrase) enjoy them, exert them every day ?

PETERBOROUGH. Only this one.

PENN. Mordaunt ! Mordaunt ! would that thy confession, frank and honest as it is, were made in another tone, and with another feeling, and to a holier than I am, or than man can be !

PETERBOROUGH. You have given me leave to speak plainly and unreservedly with you, upon every question and every objection.

PENN. Else neither were I thy friend nor wert thou mine.

PETERBOROUGH. I will venture then to declare that, in the opinion of the world, enemies as you profess yourselves to pride, you are no less proud than other men, though differently.

PENN. There are some among us, I wish I were confident of being one, who have twisted back and cut off many rank branches from this most poisonous plant, the roots whereof twine about the heart until they suck out the best juices, and until its wind-catching and ever-fluttering foliage overshadows and starves the brain.

216

PENN AND PETERBOROUGH

Self-complacency is often mistaken for pride, and stands not far from it in certain places. The consciousness of having mastered some prepotence of passion, or of having rectified some obliquity of disposition, may leave the expression of disdain for the evil subdued not unmingled with gladness, perhaps too triumphant, in the subduer. I will never animadvert on thee, friend Mordaunt, at seeing a grand illumination in thy countenance after such a victory.

PETERBOROUGH. In this warfare you are among the few great captains.

PENN. Never say it. Hear the wise one. " Hope deferred maketh the heart sick " : and mine is sick indeed ; for I myself have deferred the hope I raised and cherished. Perverse as we are, we sigh for happiness ; we know where to find it ; and we will not go for it one step. Would we increase it, we must do with it as we do with money ; we must put it out. Whatever of it we place in the hands of another, let him be improvident, let him be thankless, is sure to return to us, and without delay : whatever we keep to ourselves, lies dead the moment we have thus settled it, and cannot be lifted from the chest. I have begun to do good late, and can hope, alas ! now to do but little.

PETERBOROUGH. A truce with sighing, friend Penn ; for that is a thing in which I never can join with you ; unless I find you in debt, or with bad wine before you : these being two evils beyond my mending, and growing no better for waiting.

You have turned me aside from the conversation I would have holden with you about pride.

PENN. Dost thou find any growing in this wilderness ? or dost thou fancy I have chosen a fit spot for the cultivation of it ?

PETERBOROUGH. No, no ; but tell me whether you do not believe there are some kinds of it useful and beneficial to society.

PENN. I do not.

PETERBOROUGH. I would by no means advert to that which arises from antiquity of family, unless I were fully confident of surpassing one day, in services to my country, the foremost of my ancestors.

PENN. In regard to antiquity of family, the hedge-hog and sloth fairly beat the best of us, by a good day's run.

PETERBOROUGH. So says Moses.

PENN. And, friend, art thou wiser than he ?

PETERBOROUGH. I do not speak of the creature man ; I do not

217

speak of our commoners or peers. The only claim to distinction in the generality of the better, is, that their ancestors have lived upon the same spot for several ages : so have their groves and avenues : so have their pigs and poultry. Among us of the peerage, there are only ten or eleven whose best forefather rendered any remarkable service to his country, or distinguished his name by valour or by genius. Supposing a peer or gentleman, descended, not from one who crouched or curtsied to a frivolous fantastic Scotch schoolman, or those lying varlets his son and grandsons ; but from one who clinked his mail in close array with a Plantagenet's, or, what is more, bade him respect his equals and reverence the laws, shall not that man look back with pride upon the glorious shade gone past, and shall not he become the better for the retrospect ?

PENN. With veneration he may indeed look back, but not with pride, which ought to be humbled to the dust before such an apparition. Pride it would be, and folly too in the extreme, if he preferred the dead man, who had once done these things, to the living one who does the same at the same hazard.

PETERBOROUGH. The rarity of those who acted and thought generously in times of ignorance and violence, renders a single one such equal in value to some thousands of the foremost who act and think so now.

PENN. It [1] is easy to look down on others ; to look down on ourselves is the difficulty. Of all pride however, and all folly, the grossest is, where a man who possesses no merit in himself shall pretend to an equality with one who does possess it ; and shall found this pretension on no better plea or title, than that, although he hath it not, his grandfather had. I would use no violence or coercion with any rational creature ; but, rather than such a bestiality in a human form should run about the streets uncured, I would shout like a stripling for the farrier at his furnace, and unthong the drenching-horn from my stable-door.

PETERBOROUGH. After all you have said, I am but the more confirmed in the sentence of a poet, whose name I have forgotten, that Pride is

> Mother of Virtues to the virtuous man,
> And only hateful with her arm round Vice,[2]

---

[1] From " It " to " difficulty " added in 3rd ed.
[2] Landor, *From the Phoceans*, viii. 62.

PENN AND PETERBOROUGH

PENN. Thou mistakest another for her ; she is verily an unsober jade, who in her gravest humour will lead thee into quarrels, and in her gayest will pick thy pocket. Turn [1] away from this foul obscure vision, and discourse again about the land before us, which may constitute hereafter many states, prosperous and independent.

PETERBOROUGH. I have an insuperable objection to small states, because of their inability to defend themselves. If some day America should form herself into a republic, as it is evident she will from the political and theological tenets of the settlers, one portion must drop off after another, like noses and ears in such a climate, and everything soon be rotten and at last diminutive.

PENN. Families themselves do not hold together longer than is consistent with the welfare of the members : yet, although they may not hold together, they may abstain from fighting and quarrelling. In vain wilt thou devise new forms of government, until thou hast erected something for those forms to stand upon. Until thou hast broken in the horse, do not trouble thy head about the colour or quantity of the trappings ; for peradventure thou mayest not sit easily on them, nor long. Small republics have usually been happier than extensive ones : while small principalities serve only as seraglios for the masters of greater, out of which to take their wives : otherwise it would be expedient for them to putty up such bug-holes.

Suppose an Italian wishes to commit a murder, and he hath no cardinal at Rome to protect him, nor any friend among the domestics of the most Christian or most Catholic majesties, whose ambassadors' houses are inviolable asylums for assassins, he hath only to waylay his enemy in such a state as Piombino or Massa, out of which, if he catcheth a cow by the tail and she gallopeth, he shall be carried in twenty minutes.

PETERBOROUGH. This reminds me that there is prevalent, through the whole of Europe, a most injudicious, injurious, and iniquitous practice : the custom of protecting, I do not say murderers, for that is not universal, but fraudulent debtors and other fugitive malefactors. One would imagine that common interest and common courtesy should admit, should indicate, should dictate, the pursuit of them, even by an armed force, if necessary, passing the boundaries. No prince ought to be the patron or the protector of lawless men. In private life we not only refuse to receive such characters, but we

[1] From " Turn " to " independent " added in 2nd ed.

219

dismiss from our service those who have given a slight offence to our equals. I am not so visionary as to expect that princes should be gentlemen ; but, as they often have gentlemen about them, someone, it may be hoped, at some time or other, will have courage and influence enough to persuade them, that such a conduct is at once dishonourable and disadvantageous.

PENN. Every[1] government should provide for every subject the means of living both honestly and at ease. We should bring out of every man and every creature as much utility as we may : now much utility will never be produced, unless we render life easy and comfortable. If all men and women would labour six hours in the twenty-four, some mentally, some corporeally, setting apart one day in the seven, all the work would be completed that is requisite for our innocent and rational desires. Dost thou believe that God beholds with pleasure any poor wretch working three-fourths of his whole lifetime, reckoned from childhood ?

PETERBOROUGH. No, nor is the thing possible.

PENN. I tell thee, Mordaunt, the thing is possible, and is done.* Thou countest not the hours when thy horse is at his manger as those of his course ; not the hours when our common nature casteth him down into sleep : why then treat thy fellow man more harshly ? He too must sleep, whether he will or no : he too must replenish his veins with food and sustenance. These are as requisite to his labour, are in fact as much the implements and tackle of it, as the spade and plough. When Nature hath demanded so much for herself, what remaineth to the creature ? Allow six hours for rest in cold climates, eight in hotter, and one in each for refreshment by food ; thou wilt then find that not only three-fourths, but nearly the whole of life is hard labour. This ought not to be : and I verily do believe that God hath opened to us our new continent that it may be no longer.

PETERBOROUGH. The whole world is not in the condition you represent.

---

[1] From " Every " to " ease " added in 2nd ed.

* The House of Commons lately passed an Act that children under *nine* years of age shall not be obliged to work longer than *twelve* hours in the day. Do not the wretches deserve to be stoned to death who authorize the infliction of such labour on creatures so incapable of enduring it ? No animal, though full-grown and vigorous, should labour twelve hours, with all the benefit of open air, refreshment more regular, cessation more frequent, change of position, and variety of motion.—W. S. L.

PENN AND PETERBOROUGH

PENN. True, the whole world is not ; but only that part of it which is policied and civilized ; in other words, that very part which, possessing the experience of ages, ought to liberate itself from its trammels, and to enjoy the refreshing sweetness of well-ripened society.

What art thou musing upon with such complacency ?

PETERBOROUGH. I know that you rise early, and I cannot see why you allow to others quite so many hours of sleep. I myself sleep only four.

PENN. I could make thee sleep six, and soundly as a Board of Inquiry in the committee-room, and quarrel with him who wakened thee, swearing (for thou dost swear now and then, friend Mordaunt —God mend thee !) that thou wert already upon thy legs, and wantedst no fool to call thee, and rubbing thine eyes meanwhile with nightcap between them and forefinger.

PETERBOROUGH. Indeed could you, friend William, and without a march up the garret-stairs, to the little snug room with a square white curtain at the window, and overlooking the poultry ?

PENN. O fie ! thou wanton !

PETERBOROUGH. That indeed would make a man pant, and desire to rest himself, and take rest therein, though he were as the young cedar, even like unto the cedar that hath not many years.

PENN. Who touched thy lips with flame, that thou speakest thus ?

PETERBOROUGH. Not she, upon my honour ! not that bright cynosure with the eye of steel and bosom of snowy-cloud, that the cocks crow to, and waken me.

PENN. Be discreet ; and ponder not upon the hand-maiden.

PETERBOROUGH. In earnest then, do not you think that eight hours' sleep would be excessive for a labourer, in any climate ?

PENN. I do not. I would divide his sleep, in some countries ; four hours in the hottest part of the day, four at night. I sleep seven, and am convinced that many, and those too who do not labour, may sleep eight without ill consequences.

PETERBOROUGH. Yet those who have slept long have mostly been short-lived.

PENN. Not because they slept long, but because they ate and drank immoderately and late, and slept in consequence both long and badly. Long sleep in itself, I conceive, is far from unwholesome, though it is almost always followed by debility.

IMAGINARY CONVERSATIONS: AMERICAN

PETERBOROUGH. How can it be other than unwholesome, if followed, as you acknowledge, by debility?

PENN. This proceeds not from the relaxation caused by its continuance, but from breathing the same air the whole time, and losing that which refreshes the earth, and everything alive, animal and vegetable, soon after sunrise. If we arose when we ought to do, we should be the better for a brief and gentle sleep in the middle of the day : a thing which very active and very studious men are improvident in neglecting. Neither love nor poetry hath imagined aught more precious than the eyes ; insomuch that the poet and lover, when he hath made some idle girl believe everything else, comes hither at last as to the highest pitch of all, telling her that she is dearer to him than they are ; and, if she swallows this wafer, her faith is catholic. The eyes would remain much longer unimpaired, by dividing (I do not say equally) the hours of their employment and their repose.

PETERBOROUGH. The Society of Friends enjoys eyesight in perfection, and with the clearest title ; by rejecting with other pleasures those of literature. I never have heard of one, beside yourself and Barclay,[1] who pursued any science or was occupied in any study.

PENN. The knowledge that conduces to practical good is not restricted or undervalued by us : whatever leads away from that direction seems to us reprovable and amiss.

PETERBOROUGH. My dear Penn, you are too speculative : too visionary for this world of matter and realities.

PENN. Friend, that which thou callest matter is indeed such : but that which thou callest reality is not. There is nothing so visionary as what the world esteems real ; nothing so baseless, nothing so untrue.

PETERBOROUGH. Men, it appears to me, are incapable of that perfection to which you would, with whatever gentleness, bring them on.

PENN. We do not hope to conduct them further in the way than our blessed guide and master hath commanded. They are no worse generally in our day than they were in his, although the best governments in these ages are more degrading than Roman or Greek would suffer, until utterly subdued. It is impossible to rescue the human

[1] 1st ed. reads : " George Fox."

222

race from the abyss of sin and slavery, unless we can induce our brethren to look on Christianity in its purity.

PETERBOROUGH. Ah my friend ! nothing on earth has been or ever will be of long continuance, and least so purity.

PENN. Thou speakest untruly, Mordaunt ! Of long continuance have been folly and wickedness : shall wisdom then and righteousness be transitory or illusive ? Is that which is inconsistent and wrong, of a nature more stabile than that which is consistent and right ? Is there singleness in falsehood ? is there duplicity in truth ? Why then shall corruption stand, and incorruption sink ? or why shall the good bend voluntarily to drink, from the cup of the damned, the last and bitterest of its dregs, despair ? Let us raise up our heads unto the God who made us : even as he made us let us raise them up : and let us hope and believe that he will help us in our endeavours to render one another free and happy. We take man such as his hand hath formed him ; we lead man whither his voice hath called. Is this visionary ? is this speculative ?

PETERBOROUGH. Enthusiasm will cool gradually. Within half a century, I presume to prophesy, the society will dissolve from its very purity.

PENN. Let it continue but that period ; and it will contain, in so brief a span as the half-century thou allowest to it, a greater portion of true Christianity and solid happiness, than the sixteen whole ones past over us have contained. After which, supposing that religion may have grown much cooler, habits of industry and feelings of gentleness will have sprung up widely, and have spread far beyond the enclosures of our brotherhood.

PETERBOROUGH. Nations, like individuals, interest us in their birth and early growth : every motion, however irregular, seems to us natural, graceful, an indication of vigour or intelligence. For some time afterward the sallies of frowardness and of passion are not only forgiven in them, but applauded and admired. Soon however what we fancied a pleasing peculiarity becomes an awkwardness and uncouthness ; what was spirit is petulance ; and we confess we were disappointed in our hopes and calculations. In fact the hopes were foolish, and the calculations were traced by a clumsy finger on a moving sand.

Against our expectations and auguries, America may produce boors without the honesty, the simplicity, the frugality, of boors ;

223

and merchants not only without the quiet industry and expectant patience of merchants, but with scarcely the steadiness of the elements that waft and convey their merchandize. Do not accuse me of rashness or of incivility, when I declare to you my suspicion, that you, however unconsciously, tend toward this mischief. Whenever a part of society secedes from the general mass under whatever pretext, it grows distrustful, and renders others so : hence moroseness, and the resolution of indemnity, by the acquisition of wealth, to gratify a secluded vanity and enforce an ungracious consequence.

PENN. The ancients were of opinion that every man hath his good and evil genius. They would have believed more wisely that everything human hath about it, near or remotely, somewhat of good and somewhat of evil. There is truth, and perhaps more of it than can unfold itself at present, in thy observation. We will strive, by mutual admonition and encouragement, to make straight and even and pleasant, and to break off and to bend aside as many thorns as we can, from the path we have chosen to pursue. One would think it requireth but little exhortation to warn men against the two mischiefs thou hast pointed out : whereupon I would ask the grossest fool and sensualist, whether he doth not eat a heartier dinner, and digest it better, by keeping in good humour ; and I would ask the most dishonest rogue that ever touched a fleece, whether he gaineth not more by being trusted than by being distrusted, and whether he hath not a better chance of being trusted for honesty than for dishonesty ? Teach men to calculate rightly, and thou wilt have taught them to live religiously.

PETERBOROUGH. Pious and contented as your people seem, they are not indifferent to the good things of this world ; indeed none look more attentively to what we call the main chance.

PENN. Honest occupation is favourable to that piety and content which thou attributest to us.

PETERBOROUGH. Religious men, in other new sects, have generally placed their reliance more undividedly on Providence.

PENN. Providence uses earthly means. We rely on Providence for blessing us in our endeavours to benefit one another ; which we would do by giving employment to the needy, and aiding the laborious.

PETERBOROUGH. Fortune has favoured you above others. Industry often fails with them ; with you rarely.

224

PENN AND PETERBOROUGH

PENN. Allegorically speaking, as thou hast done, of Fortune, if we hope to be gainers from her wheel, we must now and then drive a spoke into it ourselves ; and we must take what precaution we can that it do not fire by its velocity. Industry has never failed, while she has kept both eyes upon one object, nor until she has risen from her business and gone into partnership with Speculation. Afterward she hath no better right to the name of Industry, than Thievery hath, or Gaming.

PETERBOROUGH. The world will turn round still. Industry is produced by Want, Wealth is produced by Industry, Idleness is produced by Wealth, Poverty is produced by Idleness. Here Poverty finds herself at the side of her sister Want. They agree to go in search of Industry, before it is too late, being sure of finding her, since she may be heard of in every field and traced in every gateway : and the great year proceeds again through the same zodiac. We may calculate in like manner on the order of the political globe, which is destined in all its divisions of country to one series of risings and settings. Barbarians must have a chieftain ; the chieftain must have favourites : these are jealous, and quarrel, and stand apart. Each promises what great things he will do, for such as espouse his cause. A part of these benefits is granted, a part extorted. Hence the higher power by degrees is subdivided : but the principal holder of it is never quiet, until he can recover, by force or stratagem, what his interest led him to compromise, or his weakness to concede. That which is balanced can never long be stabile ; for a time it nods to the one side, for a time to the other ; but at last it falls to that where there are the most hands to drag it down ; hence Democracy. The exaltation of spirits which democracy produces in the body politic, and the envy and hatred which every king in its vicinity bears against it, are the causes of eloquence and of war. Popular chiefs are recommended for the army by popular orators : in these chiefs the habit of command abroad is succeeded by the flagrant lust of it at home. Clamours are raised ; advantage is taken of great abuses for the entrance of greater ; and from the slips of the theatre, thus thrown into confusion, comes Monarchy again in full plumage, sometimes alone and straightforward, sometimes in slower and statelier procession, through the yielding files of a bought and bowing aristocracy.

PENN. Thy wand, friend Mordaunt, hath well pointed out those monstrous signs, under which the industry and felicity of mankind have regularly been blasted.

As the arrow of Paris was directed from behind the brightest and most glorious of the heathen Gods, and occasioned the downfall of his native city, so hath ever that of Policy in later times from behind the fairer image of Christianity; and hath likewise caused the prostration, not of a city, not of a country, not of an empire, not of a continent, but of all God's higher creatures in every quarter of the civilised world. For, without these corruptions and abominations, can we believe that Mahomedanism would have risen up, like the Simoom from the Desert, and have thrown Truth upon her face, and stifled Wisdom, in their fairest regions, in their most ancient residences? or that the Gospel would not have penetrated long ago into the furthest recesses of this half-illumined Earth? Half-illumined do I call it? Long will it be, I fear, before a few scanty rays are to fall upon a fourth or fifth of it.

This [1] we owe to Popery; to her turbulence, her insolence, her fraudulence; to her rapacity, her persecutions, her lusts; to her contempt of good faith, of equitable government, of authority both divine and human. Now every establishment of a political church is Popery: every church having a head, which head is not Christ. So long as the pure is dipped in the impure, and left in it, so long as what ought to be the most simple is made the most splendid, and what belongs to the house of God is transferred to the house of parliament, there can not be true Christianity among the people.

The religion of Christ is peace and good will; the religion of Christendom is war and ill will. Popery hath set the worst examples, and hath maintained them the longest.

PETERBOROUGH. You appear to dislike the religion of Rome worse than any other modification of Christianity.

PENN. As being more remote from the simplicity of the Gospel, and as violating more of Christ's ordinances. Popery lives on the offal of men's vices.

PETERBOROUGH. Not she indeed : she has better dishes ; though these, if well dressed, are not amiss.

PENN. For shame ! for shame !

[1] 1st ed. reads : " PETERBOROUGH. This we owe . . . human. PENN. Every establishment," etc.

PENN AND PETERBOROUGH

PETERBOROUGH. Be generous ; be just. If the pope has a couch for Vice, he has also one for Virtue.

PENN. He is fraudulent to be domineering, and liberal to be enslaving.

Can anything be so insulting to equity and common sense, as that a gang of priests and friars should be the absolute and self-elected potentates, of enough territory and population to constitute a mighty commonwealth ? Alas ! and such was it ! With less than one-half of its present extent, it was the most potent, the most free, upon the earth. Let those who doubt, or rather who profess to doubt, which is best, arbitrary power or republican freedom, lift up their eyes, if their eyes can indeed be lifted up, to the contemplation, on the one side, of equal laws, of magistrates elected by the people, of frugal habits, of voluntary industry and adequate recompense : on the other, of insolent domination, of rulers imposed by force and maintained by terror, of dissolute manners, no less in the lowest than in the highest, not springing from abundance, but permitted and thrown out as a covering and contentment for privations, a narcotic that at once assuages and destroys the appetite ; then of gaming and beggary, which follow ; of dilapidated cities, of religious per-juries in the creating of saints to people them ; and the triple pestilence of priests, monks, and marshes, of which the last only ever intermits its ravages.

PETERBOROUGH. Vigorous description ! irresistible truth ! The father of lies himself cannot find a stone to throw against it : nevertheless I doubt whether you would bring over one convert, though you were permitted to preach it in the *Piazza di Spagna.*

PENN. I doubt it equally. Both in hearing and reading, men rather look for what suits their notions and opinions, than for what may alter and correct them. By which perversity they often lose much advantage and much pleasure ; since nothing is gained by taking up that which is already theirs ; no more than by sitting astride their own horses in their own stable yards. They remain there without progression, though they fume, and chafe, and bounce as high on the saddle as if they gallopped.

PETERBOROUGH. According to most systems of religion, it seems that the original design, and every botch made upon it, was to leave the greater part in shade, requiring glosses and interpretations, and consequently those who should be paid for making them and for keeping them in repair.

PENN. We have a God who is called the prince of peace : but we seem disposed to keep him in a long minority : and we are turning our eyes more fondly on another, whom we denominate the " Lord of Hosts."

O God of peace, Emanuel ! make us forgiving as thou wert forgiving, even on the cross ! make us tolerant, equitable, and humane !

PETERBOROUGH. I am glad you have stopped, William ! If you had gone on, I should have prayed myself : for prayers and gaping are contagious. Beside, in all likelihood, you would have prayed that no hirelings should enter the temple, as being contrary to the ordinances of Christianity : and then what the devil would become of our younger children, and chaplains, and college-tutors ? Knock down the peerage at once, or keep its props fast in the ground. I will never quarrel with any man about the Church ; but we may have a word or two and a blow or two about the Church establishment.

PENN. Not with me, I promise thee. What I think it wrong to hold, I give up readily. Let us return to our discourse on Rome again. Such is the pertinacity of popes to the system from which they, and their closer adherents, draw their sustenance, that they never abandon a proven falsehood or an iniquitous demand, nor ever resign a pretension once acted on, nor pardon a reclamation made on any side for redress. Hence bishops are still nominated for villages and ruins and rocks *in partibus infidelium ;* and hence the more precious privilege of holding an empire over empires. Every tie, human and divine, will be dissolved, entangled, or knotted, as suits the passions of the sitting pope, whose incubation is best warmed by ashes and blood. In the correspondence of Pius V. with Charles IX. and Mary de Medici, he orders her to combat the enemies of Popery *until they are all massacred.* Afraid that she might not understand him, or that she might think he spoke figuratively or passionately, he repeats the injunction a few lines below, and uses the words *utter extermination.* The Protestants, vanquished by the Duke of Anjou, implore his intercession with his royal brother : on hearing which, his *Holiness* writes to his *Nobleness,* that he ought through piety to be inexorable to all. Furthermore he tells the king that his Majesty will *tire God's patience* and provoke his anger. Suspecting that the gentle Charles might be influenced by the generosity of his brother, he commands him not to listen to the voice of friendship or of consanguinity. In another letter to Catherine, he says authoritatively, " Inflame the spirit of the King to annihilate the last remnant of civil war." Afterward, when peace was concluded, he writes thus to the Cardinal de Bourbon : " We expect you, in your prudence, to confound and overthrow the conditions of so pernicious a treaty. You owe this proof of zeal to God, to the King, and to the character you sustain."

No people are so deeply interested in abolishing the political power of Popery, as those who believe in its religious doctrines. For where such doctrines are coupled with such perfidy and cruelty, they expose the holders of them to the worst suspicions, in many cases unjustly.

And what is the inscription on the walls and doors of Roman Catholic churches and chapels ? is it any commandment from the Decalogue, any proverb from Solomon, any precept from Jesus Christ ? No : it is, " Pray for the souls " : and for what souls ? Not for thy own, which 'twere easier to darn before it is turning to tinder ; but for those in the fires of purgatory. *Praying* means *paying :* the substance of the prayer is a compost of pounds, shillings, and pence. The salt water at the font, into which everyone dips a finger, serves for tears ; and the money-box, nailed above it, for repentance. These are essential parts of the religion, and not accidents : but if they were accidents, and not essential parts, a prudent man would keep away from a labyrinth, at every turn and passage of which there is a thief to pick his pocket, to tie his hands behind him if he resists, and to gag him if he speaks a word. How long, O Lord !——

PETERBOROUGH. Ten to one, the Lord will give you no answer, friend William ! and in this instance I am more pious and resigned than you are ; for I never ask of him how long he will be about anything, particularly such as these, in which I know he likes to take his time. If you wish to know it, I can answer the question, and you need not look up into the clouds for its solution. It will be just as long as the rich can drive the poor before them, and the cunning can lead the rich. I wonder you should object to the order of priesthood, and to the quiet seizure of your property by this order, on your hesitation to deliver up as much of it as the venerable members may demand. Are they not wiser than you ?

229

PENN. They are wise in their generation.

PETERBOROUGH. That is enough for anybody.

PENN. Thou misunderstandest me.

PETERBOROUGH. Ho ! ho ! if I had taken the other sense, I should have replied, they ought to be, for they have a good deal of practice in it. Being wiser than you, which they tell you they are, and are ready to fight you with fists if you deny it, they know better than you do what they want, and what they are worth.

PENN. What they want they can not tell, forasmuch as their wants increase with their possessions ; but what they are worth we may well nigh guess.

PETERBOROUGH. They have texts from Scripture proving their divine right to tithes. The Jewish priesthood had them.

PENN. I do not deny their similitude to the Jews, if the old ones were like their descendants : but it pleased God to abolish this priesthood, and the law it followed.

PETERBOROUGH. It did not please God nor the servants of God to abolish tithes.

PENN. We must wait.

PETERBOROUGH. Indeed must you, and in the mean time count out your money. Now take another text : " The labourer is worthy of his hire."

PENN. Pay the labourer, if he *hath* laboured and thou hast hired him : if he hath never laboured, and if thou hast never hired him, bid him good morrow. Pay the labourer ; I repeat it ; but pay not the priest. If thou calledst him a clown or a hind, he would maltreat thee for miscalling him ; while he is fain to call thee somewhat less ; not clown or hind, but cattle. Use and custom reconcile men to anything ; otherwise there are of such tempers, that, on receiving so unseemly and rude an appellation, they would look into the hedge-row for some lithe ash-plant, and feel in their pockets for where-withal to cut it—that is, if no discreet friend were at their side to moderate their inclination and to withhold them.

PETERBOROUGH. Mounted on a stout contemplative black mare, with a bushy mane and tail, a broad white streak down the forehead, white likewise one fetlock and hoof.

PENN. Ay, ay, more likely to find him on such a creature, than on one opening and shutting his nostrils like a fop at a perfumer's ; one as ready to snap slily at his comrade as a competitor in the cabinet ; one touching the ground with the extremity of the foot whenever he stops for a moment, as though forsooth that same foot of his were a divining rod ; so important and majestical doth he appear to hold himself; a gelding with a silvery tail, and scarcely enough of it to whip a syllabub or fray a gossamer, with a body bright and flashy as a marigold, thin and bony as a Mordaunt, and just as unsteady, and trickish, and mettlesome ; and loud in his snorting as a young patriot under the hammer.

PETERBOROUGH. Egad ! if ever my gelding should be stolen, I will beg a copy of this description for an advertisement.

I see I must clap spurs again : we are off to the steeple-hunt.

Whatever may be objected to the Catholic faith, I find the members of it better-tempered people, when the pope and his *posse* do not stir them up, than other sects. Even the priests and monks, if you leave their temporals untouched and unthreatened, are jovial and rational. I have known many instances of it, for a person who has had so little to do with 'em ; one of which I am certain will amuse you.

When I was in Paris, I was admitted to visit a young lady of some attractions. Going out of the door, one morning, I met a capuchin on the steps. I had seen him in the street too frequently, and having remarked that he eyed me more curiously than I liked, I asked him somewhat fiercely what he wanted there. He bowed profoundly, and answered that he came to supplicate for relief to the necessities of the monastery.

" You capuchins and other monks," replied I, " never enter a house where there is only an ugly woman or a poor one."

Again he bowed, and more profoundly than before. " Sir," said he, " we have ugliness and poverty enough among ourselves : I came, as I told you, to obtain what the convent wanted."

I then observed that he was a handsome man, about thirty years of age, of a correctness in his language that indicated a good education, and of an easiness in his demeanour that mere impudence may lend for a moment, but can not long sustain ; it was such as gave me an assurance of high birth, and of excellent connections formed early. Vexed and ashamed that I had treated as a *roturier*, a gentleman whom perhaps nothing but the hope of gratifying his amiable passions had cowled and frocked, I shook him cordially by the hand, dropped a louis into his hood, and apologised for offering only the yellow of the egg, having but that part remaining from my collation. He hesitated a moment ; then said he never could object to partake my fast with me, and should be contented in future with a less complimentary distribution.

PENN. I have no proof before me that the capuchin, as thou callest the man, came to the female's house with any pravity of intention : yet he sinned ; forasmuch as, having made and sworn to vows of poverty, expressing the rejection of money, he received thy gold, knowing it to be gold, and other than, what thou calledst it, the yellow of an egg. Therefore, whatever might be the placidity of his temper, and certain, as thou wilt have it, that another day he fasted on the white, I can not in my conscience acquit him of offence.

If Popery however displays the dexterous filcher, the Church of England hath greatly the advantage over her in the exertion of brawny strength in the meadow and farm-yard. Neither the Catholic priesthood, nor any other that ever existed among men, even in times of ignorance and paganism, hath been so litigious and oppressive. In another age or two they may grow weary of kicking and cuffing us : but they will never cease to exhibit their agility and spirit in leaping over the palings of our corn-stacks, or their observance of the most rigid rules of right in watching our garden-gate for us, and weeding out the tithes of our beet and parsley. The Catholic priest, when he enters a family, bringeth at least a pretext of some spiritual concern, some confession to hear or some admonition to impart ; but your Church-of-England text-and-tithe collector holdeth in derision all such idle occupations, and intrudeth on your substance with a pistol in the fist, and with a curse upon the lip, as little a time in discharging.

Surely men can judge for themselves what instructor they shall place the most confidence in : as surely ought they to take his instruction rather than a stranger's, whose first step is intrusion, whose second is violence, and whose every succeeding one leaves defiance and hatred behind it. What wonder that the beneficent hand of Religion should be swollen, festered, and palsied, nailed as it hath been so long to the posts of Palace-yard ! If she be spiritual, she belongeth not to the state : if she be carnal, she belongeth not to heaven.

Is not religion, of any plain, honest, unadulterated kind, as easily taught as morality ? Again, is it not taught as easily as agriculture

232

or chemistry ? Yet we have no establishment, no order of citizens set apart for teaching one or other of these, and demanding from the remainder, willing or unwilling, a tenth of the produce of their land, and another tenth of their labour upon it : though agriculture and chemistry require more study, more exertion, more attention, more precision, than the acquiring and holding forth of those dogmas, which, while they tell us to love our neighbour——

PETERBOROUGH. As ourselves : a thing impossible.

PENN. If thou findest it so, leave it a little on the way side, and let me go on. The dogmas of your gentry in lawn and purple, while they persuade us to love our neighbour, order us also to damn him everlastingly ; and are slower, I opine, than the other two sciences, those of agriculture and chemistry, in giving the labourer a clean shirt and good dinner, and in shutting out the fiercer or the subtler marauders, from which no path of life is exempt, active in spring and autumn, active in winter and summer, at undermining or battering his frail corporeal tenement.

PETERBOROUGH. People must be imposed upon for their good. He who said in his heart that all men are liars, was none himself on that occasion. Lies and liars are the things and persons the most necessary in our sublunary condition ; and without a tinge of falsehood the colours of the fairest character are faint.

PENN. Hold : hold ! or I whip thy horse before me, since I may not ride faster. One would think the cloven hoof surmounted the uncloven.

PETERBOROUGH. I will proceed more circumspectly. Grant me this. A man in a wig gains credit, where one with a cropped head would be kicked out of doors. In religion too, a white hand waves about it more persuasion than a browner ; and a hairy one in church would be looked at as suspiciously as Esau's. My father was fond of repeating two couplets, which he was likewise fond of attributing to a maiden aunt : she, however, although the stoutest of episcopalians, disclaimed them.

> Little that theologian teaches
> Under whose text hang tattered breeches.
> Devil take him who disbelieves
> Verities shaken from lawn-sleeves.

PENN. There is soundness of observation in the first stave of the canticle : let us hope that so sedate and curious an observer spake the remainder more in levity than in malice. Otherwise it were well if we ascribed it to the sudden influx of melancholic humour, which we may collect from the import of the words preceding.

PETERBOROUGH. Even had we no establishments, we should still have sects.

PENN. What then ? whom would they fight for ? who would pay them ? Although there were no establishments, there might indeed be sects in religion, as there anciently were in philosophy : yet either we must suppose that Christianity is prouder and crueller and more avaricious than philosophy, or we must admit that establishments, and not Christianity, have, wherever they existed, raised such tumults, seized upon such wealth, and shed (O blessed Redeemer, was not thine enough !) such torrents of human blood. If philosophy has not done it with her sects, neither would Christianity have done it with hers, without her purple and pretorians. These are as unfriendly to the one as to the other ; and, while they exist upon earth, the more civilised parts of it can expect no better state, long together, than external wars, internal discord, and universal oppression. Revolutions may for a while relieve them ; chastisement and the fear of it may render the princes more conciliatory and submissive : but the poison will be poured again into the drowsy ear, by those upon whose pillow they slumber. Hence even the recluse and quiet reasoner will be tempted to point toward the natives of these wilds : and someone, in the moroseness of sad triumph, will say to the inhabitant of the city, Are not such men more happy, are not they more virtuous, are not they more dignified, and, O slave, so bruised and abject as to be insensible to thy slavery ! are not they more deeply enlightened, more vitally wise, than thou ?

PETERBOROUGH. There is a strange idea gone abroad for a long time, and moving about much at its ease, by which we are to understand that *minister* means *master ;* the exact opposite of its original and right import. Thus the ministers of the church call themselves the church, and the ministers of the state are the state. Now, in my humble opinion, the state is composed of all the *people* in it, and the church of all the *Christians.* If this opinion is correct, and ever should be acted on consistently, what will become of our princely hierarchy ? And may it not happen that some of those who carry white and black rods, shall lay them aside, and with equally kind

234

officiousness help the traveller to mount at the inn-door, and snatch his skirt from between him and the saddle-bag ?

PENN. Political institutions, or *establishments*, should be founded on Christianity, and not Christianity on them. This perverts the order of things ; which order, insomuch as passive example can effect, we would set right. But what is example, what is reason, what is Christianity itself, in opposition to the force of wealth under the shield of government ! Every rich family sees or imagines its interest in the present system, which, whatever it may be called, is no better nor other than Popery in any state throughout Europe ; and every poor one hopes it, excepting those few who look to one rule of faith, under one immutable and immortal teacher, where they indeed find room enough to place their interests and rest their hopes.

Nothing can exceed the impudence of men pretending to be Christians, professing to follow the ordinances of Christ, reproaching the pope for his perversion of them, and themselves at the same time violating the most positive and unequivocal command of our blessed Lord and Saviour : " Call no man your *father* upon earth : for one is your father, which is in heaven." Now, though dignities of state were left untouched, dignities, as men vainly call them, in religion are here distinctly and solemnly forbidden. I say nothing of the prevarications and perjuries that must be crossed to reach them. Can the calmest face, can the best-plaited lawn-sleeves, can the highest-drawn pink stockings, can the comeliest thigh-cases,[1] the most nicely puckered at the knee-band, or can the most virginal apron, do away with or cover this ? In the ritual of the Apostles there was no string of prayers ordained, no dressing and undressing in the public place of worship, no pagan ceremonies, no other precedency than eldership. Priests, we have heard, were appointed to put down the devil. If they have been seventeen centuries about it, and could neither do it while they were holier men and worked miracles, nor afterward, when they became less holy but more wise, and had learned all his tricks and devices, it is time methinks they should give in, and own themselves worsted. If, on the contrary, they have put him down, or if he has been put down without them, or if we have brought him to decent terms, or if he lieth quiet by his fireside of his own accord, and we no longer feel ourselves in danger

---

[1] 1st ed. reads : " comeliest breeches, the most nice puckered at the knee-band, do away," etc.

from him, we may just as reasonably and constitutionally demand from parliament the disbanding of them as of any other body of troops, appointed for any other service, when that service hath been performed. But if, after so many thousand years, he fighteth only the more desperately for the blows he hath received, I would try other methods of attack and other implements of warfare, or I would keep myself shut up close in my fastnesses at home. Are scouts and watchmen here likewise necessary ? Enow of men for the purpose will ever be remaining, whose vanity and ambition, whose love of teaching and of talking, whose impatience to display a fine voice, a fine person, a fine gesture, a fine doctrine, a fine metaphor, will clothe them in the garb of piety, and place them astride the gate of the sheepfold. Furthermore, let us hope that better inducements will exist at all times, and that the necessities of the soul will be supplied in their due season ; that every father and mother, every experienced man, every considerate woman, will exercise the duties of private life and social, by inculcating those morals wherefrom arise the listener's content and the teacher's security ; and which, if no other benefit accrued from them, would detruncate our rank expenditure on the three most wasteful and unprofitable of consumers : on him who carries the sword in his hand ; and on those two wilier ones who carry it in their mouths, flaming and empoisoned.

PETERBOROUGH. But Christ himself said, if what I fancy I once heard at a sermon is exact, which indeed it may not be, for I was half-asleep, " I bring not peace, but a sword."

PENN. Christ never said anything like it ; for Christ never contradicted his own doctrine. We find the words among better ; and we find them attributed to him : falsely, falsely. No construction can ever make Christ a murderer ; though his name hath been used among men for hardly any other purpose. Either the words were reversed by accident, which is the more charitable supposition ; or were corrupted by design, which I am afraid is the more probable and correct one. Some conciliatory and harmonizing theologians would assure us, that they never were changed, interpolated, or transposed ; and that they signify the hard service of the first Christians, and the persecutions they must suffer. This is foretold plainly enough in other places : *here* the expression would show the *object* of Christ's mission, and not its accidents ; that he came to bring slaughter, and not peace. Therefore, even if we found it in

236

PENN AND PETERBOROUGH

the writings of all his disciples and of all his apostles, in the same terms, we should at once reject it ; because it never could have been said by the person who proclaimed universal good-will and unqualified forbearance, supposing him sent, as we do, by the God of mercies, and breathing the spirit of truth.

PETERBOROUGH. There is one text of Scripture, and only one, upon which all establishments and sects agree, excepting yours : which makes them all think you an unconscionable set of people.

PENN. That text doth not occur to me at the present time.

PETERBOROUGH. Priests and rulers preach and proclaim it incessantly ; and, what is more remarkable, act as they proclaim and preach.

PENN. Canst thou repeat it ?

PETERBOROUGH. " Kill and eat."

It appears to me that there was more Christianity before Christ than there has been since.

PENN. Hast thou any objection that there should be more after than there was before ?

PETERBOROUGH. None at all.

PENN. Let us then begin to speed it, and to recover as much time as we can. It consoleth me to find that thou occasionally dost think on worship.

PETERBOROUGH. I have left it off.

PENN. What was thy motive ; if indeed thou didst not drop away from it through lightness of mind ?

PETERBOROUGH. I dropped away from it through piety itself.

PENN. I am afraid to question thee further, lest thou say aught irreverent.

PETERBOROUGH. Reverence urged me. The clergyman told us repeatedly that we were all children of Satan, and ordered us in the next breath to turn him out of doors. Lear's children were detestable for this very proceeding : yet Lear was neither older nor madder, nor was he worse pelted.

Religion is apt to wince if you handle her quarters near her stalls and mangers. Here however one may treat her as having grown more tractable : and since her price is out of the question, and no dealer is within ear-shot, we may express a wish that those usually about her had consulted their own interests better, and had

237

attempted to show us that she can bring us to happiness somewhat less circuitously, and without relay and baiting.

PENN. The road hath been pointed out unto us by the same divine hand that made us ; and such is, and such was ever, our hanging back, I do not wonder that God repented of creating man.

PETERBOROUGH. Nor I, since he must have foreknown the trouble we should give him, and that we should be even less obedient to his Son than our first progenitor had been to *him*. But it is surely by some unfair interpretation, that the living God is represented to us as hardening the heart of Pharaoh, expressly that he might disobey his commands ; which disobedience caused the death of that king, and of thousands with him ; of thousands who were innocent even of having their hearts hardened, on the contrary, who were engaged at the very moment in bringing God's tragedy to the close, and performing the duty which he himself inculcates, of obedience to the prince.

PENN. Worm ! worm ! thou wouldst question the Lord.

PETERBOROUGH. Not I indeed ; but I would question those who dress him in their own dirty suits, to frighten folks out of their senses and their money. And even them I would let pass on, when I had joked or reasoned them into a passion : for I am as much an episcopalian at heart as any of them, and see the matter in the same light. Nevertheless I can allow my zeal for the Church of England to subside a little, in compliance with the humours of the weak and lukewarm ; and indeed I hoped to fall in with your opinions and feelings, when I showed the folly and culpability of men who would represent our Creator as inconsistent and cruel.

PENN. We appeal to the Gospel, not to the old Jews.

PETERBOROUGH. Perhaps there are some reasons why I should hit upon the old Jews first. Now then we here have done with them : and I beg you to give me a little light on the sepulchre of our Saviour, as there appears to be some discordance in the history of those who visited it, and of those who were found at it by the visitors, and in the number of times that their master came among them afterward.

PENN. Follow thou the righteousness of Christ, his gentleness, his forbearance ; and leave his ascension to the more speculative, and his sepulchre to the more devout.

PETERBOROUGH. Would he, with such righteousness, such gentle-

238

ness, such forbearance, have treated Ananias and Sapphira as Peter his successor did ? Certainly the popes descend in a right line from this prince of the apostles ; who very properly bears in his statue the head of Jupiter the thunderer. If he really did toward Ananias and Sapphira, what we are bound to believe he did, he neglected the example and disobeyed the commands of his master, and he infringed the laws and usurped the magistrature of his country. Would any modern king, Christian or Mahomedan or idolater, would any republic of any age, permit a private man to enforce, under pain or threat of death, so rigid and bitter an equality ? Would you yourselves, who come nearest to the discipline of Christ, insist upon it ? I do not ask whether you would point out for reprobation, I do not ask whether you would strike with extinction, a virtuous, generous, unsuspicious couple, who had given to the indigent the greater part of their possessions. Extinction for what crime ? the crime of holding back from their enthusiastic prodigality a slender pittance, with an object perhaps as justifiable and as sacred as charity itself. Their motives were unexamined, their cause unheard. We may suppose them desirous of repurchasing some quiet country-house, some shady little meadow, some garden with its trellised alcove or its woodland path at the end of it, the scene of their earliest tenderness and first caresses. There may be things about us so dear to us, that we should almost bear our soundest flesh to be cut away, before we could surrender them to another ; and from a feeling so very different from avarice, that the avaricious man is perhaps the only one who is quite incapable of it. There are localities that have in them somewhat of an identity with ourselves : insomuch that, in almost all ages and countries, the poets have appealed to their consciousness : and poets search out and seize on resemblances of truth, even more striking than truth itself.

PENN. What does that prove ?

PETERBOROUGH. It proves the affection we may naturally bear to certain parts of property, consistently with the most generous spirit, the most exuberant and profuse liberality. We [1] must believe the sudden and almost simultaneous death of this unfortunate couple to have been designed and exhibited by Saint Peter, in order to strike terror into the disobedient, who might withhold from the common stock any particle of their property.

[1] From " We " to " PETERBOROUGH " added in 2nd ed.

IMAGINARY CONVERSATIONS: AMERICAN

PENN. Be candid, be just and veracious. Remember, he told Ananias it had been at his option to give in, or decline to give in, the whole; to enter or not enter into that society of Christians which agreed to hold all property in common. The punishment of perfidy was exemplary, but not severe : it was striking, but not painful. Thou appearest to intimate that the apostle called it down on the offender, who brought it on his own head. The chastisements of the Almighty may (we hope) be averted, never can they be accelerated or aggravated, by human prayer. Paul, after his conversion, never was intolerant or inhumane.

PETERBOROUGH. As we can not see clearly, though we may suspect, the aim of such an institution, let us try whether we can not find out the natural and necessary end of it. Nearly all Christian sects, and mostly the episcopalian, have greatly corrected the practice of the apostles : which they never would have done if it had been ordained by God. So much my mother the Church of England will not permit me to doubt of : and now from the motives we will proceed to the results. You, who calculate better than I do, may inform me how long could have existed, if the laws had allowed it, the order of society laid down by Saint Peter, for those who followed the apostles. Since it was necessary that all the new Christians should sell their property, the purchasers would have the whole at nearly their own price. Hence the greatest misfortune that could befall the faithful would be the propagation of the faith itself. If the apostles worked with equal zeal and success, and converted the rich as well as the poor, where could they find purchasers ? They sold both lands and houses : where would the people live in winter ? For the mountainous parts (and nearly all Judea is of that quality) are cold and stormy. In the imagery of the Psalms, we find flakes of snow and violent winds and tempests. After the sale and alienation of their houses, both sexes must herd together. In fact, they did so ; and their guides were, in the nature of things, obliged to make loud and incessant complaints against certain immoralities, which they did not or would not believe to be dependent on their own system, and inevitable in it.

But my main and plain question is, how long could the money have lasted ? Certainly not for two whole generations : what then would have become of the next ?

PENN. We want leisure, and pen, ink and paper, for these calcula-

240

PENN AND PETERBOROUGH

tions. The Lord would have taken care that nothing should be deficient for such as believed in him.

PETERBOROUGH. I am answered.

PENN. Ride on then in quietness and sobriety. Every child, six or seven years old, thinks his father can do everything and knows everything : and we smile at his simplicity. Are there no intelligences that smile at ours, who, in the meridian and maturity of the faculties, so act toward others and toward ourselves, as if our father in the heavens knew nothing and could do nothing ? The little boy of that age, whom thou tellest he is older than the great and strong coach-horse, will disbelieve thee, forming his idea of age from size and strength : again thou smilest at such simplicity : yet here the reasoning powers are coming into action, although the powers of reflection are yet dormant and inert : here likewise I could point out to thee in riper years a worse and weaker inconsistency of unbelief.

Law should provide that the inhabitants of the land be brought up religiously : but never let her dandle Religion in her lap, play with her at the desk, cater for her, pamper her with sweetmeats, indulge her in childish freaks and acrimonious passions, teach her cant and cozenage, mimic steps and sidelong glances, and take her thus accomplished into partnership.

PETERBOROUGH. I never was fond of questioning or debating on matters in which I have no practice or skill : otherwise I would ask how it happens that you, the most remote of all Christians from the papists, employ nevertheless excommunication. If going to places of worship is good and needful, it certainly is most so in those who have done wrong. The pope on the contrary does not wait for an incorrigible fault : the moment an order of his is transgressed, let the offence itself be the lightest possible, he shuts the doors of Saint Peter in the face of the transgressor, and forbids him to say his prayers and seek forgiveness in any church upon earth.*

PENN. We have nothing to do with such a fisherman, or such fish. We never excommunicate, while the moral character of the sinner hath a sound or curable part left, or while a hope survives of reclaiming him. We can not issue an arbitrary order, nor receive one. Paul recommends to his disciple Titus, that he should admonish a

* Qui contra mandatum hoc nostrum fecerit, is universæ Dei ecclesiæ toto orbe terrarum expers esto.—W. S. L.

heretic *once or twice ;* and, if he can not convert him, that he should *leave* him : a punishment (if one at all) very different from the pulley and the gridiron. And what was heresy in those early days ? Not a diversity of opinion on a metaphysical point, for such questions were started later, but a rash determination to set aside the ordinances of Christ himself, at that time the sole authority and guide. Moderate as this chastisement is——

PETERBOROUGH. Chastisement !

PENN. Without talking of chastisement we can not talk agreeably with any denomination of Christians. Paul, I was about to remark, is severer than his master, who orders that the admonition shall be repeated *thrice*.

PETERBOROUGH. How ! alter his master's message at his humour ! and scratch out the best line in it !

PENN. He hath only too much zeal.

PETERBOROUGH. All the rogues that ever lived have brought little misery upon the world, in comparison with those who had too much zeal.

PENN. True : but take heed lest thy mouth offend, and thy speech give offence.

PETERBOROUGH. I am called an infidel ; and an infidel I am : but is my infidelity so mischievous in itself, or in its consequences, as the conduct of that man who exaggerates the words or changes the directions of his master ?

In what and against whom am I an infidel ? At worst I do not find reason enough to believe what others do. If I believe I see a tree, it may not be a tree : but how can I help believing that I see a tree ? and if I see no tree, and can not by any stretch of vision see it, will the smoke of faggots mend my eyesight ?

Do not groan, William, nor let your arms hang down in that manner : for, if your mare should stumble among these old charred roots, it might do somewhat worse, I apprehend, than blacken your dove-coloured thigh-case.

PENN. Wonderful, but saddening to the soul, unless we had better hopes from better justice ! Whoever thinks worthily of God is in danger of being styled an atheist, and whoever would frame his will to the rules of the divine one, a visionary, an enthusiast, or a hypocrite. Fears and formularies, received by men from men, are called religion ; belief and trust in Providence, truth, kindness, equity, mere things of this world. O ! were they so, were they so indeed ! then the confines of this world would touch and almost be confounded with the other ; and our hearts and imaginations might every day take exercise and repose there. Why are so many folks necessary with parliaments and penalties, with castles and battlements and bayonets and bells, to make us of a true religion ? Why are we in a state of despondency without plush, and damned without the dyer ? We friends are reprobated : wherefore ? because we offer no sureties to God for infants whom we may never see after they grow up, and about whose conduct it is deemed needless to be solicitous, and unbecoming to be inquisitive ; because we have no hand laid for a moment on our heads in childhood to make us upright and steady for life ; because [1] we do not take a morsel of bread and a sip of wine in the morning, to remind us of eating a supper, of which others were in fact the eaters.

PETERBOROUGH. This part at least of the vital in religion is, methinks, what the imitators might imitate better, with little pains.

PENN. I do not approve of thy scoffing at the *vital in religion*.

PETERBOROUGH. Friend Penn ! every man hath his favourite guard and pass. You made several lunges at the midriff ; I made but one.

PENN. Thy words were inconsiderate, and might become a stumbling-block of offence.

PETERBOROUGH. I now perceive, my worthy friend, no man ever fought for religion : it was for some little idol which his own heart had fashioned, or which, whether bought or given or snatched up and run off with, he carried in secret under his doublet, either to help him in his crimes or to keep him at least from punishment. You need none such : but every kind of love must have its object ; self-love among the rest, an object the most distinct and definite.

PENN. Thou art hard upon me : and yet, who knoweth whether God hath not given thee on this occasion the spirit of truth, to strike me the more forcibly. I have suspected in myself the thing thou sayest : nay, I have found it, and have cast it out. It may have entered again under the haze of zeal, and have stood invisible in the high place, in the rock of Zion, in the shadow of the temple.

---

[1] 1st ed. reads : " because we do not sit down on our knees with a book for the sake of society, nor take a morsel," etc.

Come over unto us ! come over unto us ! come into our camp ! and thou shalt rejoice with exceeding great joy.

PETERBOROUGH. I am not so wild : I am on leave of absence.

PENN. Be persuaded at least that with us excommunication is according to the command of Christ, although in churches it be not. Excommunication precluded no man formerly from the enjoyment of legal protection and of civil rights ; but only from the communion of believers, from their assemblies, their contrition, and their fasts : a penalty by no means intolerable to people of such a turn.

PETERBOROUGH. I could have borne it myself, though none of the meekest. These humble men however would not let their superiors sit quiet.

PENN. Thou wrongest them. When they grew rich they grew restless.

PETERBOROUGH. I could have cured this disorder in them.

PENN. Even bishops, and those of Rome too, so far from assailing the rulers of the world, requested and implored their protection : so far from excommunicating them, as they did afterward, and ordering their subjects to rebel against them, they came forward as suppliants for gratuities and favours ; and boasted of deserving them, by having prayed in their churches for the safety of the prince and the prosperity of the empire.

PETERBOROUGH. Ho ! ho ! they did, did they ? I always had heard and believed that our own holy fathers bore no resemblance whatsoever to the old ones : I see they differ little in essentials.

PENN. Christianity, in my view of her, not only makes us able to bear our sufferings, but in great measure to avoid them ; not only to obey, but to select the proper objects of obedience. She enlarges the intellectual and moral world about us : and by this enlargement the horrible signs of thy zodiac, friend Mordaunt, if gape upon us they must, will gape upon us after longer intervals. But I trust that a new order of things hath commenced and will continue. In England you may want perhaps, for some time longer, kings, bishops, chancellors, lords : in America our wishes are humble and tranquil, by not having such objects of excitement and delight before our eyes. We shall be contented with equality of rank and right, with honest unpresuming plain-spoken Christianity, and with a paternal distribution of uncostly justice.

PETERBOROUGH. Though addicted to no particular system of philosophy or religion or government, I am convinced that if you destroy the institutions and customs of men, however bad a great part of these may be, you also chill the blood of their attachments, which are requisite for the prosperity and indeed for the safety of nations. At the same time, I am not sorry to find you setting an example here of sobriety and forbearance. These virtues will gradually allure and conciliate many, by the wealth and respectability attendant on them. If, however, all Englishmen were at once such as the Society of Friends, they would have their throats cut before the next harvest : a consideration which has hindered the greater and better part of Christianity from being yet admitted in any European state.

PENN. My young friend, genius with thee is like the bird of paradise, all wing : should it wish to alight and settle on anything, it finds under it no support.

PETERBOROUGH. Penn, I was once a great admirer of Rochefoucauld, and fancied his *Maxims* were oracles. It happened that, quoting them one day at dinner, my adversary told me I had reversed the sentiment : I found I had. Upon this, I began to reverse, for curiosity's sake, almost every third sentence of my shrewd and smart philosopher ; and discovered that, like superfine cloth, they look as comely the wrong side outward as the right, wherever I could give as easy and quick a turn as that of the original. This persuaded me that we receive for the wisest things the gracefullest and the boldest, and that what are called speculative truths are in general not only unimportant, but no truths at all. Industry, cleanliness, equanimity, beneficence, are the intelligible parts of your system : these constitute civilisation, and will not suffer it, I hope, to slide or bulge or decline. It is quite a new and ingenious thought, to try whether Christianity can stand alone : and the experiment is well worthy of our attention.

PENN. Thou speakest with levity and indifference, young man, upon matters of eternal interest.

PETERBOROUGH. I know nothing, I must repeat it, about these affairs ; but I have experienced that some of eternal interest, if there be any such in reasoning, ought to be held as lightly as a rapier, or they may be twisted out of our grasp into the air. Having asked the discreet and pious of several persuasions, whether in their judgment God alone is uncreated, infinite, and eternal, each, however he might differ from the rest on other topics, replied in the affirmative. What an opinion must I form on the perversion of the human mind, afraid as I find it everywhere of admitting that time and space must also be eternal, infinite, and uncreated ! Day [1] and night only mark time out, and are in regard to it what clocks and watches are. God himself, although he may be said to extend through all space, can not be said to extend any farther : yet what is *through* is *beyond*. Are we not here in want of terms ?

PENN. Rather,[2] in want of curbs, to check us on a precipice.

Those doctors you have cited would have acted more judiciously and honestly in owning that they knew nothing about the business, and that it is a question which our Saviour did not come upon earth to agitate or to solve. We have already more knowledge than we are disposed to bring into use : when we have well practised the whole of it, perhaps he who gave us it may give us more. One would imagine that the wisdom of those who govern might be better for a supply now and then from the wisdom of those who reason in retirement. Instead of which, politicians and philosophers are the two classes of men the most opposite in the world, standing with their eyes fixed one upon the other, in suspicion, or indignation, or scorn. The most extravagant are the oftenest quoted : but it is merely to exhibit the futility of innovation or reform. I do not assert that there is a single axiom in Plato, which a minister in any country or any age ought to receive and act on : but many of them, taking up his fame when it suits their purpose, announce him as a high authority, holding in derision those who stand nearer, such as Harrington and Milton, superior to him in gravity and in virtue.

PETERBOROUGH. I remember one axiom of the divine man, which every minister in my time has both received and acted on.

PENN. Although I perused his dialogues on polity a little while ago, I can not recollect it.

PETERBOROUGH. He forbids the use of falsehood to the community at large, but allows it to the rulers : just as the papal priests do with the wine at the sacrament, giving it one to the other, but withholding it from the people. Plato calls it a medicine, and tells us we must concede it to the physician, in order that we may use it as he pleases ; but we must let no other man meddle with it. Surely, my friend

---

[1] From " Day " to " terms " added in 2nd ed.
[2] From " Rather " to " precipice " added in 2nd ed.

PENN AND PETERBOROUGH

Penn, you can not deny that persons in authority, with us, cherish this Platonic sentiment with somewhat more than Platonic affection.

PENN. I grieve at the man's vacuity, who imagines that falsehood, of all vices the easiest to take root and the hardest to extirpate, is likely to be long in overrunning the country, when the breath of those who govern us blows it abroad at will, in every direction. Beside, did he not see that, sooner or later, the lie must be exposed? and that not only the bad example would ramify in the closest and most sheltered concerns of life, but that the government itself must be rendered unstable, when the governors were found cheats and liars.

PETERBOROUGH. He would not permit the soldiers to reside in the city.

PENN. In other words, he would not permit them to care a farthing for the townsmen they are to protect : in that case a slight matter would incline them to the invader.

PETERBOROUGH. Not at all : he provides against it, by informing them it is idle and sacrilegious to aspire after the poor corrupt money current upon earth.

PENN. They would buffet him for an impostor, or tie him to his bedpost for a madman.

PETERBOROUGH. He has provided against that also. He tells them another story first : he says to them, " You and your arms and your equipments sprang up from the bosom of your mother Earth. You must protect your mother Earth, and likewise her weaker children, your little brother fellow-citizens. As for gold, the Almighty mixed a quantity of it in your primary conformation, which adapts and entitles you to command ; while in your little brother fellow-citizens he mixed up only brass and iron, rendering them fitter for artisans and husbandmen."

PENN. I remember this foolery.

PETERBOROUGH. Now tell me, friend Penn, whether you yourself are not, in some sort, equally liable to be taken for a visionary.

PENN. Thou mayst take me for a visionary, friend Mordaunt, but thou shalt never take me for a liar.

PETERBOROUGH. Of that indeed there is no danger. I would have added the chief reason on which you might appear as a visionary to many, or rather indeed to most people.

PENN. Prythee add it : since, should it be wanting, I see not how thou mayst so soon correct me.

PETERBOROUGH. You fancy we can live without war.

PENN. That is, I fancy we can live without slaughter. It sounds absurdly, no doubt. A strange fancy, a hot, wild, wrong-headed aspiration, in me and my brethren! No wonder thou laughest at so novel, so irregular, so awkward a stretch and strain of my humble and squat imagination.

PETERBOROUGH. Do you believe that others would let you remain quiet, and admire, with uplifted and united palms, your industry and your innocence? or rather that to flourish is not to invite the visit and quicken the appetite of spoliation? Do you expect that the bad man will forbear because the good man will?

PENN. I believe that the desire of possession is universal, or nearly; that it may produce good, and that it may produce evil. Property is the bond and seal of civilisation. The sight of it, however, will arouse in those who have it not, and in some also who have it, the lust of violating it. Prisons and chains and halters are coarse reproofs at best. If we would be rather less dignified, and rather more humane, we should be safer and usefuller. Can not we go among those whom we suspect of rapacity or cruelty, and speak tenderly with 'em, and remonstrate reasonably? Can we not lead them to our garners, our growing corn, our furrows, and say to them, " These very things which you so much covet are your own upon the same conditions as they were ours or our fathers'. They were laboured *for* before they were laboured *in*. Believe me, friends, there is less *wear and tear* in the body and in the mind to obtain them as we have done than as you would do. Doubtless you love your children : provide then for them, as ye may with certainty, by teaching them how to provide for themselves ; how to be out of want and danger, out of grief and sorrow ; how to form those marriages which will bring them into peaceful and plentiful houses, where they will be welcome and respected."

Reason, preceding a chastisement, forming no portion of it, and unconnected with it, has an effect on all ; following one, it comes as a scoff, or as a section of the sentence.

Ideas of property can not be very correct where there is little distribution of it ; and those whom we call savages we often may find thieves. But heavier injustice is done every six months in our English court of chancery, the Acropolis of Themis, than by all the savages on our borders in as many years. I have found them universally just, whenever I argued patiently and mildly, and greatly more calm and civil than our silken sergeants. Men are never very unjust until they see and enter and grope their way along the perplexities and subterfuges of law. Feeling at first no reluctance to run into it, they experience at last no compunction to run through it.

In England the statutes are often in opposition to religion, and religion to God's anointed, as you call the thing. Why can not both together rest upon one foundation ? Is Christ unable or unworthy to lead us ? reject him then totally. But if his example and precepts are such as of themselves can make us virtuous and happy, should we not follow them without any deviation ; and without stopping at any half-way house, to assemble a riotous and roaring party, to elect a toast-master, to booze and confound our intellects, to quarrel and fight, to slaver and slumber, and, after such heartiness and manliness, to toss about and tumble, and find ourselves at last unfit for the prosecution of our journey. Our master doth not permit us to compromise and quarter with another : he doth not permit us to spend an hour with him and then to leave him. Either our actions must be regulated by him wholly, both individually and socially, both politically and morally, or he turns us out. We must resign the vanities and vices, the prostrations and adorations, of the heathen world altogether, or avoid his presence ! We must call no others by his name, until those others shall possess the same authority and power. He did not place himself, great as he was, on the tribunitial chair with Cæsar, nor on the judgment-seat with Felix : he governed, but it was in spirit ; he commanded, but it was of God. Christianity could never have been brought into contempt or disrepute, unless she had been overlaid with false ornaments and conducted by false guides. Her expounders and high priests, in all monarchies, are prompt and propense to be keepers of the regalia, and studious how they shall be, externally and intrinsically, as unlike as possible to the disciples and apostles.

PETERBOROUGH. I am afraid, my friend William, you will generally find men of genius indifferent to the externals of religion.

PENN. What are its externals ? Canst thou point out to me the place where vitality and feeling commence, in this purest and most delicate of existences ? By *externals* thou canst mean nothing but *administration*. Men of genius then, I am to suppose, are utterly

249

indifferent to the administration of religion and law, if the law or the religion in themselves be good.

PETERBOROUGH. I did not say law.

PENN. I insist that religion is law : not the law of popes and parliaments, but the law of God. I do not contend that it is graven on the heart of man : nevertheless I must ever think that the heart of man is the better and the richer for receiving it. I will not assert to thee that corn was scattered by Providence on each side of us : yet how pleasantly these green waves do rustle in the air, whispering to us of divine bounty, and displaying to us how much better is a state of peace and industry, than of ferocity and idleness. And what is genius ? so elevated in its disdain, so glorious in its indifference ! This is a question, one would conceive, to be solved more easily. I will not take it however, where thou wouldst rather let it lie, from among our dialecticians ; although there can be no great genius where there is not profound and continued reasoning. I will not lead thee to Hooker or Taylor, or that loftier man now living, Isaac Barrow, but among those rather who delighted more in the excursions of fancy and imagination ; which the above-mentioned had not to seek, but entertained with equal fondness and better mastery at home. Was Chaucer then indifferent ? was Spenser ? was Milton ? Did they not all oppose abuses and corruptions ? did they not all turn the acuteness of their wit on these externals ? By the help of God, my own industry shall be employed in brushing off the tender-bellied grubs from the beautiful plant which I hope to leave behind me, flourishing in this wilderness. We friends are reported to believe too little : yet we believe that God can hear our voices five feet eight inches from the pavement, as easily as with the calves of our legs tucked up against our breech, and leaving us but four feet above-ground.

PETERBOROUGH. This is only a childish trick : who would object to it, or care about it ?

PENN. It is among those postures and pranks which enable the bustling and authoritative of the place to pick our pockets, and master us, and hold us down, and scourge us, at their greater convenience. The plainest and simplest things are the wholesomest ; mostly of all in religion. Peace and equity are its only ends : if no system in Europe hath yet produced them, it is time to try another : for without them, we are not Christians, and but corporeally men.

PENN AND PETERBOROUGH

PETERBOROUGH. Some latitude, some dignity, should be allowed to religion, in highly civilised nations.

PENN. What would be thy feeling, if a simple beauty were introduced at court in silks and flounces and rubies, and spoke the first sentence in her own plain homely dialect, the second in the conventional language of the palace ? Surely the maiden would lose thereby much of her loveliness in thy sight, even though thy passions had been engaged : how much more then must Christianity lose in the like condition, when the passions are very far indeed from any engagement in her behalf !

PETERBOROUGH. I can not answer that satisfactorily : and can you answer me any more so, when I ask whether you do not wander from your own principles, and from the command of Jesus Christ, in refusing to pay taxes and tithes ? Your master says, " Give unto Cæsar the things that are Cæsar's, and unto God the things that are God's."

PENN. He doth ; and we obey him.

PETERBOROUGH. How ! by refusing the surrender of tithes and taxes, you obey the gospel, or the higher powers !

PENN. Certainly ; the higher powers are God and his eternal justice. After giving up to God all that belongeth to him, prythee, friend Mordaunt, what remaineth to Cæsar ? Verily that broken switch in thy hand, or that foam about thy horse's bridle, would overpay him his right demands. He who delivered the ordinance, enabled those to whom he delivered it, to understand its import.

PETERBOROUGH. It is pity that everything in the *New Testament* is not plain and explicit.

PENN. No pity at all : it is explicit and plain enough for whoever is earnest to emend his life by it. The little that is difficult to comprehend, serves to occupy attention and stimulate inquiry. Thou mightest say, it would be better still, if everything it conveyeth were impressed upon the heart, without any book whatever. Not so : the human heart and intellect want exercise and excitement ; and the eye is the first organ of meditation, although in the end meditation is abstracted from the visual sense, and every other. Many are no less mistaken in an opposite judgment on the *New Testament,* and imagine there is more philosophy in abstruser volumes. Such volumes being merely didactic, should be clearer, more systematic, more explanatory. If the authors could have rendered them so, they would have done it ; just as the maker of glass would have made it whiter. Nothing is easier to men of genius, nothing more certainly a proof and part of it, than to compose what raises men's wonder and admiration : nothing more difficult than to show them distinctly the simplest and most obvious truth. They can no better see or comprehend it than they can see or comprehend the air, until thou hast quickened their sight by purifying their affections. During this operation they will call thee pedant or enthusiast, and throw perhaps some heavy book at thy head, bidding thee to read it again and again, and to be modester and wiser. Little as I shall ever be contented with my modesty or my wisdom, I hope to improve and to increase them daily, by a patient and kindly intercourse with my fellow-men, and a humble unquestioning obedience to our heavenly father. Peace and quiet are, in this happy climate, the unfailing fruits of concession and forbearance ; fruits which I hope may be transplanted and husbanded, with all the attention and solicitude they ought to be, in countries where at present they have been but heard of, and with indistinctness and with incredulity.

Thou thyself art inclined, my friend, to doubt and dispute the verities of Revelation. I shall not argue with thee on the tenets of any particular sect, nor speak in my own person, nor according to my own belief, but generally and loosely, and as an indifferent man might reason, when a scheme was laid before him for the improvement and emolument of his kind. Something of fear, thou wilt acknowledge, is requisite, for the coercion of the ungenerous and unjust : something of hope, something of promise, something of security, for the beneficent and righteous, for the afflicted and oppressed. Thou thinkest thou art doing no wrong in removing the foundations of hope : to think it, is a folly ; to do it, is a robbery.

PETERBOROUGH. In what way a robbery ? Come, tell me ; for you stopped to expect my question.

PENN. Hope is the best of possessions.

PETERBOROUGH. Of possessions truly !

PENN. Ay, that it is. The provident rear it early in their bosoms ; and the improvident, when everything else is squandered, cling at it to the last.

If we find a few stubborn texts of Holy Scripture that would

252

exclude many good men from their rewards, we may reasonably think them the dreams of hot enthusiasts, exhausted by their aspirations and distempered by their zeal. We should more wisely turn to the words of the teacher than to the glosses of the interpreter, and press toward him through the clouds that surround him, in which alone is darkness and dismay : for his countenance is irradiated, his speech is simple, in his voice is confidence, and in his mien is peace. Why wouldst thou push men away from him, even if thou wert persuaded that he has nothing for them ? They are better by trying to merit it, and happier by continuing to expect it. Neither of us can say to a certainty that it is unattainable : on the contrary, the means, we are assured, are not difficult, and the mediator is not repulsive. There may be folly in most religions, and if thou wilt, in all ; but the greatest of folly is to hinder men from happiness, to render them turbulent, disorderly, lawless, desperate.

PETERBOROUGH. Certainly it is wiser, when you have broken their bones, to tell them that they may pick them up again and case them better hereafter.[1]

PENN. Oppression and injustice are not wanted to make the promises of a man's own heart acceptable to him, and to expand his breast with joy and gladness, at the responses given to him (as he believes they are) from above. These he may have without purchasing, and without going to seek them at another's door.

If commerce itself is generally bad and iniquitous when it falls into the hands of a company, what is religion ? At first a craft, and afterward a cheat.

Woe ! woe ! to those who make it one : woe ! woe ! to those who enter into it——

PETERBOROUGH. Without a patron in the chancellor, or a friend in the huntsman of the squire.

PENN. Thy light spirits will one day carry thee into the wilderness, and there leave thee sore smitten and without strength. Unworthiness ! thou laughest at men's wrongs.

PETERBOROUGH. Because men are made now as they were made

---

[1] 1st ed. reads : " hereafter ; that is, if they will but hold their tongues about it, or employ them in praising the Lord for His loving mercies. PENN. Oppression . . . above. PETERBOROUGH. If commerce . . . religion ? This is now a craft. PENN. Woe ! " etc.

formerly, and yet bear them. Such being the fact, I think I have esteem enough for them in ranging them with my other instruments, lead and iron.

PENN. Great God ! the proud themselves decry and detest the oppressor, while only the powerless pity the oppressed.

PETERBOROUGH. Nations are to be commiserated for few other evils than what the elements cast among them ; such as famine and pestilence. A quiver of arrows, well directed by half a dozen boys, would remove in a single hour the heaviest that philosophers and patriots have tugged against for ages. Injuries [1] grow up quickly and rankly under impunity. I do not deliver such an opinion because I have acted on it ; for I may say to you in confidence, that I often have forgiven injustice done against me, not indeed to bring a Christian spirit on the parade, but for the satisfaction I feel in the consciousness of superiority, and in the intensity of contempt. It was wrong to gratify my humour at the expense of society, as I have frequently ; and the only counterbalance is, to serve society at my own peril and loss : and this, as you must acknowledge, hath been my conduct in regard to King James. It is just and necessary to shake a salutary fear into the breasts of insolent stupid despots, when they shake an unsalutary one into thousands, who, without such nuisances, would be brave and free. Whoever lets a prince escape him after suffering an act of arbitrary power, neglects his duty to himself and others ; and neglects it from the worst motive, indifference to public security and private honour. Never let me hear that it is no easy matter to accomplish. I have only one reply ; and an obvious one is it : that it may be no easy matter to catch or poison a rat at the time of its depredation : but let traps and arsenic be always in its way ; and finally, you are certain of success. Here indeed you may more justly censure me as cruel : for these poor creatures do us little harm comparatively, and consume what is as much theirs as ours, and what they are guided by instinct to partake with us. But animals without hearts are not directed by Nature or Providence to consume the hearts of others, and the most generous with the most voracity. These now and then recoil, swell against and overpower them.

PENN. Hold ! hold ! less animation and heat, I do beseech thee ! *Vengeance is mine*, saith the Lord.

[1] From " Injuries " to " tragedy " added in 2nd ed.

254

PENN AND PETERBOROUGH

PETERBOROUGH. We can not do better than imitate him on it, when we find him ready to help us.

PENN. By long and patient endurance thou mayst make unrighteous princes ashamed.

PETERBOROUGH. You may make a dog ashamed by looking him fixedly in the face ! You can only make a prince afraid by it : and if you do, and nothing more, he hangs you. We never play the farce before the tragedy.

PENN. I [1] am slow and reluctant to admit what I am afraid must be admitted ; that certain plagues, like certain weeds, ought to be cut down rapidly three or four times in the season : this alone kills them. Happy the land where such cutting down can be avoided !

PETERBOROUGH. And [2] where it can not be, your friends will supply neither hatchet nor rope. The better your institutions are, and the purer your religion and morality, the less likelihood is there that your numbers will increase. Want indeed may compel a few to emigrate from England : but what gain you by such colonists as those ?

PENN. A pledge ; a security. Whoever emigrates from want, presents a token that he would rather work than steal, rather help his neighbour than beg. In England a family may often be a curse ; in America it will always be a blessing. In England a child brings with it poverty in most instances ; in America wealth.

PETERBOROUGH. In England they are swamps and bushes, in America ploughs and oxen ; ay, Penn ?

PENN. Without them, and in greater proportion than the luxuries of England can afford, our ploughs would rot, our oxen run wild. Wherever I see a child before me in America, I fancy I see a fresh opening in the wilderness, and in this opening a servant of God appointed to comfort and guide me, ready to sit by me when my eyes grow dim, and able to sustain me when my feet are weary. Look forward, and behold the children of that child. Few generations are requisite to throw upon their hinges the heavily-barred portals of the vast continent behind us. Thy horse appeared to scent by instinct the high-road across it ; and thy heart, Mordaunt, panted with prescience to pass the barrier, which, the tyrant and his fool would tell thee, Nature hath interposed. Who knows but,

[1] From " I " to " admitted ; that " added in 2nd ed.
[2] From " And " to " rope " added in 2nd ed.

255

a century or two hence, we may look down together on those who are journeying, in this newly-traced road, toward the cities and marts of California, and who are delayed upon it by meeting the Spaniards driven in troops from Mexico.

PETERBOROUGH. You began with a dream, you are ending with a vision.

PENN. Everything good hath been ever called so : my answer is, past events shadow out future ones.

PETERBOROUGH. We move in the midst of these shadows, but discern not their forms and tendencies.

PENN. Perfectly we do not discern them : nevertheless, from the invariable practice of hereditary potentates to abuse and arrogate power, and from the spirit of agricultural states in their adolescence, and from the vantage-ground whereon that spirit stands when it settles but to soar away, he who is not an idiot must be a prophet.

First the brutes possessed the earth : afterward they and men contended for it, and held it equally : by degrees men acquired the ascendancy : lastly, as the monsters were thinned and scattered, men contrived to raise up artificial ones, covering them with furs and hair, and admiring their truculent looks and flaring colours. These creatures, like the pig-enactor in the fable, did bravelier than those they represented, and allowed no better than a precarious and merely animal existence to their fanciful dressers and complacent fosterers. It was not the tree of folly that

> Brought death into the world and all our woe ;

it was the tree of wisdom. As this apologue is liable to many interpretations, it may admit mine among the rest.

PETERBOROUGH. Let me hear it : a fable is sometimes a refreshment.

PENN. Mine is, that neither the ignorance nor the passions of mankind are immediately and of themselves the causes of their corruption and wretchedness, but the uses and ends to which they have been converted by the warier.

PETERBOROUGH. I [1] think so too ; and, although our creeds are not quite homogeneous, one thing peculiarly pleases me in your religious doctrines.

PENN. I rejoice to hear it : say which.

---

[1] From " I " to " homogeneous " added in 2nd ed.

PENN AND PETERBOROUGH

PETERBOROUGH. You pay nothing for them.

PENN. To suppose that we want hirelings to teach us our duties, is to suppose that our fathers and mothers have given bad examples and appointed bad executors. Taking a different view of the subject, holiness, you may tell me, hath little weight with most people : I know it : but every man who wishes to leave his children either rich or respectable, will provide that they first acquire from him what shall preserve their riches and promote their respectability ; that is, frugal habits and civil demeanour. Quarrels for tithes, and appointed prayers, imperfectly serve the purpose. They supersede those endeavours which would be made for every man's own interest, in every man's own house ; not perhaps by psalms and sermons, but by exhortations and examples.

PETERBOROUGH. There is something grand and imposing in our hierarchy.

PENN. Troth is there ! and more than enough of both : yet there was nothing grand or imposing in Christ and his successors, who gained more proselytes than your hierarchal folks lose.

Grandeur is what the eye makes it. For my part, I see nothing grand in frocks and flounces : I see nothing grand in a fellow who wears one shirt next his skin and another over his coat. I find in your church

Luxuriam spoliorum et censum in damna furentem,

as the pagan poet hath it ; and we brethren are convinced that it not only is no help or assistance to true piety, but that it torpefies and impedes it. I speak of its effect on the whole ; not on one individual, one family, or one parish. Moreover we think, and can prove by figures, that its revenues are more than sufficient to maintain an army (since armies you will maintain) of such strength as should repel the most obstinate aggression. This is not always to be expected : suppose then that warfare shall exist among us, even when we grow wiser, one year in three ; the other two years' income might be applied to the education of the poor : shortly, it would leave none in that predicament. We demonstrate in our society the practicability of the thing, without any such abundant means at our disposal, and suffering under the aggravation of war-taxes, as may happen, and church-taxes, as must befall us irremissibly.

PETERBOROUGH. In this you have done admirably, divinely.

Religions are calculated for climates. Popery is lax enough for the warmest. Its modification in the Church of England, stiff but elastic, serves best for the variable atmosphere it was composed in. Yours is the most judicious where there is a trade in beavers : the thornier and rigider Calvinism takes root and flourishes under the Alps and Ben-Lomond. I [1] could dandle the pretty baby of Catholicism, with its whistle and bells and coral and flounces about it; but in regard to the capricious and ferocious Tiger-God, that looks at it with such growls, I think it prudent to stand on this side of the grating.

PENN. Governors, who are the gainers, will allow any creed, provided the people pay them regularly, and ask no questions. Calvinism is the product of cold and gloomy countries ; and such countries being likewise poor, nobody is at the trouble to extirpate it out of them, if the natives will but abstain from leagues and covenants. Let it however sprout up for a season in any rich soil and sunny exposure, and thou shalt find dragoons turned into the field against it, with such hoes and harrows as the like husbandmen use most expertly. Languedoc has witnessed this. The Catholic priest himself is less intolerant than one might imagine : and it is not the reprobate creed that troubleth his slumbers : it is the new-fangled bolt wrapt up in it, made on purpose for the apartment of thy daughter. An accursed creed ! it turneth him out of more dormitories than were contained in the palace of Priam, and strippeth from him the supervisorship of more kitchen-stoves than smoked for Elagabalus. With one foot upon thy bed and the other upon thy belly, he fancied thee fairly his : and now he thinks the devil must be in thee if thou hast turned thy back against him. He curses thee, kicks thee, and leaves thee to that *Evil one's* disposal.

PETERBOROUGH. I am not sordid nor avaricious ; yet, in my opinion, the worst of the matter is the money we are obliged to contribute, although we have no appetite for the ordinary. Those who receive the best education, and who want no new instruction, pay the most : those who, being seceders, decline the doctrine and follow another, pay for both, and perhaps thrice as much for that which they reject as for that which they cherish. This in another age or two will be incredible, at least in England and in America.

There are two reasons however why I never could become a member of your society : first, I never should be quiet or good

---

[1] From " I " to " grating " added in 2nd ed.

enough : secondly, supposing me to have acquired all the tranquillity and virtue requisite, my propensity toward the theatre and its fair actresses [1] would seduce me.

PENN. Thy language is light and inconsequent. Thou couldst not indeed be quiet and good enough for any rational and sedate society, and oughtest not even to discourse with any confidence on virtue, unless thou hadst first subdued such an idle fantasy as that of mockery, and such vile affections as those for paint and fiddles, and wind-instruments and female ones.

PETERBOROUGH. They who are to live in the world, must see what the world is composed of; its better and its worse.

PENN. No doubt; he who is to live in a street, must see the cleaner parts of the pavement and the dirtier : but must he put his foot into them equally ? or, according to thy system, step over the plain flagstone to splash into the filth ?

PETERBOROUGH. Philosophers tell us our passions and follies should be displayed to us together with their evil consequences, that we may regulate and control them.

PENN. In my opinion, who am no philosopher, we should grow as little familiar even with their faces as may be. We ought to have nothing to do with such as are exhibited on the tragic stage : if they really exist, they are placed by Providence out of our range ; they can not hurt us unless we run after them on purpose. Then do we want strange characters of less dimensions, such as can come under our doorway and affect us at home ? We meet them everywhere ; nay, we can not help it.

PETERBOROUGH. Elevated sentiment is found in tragedy ; elegant reproof in comedy.

PENN. Comedy is the aliment of childish malice ; tragedy of malice full-grown. Comedy has made many fools, and tragedy many criminals. Show me one man who hath been the wiser or the better for either, and I will show you twenty who have been made rogues and coxcombs, by aping the only models of fashion they can find admittance to, and as many more who have grown indifferent and hard-hearted, and whatever else is reprehensible in higher life.

Who, being thoughtless, ignorant, self-sufficient, would not be moody, vindictive, unforgiving, if great monarchs set the example

---

[1] Peterborough, having married a singer in 1722, only avowed the marriage in 1735.

before him ? and who fears those chastisements at the end, which it would be a thousand times more difficult for him to run into than to avoid ? There is only one thing in either kind of scenic representation which is sure enough never to hit him ; the moral.

If however thou visitest the theatre for reflection, thou art the first that ever went there for it, although not the first that found it there. Reflection, from whatever quarry extracted, is the foundation of solid pleasures, which foundation, we think, can not be laid too early in the season.

PETERBOROUGH. Solid pleasures, like other solid things, grow heavy and tiresome : I would rather have three or four lighter, of half the value, readily taken up, and as readily laid down again.

PENN. The time will come, young man, when thou wilt reason better, and wilt detest that wit, the rivet of sad consistency. Thou hast spoken, as thou fanciest, a smart and lively thing ; and, because thou hast spoken it, thou wilt tie thy body and soul to it.

PETERBOROUGH. Possibly the time may come, but it lies beyond my calculation, when the frame of my mind may be better adapted to those cubic joys you were proposing for me : but I have observed that all who in their youthful days are the well-strapt even-paced porters of them, have been the first broken down by calamity or infirmity.

PENN. The greater sign of infirmity, the greater of calamity, is there apparent, where the intertexture of pleasures and duties seems intractable.

PETERBOROUGH. If the theatre were as hostile and rancorous against the church, as the church in some countries is against the theatre, we should call it very immoral, not because it had less justice on its side, but because it had more virulence. Splendour and processions and declamation and rodomontade are high delights to the multitude. Accompanied by lofty and generous sentiments, they do good ; accompanied by merriment and amusement, they do more good still : for lofty and generous sentiments are so ill fitted to the heads and hearts of most men, that they fall off in getting through the crowd in the lobby ; but the amusement and merriment go to bed with man and wife, and something of them is left for the children the next morning at breakfast. I have no greater objection to parade and stateliness in that theatre where the actors have been educated at the university, than in that where one can more easily be admitted behind the scenes : what I want is, a little good-nature and good-manners, and that God should be thought as tolerant as my lord chamberlain.

The worst objection I myself could ever find against the theatre is, that I lose in it my original idea of such men as Cæsar and Coriolanus, and, where the loss affects me more deeply, of Juliet and Desdemona. Alexander was a fool to wish for a second world to conquer : but no man is a fool who wishes for the enjoyment of two ; the real and ideal : nor is it anything short of a misfortune, I had almost said of a calamity, to confound them. This is done by the stage : it is likewise done by engravings in books, which have a great effect in weakening the imagination, and are serviceable only to those who have none, and who read negligently and idly. I should be sorry if the most ingenious print in the world were to cover the first impression left on my mind of such characters as Don Quixote and Sancho : yet probably a very indifferent one might do it ; for we can not master our fancies, nor give them at will a greater or less tenacity,[1] a greater or less promptitude in coming and recurring.

You friends are no less adverse to representations by painting than by acting.

PENN. We do not educate our youth to such professions and practices. Thou, I conceive, art unconcerned and disinterested in this matter.

PETERBOROUGH. Nearly, but not quite. I am ignorant of the art, and prefer that branch of it which to many seems the lowest ; I mean portraiture. I can find flowers in my garden, landscapes in my rides, the works of saints in the Bible, of great statesmen and great captains in the historians, and of those who with equal advantages had been the same, in the *Newgate Calendar*. The best representation of them can only give me a high opinion of the painter's abilities, fixed on a point of time. But when I look on a family-picture by Vandyke ; when I contemplate the elegant and happy father in the midst of his blooming progeny, and the partner

---

[1] 1st ed. has a note : " In my youth I was fond of reading the *Nouvelle Héloïse*, and purchased a fine edition of Rousseau's works in which were engravings. Opening the *Nouvelle Héloïse*, my eyes fell upon one of them ; and never afterwards have I looked into the book, which I instantly closed with more sorrow than ever merchant did his ledger, when he found an insuperable balance against him."

261

of his fortunes and his joys beside him ; I am affected very differently, and much more. He who there stands meditating for them some delightful scheme of pleasure or aggrandizement, has bowed his head to calamity, perhaps even to the block. Those roses gathered from the parterre behind, those taper fingers negligently holding them, that hair, the softness of which seems unable to support the riot of its ringlets, are moved away from earth, amid the tears and aching hearts of the very boys and girls who again are looking at me with such unconcern.

Faithfullest recorder of domestic bliss, perpetuator of youth and beauty, vanquisher of time, leading in triumph the Hours and Seasons, the painter here bestows on me the richest treasures of his enchanting art.

PENN. Vanity! vanity! vanity! as thou hast proved. The fine arts, as you call them, have always been the attractive clothing of a venal religion. Ours is none such, and needs no such lures. Come away : let us leave the vain, and look once again at the grasping. Religion ought no more to be forced on us for payment, than soap and candles.

The first property was a portion set apart for the Gods ; that is for the conjurers or priests. Shortly, those who decided on subjects of litigation, took presents for their good offices, and by degrees claimed rewards. Hence originated two classes or professions, which have absorbed in the course of ages more by many times than the fee-simple of the whole cultivated earth. They are contrary to Christianity and subversive of it.

PETERBOROUGH. I know enough of both to see this. Here indeed you stand beyond controversy.

PENN. Friend, whenever thou hearest it said, as thou often must do, that there is some excellent sense in this man or the other, thou mayst always find it in strict correspondence with the preconceived opinions of the sage observer : and where the author or speaker is wrong, he is wrong exactly where he would set his reader or hearer right, and can not. If we are weak in proportion to our failures, the best intellects, as ye would call them, are the feeblest of all : for the most rational advice has the fewest followers, the plainest reasoning the most obstinate opposers. We have no right to be angry or vexed at any such disappointment. When a wise man can not make an unwise one better, shall he therefore let the unwise one make him worse ? Shall the weak, while he holdeth pertinaciously to his ignorance, snatch away temper and discretion from the strong ?

PETERBOROUGH. Argumentative enough : but the business is, to remove those insects, which, deriving their sustenance from the juices of the state, take its colour and seem its substance.

PENN. Our society, although it be extinguished, and although its extinction be as early even as thou prognosticatest, will at least leave behind it the remembrance that it marched foremost of the vanguard, and opposed those inveterate unrelenting pestilences, in the spirit of justice and in the gentleness of consistency. That communities, in their most depraved and rotten state, stand more upright without them, is plain and evident ; in regard to one, from the practice of your judges, who, whenever a case of property is most difficult and delicate, recommend it to the arbitration of friends ; in regard to the other, from the manifestation of more quietude, regularity, and happiness, in those who have seceded from the toilet, the feast, and the theatre, of a city-bred court-aping religion, into their own family party, their private sheltered walks and noiseless untrampled grass-plots. I do not calculate here on worldly loss and profit. I do not demonstrate to thee, as I might do in figures, that after government hath fairly done its worst, a fifth of every man's remaining goods and chattels are piled up and swept away ; and we are at last so pressed and elbowed, so jostled and trodden on, between the bar and the pulpit, while we clap our hands to our seals our pockets are slit to the very bottom, with little care or concern for the skin under ; and, if we cry out, there is always a hand in readiness to stop our mouths, and to stifle and strangulate such as would resist. Where the lawyers flourish, there is a certain sign that the laws do not : for this flourishing can only arise from the perplexity or the violation of them.[1] If an English lawyer is in danger of starving in a market-town or village, he invites another, and both thrive. Hence, though litigation is their business, they usually are courteous one to another, whenever and for whatever purposes they meet : on the same principle of abstinence as is displayed by vultures, which, however hungry and strangers, do not attack the stronger the weaker, but, sullenly concentrated, await in calm providence the weltering breeze, laden with glad tidings of pestilence or of battle. What is more wonderful

---

[1] A long note in 1st ed., on Landor's legal experiences, is reserved for the Appendix to the final volume of Conversations.

and inexplicable to a man who thinks on it, than that, after many hundred years of the same government, and this government called a good one, a wise one, an example to others, some new statute should be deemed requisite every week ?   When children break their toys and cry for fresh ones, we attend to them only because they are children : when men break those bonds which hold them together, and, as often as the gravest of them assemble, want some of another colour and quality, we give them honourable names for it, instead of scourging and sending them supperless to bed.   I fear, my friend, that laws are contrived rather to increase the fortunes of the few than to secure those of the many.   The makers and menders of them do a great deal of work in a little time, and have hardly put into their pockets the money for it, when our victuals drop out of some un-soldered chink into the fire, and the same tinkers must hammer, and the same payers must pay, again.*

PETERBOROUGH. English law, like the torpedo, kills only those who have no metal to put between it and them.   It does not appear that God will ever let the world rest, without one or more of his curses on it.   When the rattle-snakes and alligators are exterminated in this country, barristers and attorneys may shoot up.

PENN. Our Maker's plagues upon wealth and avarice !—but the religion we profess will never allow such a dreadful scourge to infest our people.

PETERBOROUGH. Our English Themis, venerable for her paunch, and glorious in the rich array of native carbuncles, makes her scales of gold, her weights of rubies.

PENN. Truly doth she, and rubies concreted from the heart-blood of the people in her cracks and crevices.   If, after what goes among the lawyers, the English are to pay a tenth to the clergy, and a tenth to the civil power in taxes, they, on the score of property, derive no advantages whatever from the social state.   For, supposing the whole island to be as much over-run by robbers as any part of the globe ever was, you can not yet suppose that these robbers could take to themselves a fifth of all property, immovable and movable. Districts the most infested by them would suffer in a much less

---

* General Bathurst, examined before a committee of the Commons on the county rates, stated that poor persons were recommended by their solicitors to plead guilty, to avoid the fees : the fee for an acquittal in the Western Circuit being one pound six shillings and eightpence.—W. S. L.

degree than this : and common sense and common interest would
unite the population, however rude and scattered, however timorous
and abject, against such despoilers. The most exposed to their
outrages would be exposed to less ruinous demands ; and these
demands themselves would soon cease : whereas there is no appearance that those heavier ones under which our mother country
labours, will have any other termination than such as our peaceful
habits and humane religion teach us to deprecate and avoid.

Tithes, according to the practice of the Anglo Saxon and British
church, never were intended for the priest alone ; but, beside the
maintenance of the clergymen, for the repairs of the church, for the
relief of the poor, and for the entertainment of the pilgrim and
stranger.[1] Thus we can not suppose that more than a third of them
went to the parson ; particularly as the distribution was left to the
bishop and his assistants. The tithes of a whole diocese were
collected, and as the duties in each parish were the same, so the
stipends of the ministers were equal. Men in those days fled from
the sword to the church ; in these we flee from the church to the
wilderness ; a longer flight indeed, but a safer refuge. Value the
life of every man, in possession of goods, at ten years' purchase ; he
pays two years' income to be allowed the other eight : and on what
security ? How does he know that the *posse curiæ* may not encroach
as deeply on the rest ? Can any wise man endure this state of
things, with the power of avoiding it ? any brave man with the
power of overturning it ?

PETERBOROUGH. Faith ! no. But we always are either staggering-
drunk with war, or fast asleep with peace.

PENN. Here in Pennsylvania, those who guide us are chosen by
us for our guides ; those who protect us are chosen by us for our
protectors. We do not ask favours from them ; we do not solicit
that a portion of our own be thrown back to us, like the entrails of
a beast to the dogs that have been chasing it ; we do not stipulate
that one of our sons may have, openly or secretly, a part of what his
brothers and cousins, and many houses round, have contributed.
Our agents can not form themselves into gangs against us ; can not
board our vessels, burn our plantations of tobacco, enter our houses,
break open our cellars, cast out the materials of our beverage, whip us
into their worship, or fine and imprison us for neglecting to attend it.

[1] 1st ed. has a note : " Southey's *Book of the Church*, vol. i. p. 80."

IMAGINARY CONVERSATIONS : AMERICAN

PETERBOROUGH. You lay rather too much stress upon what you call liberty of conscience, and are inconsistent in hating King James for having too much enlarged it. In fact all people in all countries may worship what objects they please, if they will only be contented to keep within doors. But even the quietest love display and dominion in worship. Political freedom is more material.

PENN. Be it as thou sayest. According to the clearest, simplest, best definition, the office and nature of Justice is to give everyone his due. Now, under kingly government, a man not only hath not his due, but hath not the means or even the chance of obtaining it. Those who are most intimately acquainted with his abilities and his virtues, are without the power of placing them where they shall be serviceable to the community. He withers with his fruit upon his branches : and the sycophant, sunned in idleness and vacuity, points at him as a *lusus naturæ*.

PETERBOROUGH. If the world were not composed of opposites, and if the actions of men were not in eternal contravention to their reasonings, I should have imagined that the peaceful manners of your people, and your abstinence from resisting, not only against authority, but even against wrong, would have rendered you more favourable to monarchy than to republicanism.

PENN. Although we resist not against wrong, we may like right better.

PETERBOROUGH. Quiet is the principle of your institution, the rule of your lives and thoughts : now nothing is further from it than the spirit of democracy ; as we may clearly see in the democratical portion of our constitution at home. Go, at the time of an election, to some borough unbiassed by aristocratical influence and ministerial seduction : you will not find the wisest or most upright of its burgesses in the chair ; but either a stranger from a distance or an intriguer in the town : and not only the rabble are his partisans : the better sort, as they are called, lean toward him, rather than toward one whose shadow chills them, whose genius is a sting and whose grandeur of soul a reproof to them. Newton, Milton,[1] and Shakespeare, would never have been proposed or thought of, in any borough where they might happen to be born, supposing them likewise to have received the requisites of fortune. Had they offered themselves, they would have been told, " We do not want men of

[1] 1st ed. reads " Locke " instead of " Milton."

266

books or genius, but men of business " : as if men of genius are not men of business in the higher sense of the word ; of business in which the state and society are implicated for ages.

Common minds revolve these reasonings about them. Let them be contented with the prospect of their future glory ; let us be, with the certainty of never being heard of hereafter : which saves us a great deal of concern, and allows us a perfect freedom of action.

PENN. Thou reasonest well, and from observation. Thy arguments are the surest proof I could adduce, that a sounder morality and a purer religion are necessary, to guide the inconsiderateness of those whom thou callest (I wish the word were gentler) the *rabble,* and to mollify the malignity of (here too the expression is susceptible of improvement) the *better sort.*

Institutions can not make men perfect. Fraud, injury, violence, may be discountenanced and diminished, if thou removest those whose authority began upon them, rests upon them, and must go upon them. Keep thy fellow-creatures temperate, keep them sane, strong, tractable, by early and late discipline : speak mildly to the obedient ; more mildly to the refractory ; and on one side of thee thou wilt soon find friendship in the bonds of peace, and violence on the other self-disarmed.

PETERBOROUGH. We should imagine, if we did not much reflect on the subject, that equality is a very natural sentiment ; yet there is none to which nearly the universality of mankind is constantly so averse. Bring before you the whole train of your acquaintance, of all ages, tempers, and conditions, and you will acknowledge at once the justice of my remark. I have observed among the peers whom I was accustomed to meet at my father's and uncle's, that they invariably bear toward one another a constrained familiarity or a frigid courtesy : while to their huntsmen and their prickers, to their chaplains and their cooks, or indeed another man's, they display unequivocal signs of ingenuous cordiality. Baronets are prouder than anything we see on this side of the Dardanelles, excepting the proctors of universities, and the vergers of cathedrals ; and their pride is kept in eternal agitation, both from what is above them and from what is below. Gentlemen of any standing are apt to investigate their claims a little too minutely ; and nobility has neither bench nor joint-stool for them in the vestibule. During the whole course of your life, have you ever seen one, among this our King

James's breed, that either did not curl himself up and lie snug and warm in the lowest company, or slaver and whimper in fretful quest of the highest ?

PENN. Without any disposition to answer what never engaged a moment of my attention, let me suggest to thee, that whether thy remark be well or ill founded, the desire of equality is not the less nurtured by reason or the less approved by Christianity. Mankind is certainly quite as averse to patience, to forbearance, to returning good on receiving evil : still I never heard of the preacher who discountenanced the recommendation of them.

PETERBOROUGH. I mean only to show you that, founded upon abstract principles, your society can not last long.

PENN. Not among the meal and tallow that breed the grubs thou hast thrown out before me : I know it : but friend Mordaunt, there are sieves and ventilators in the world, and there will always be people who know alike how to make and where to exercise them.

PETERBOROUGH. Men can only be kept in concord by their vanity ; which, weak as you may call it, is the strongest and most sensitive nerve in the human heart. If you will not let them be unjust, nay, if you will not be unjust toward the greater part of them, this greater part itself will scorn you. Nothing would raise such violent and such general discontent, as giving to every man his due.

PENN. Such alas is the world ! May we not improve it ?

PETERBOROUGH. May you not turn wolves into fawns, thistles into wheat, granite into peas and clover ? Try this first.

PENN. By the help of God I will undertake the other experiment. If I am to raise discontent, be it on this foundation ! if men are to scorn me, be it for this offence !

PETERBOROUGH. The object of your institution is to establish universal peace on universal equality. I do not assert that equality, inasmuch as relates to rights, is impracticable ; which many have done too rashly : but I doubt its extent ; I doubt its durability. Beside, since violence is the thing most hateful to you, I must remind you again and again that republics are usually more turbulent than monarchies.

PENN. The mother who gives her own milk to her infant, hath often more trouble to make him quiet, than a boon-companion hath, twenty years afterward, to make him drunk, and may seem severer to the dissolute. Monarchy lets the wood run wild, lets swamps

268

extend through it, and reptiles infest it : this is her easiness, this is her providence, this is the blessing she imparts. If in a republic thou tracest the mark of the waggon-wheel and of the hatchet, do not suddenly set it down among the certainties, that they were brought in for devastation : look round a little : see whether the plants are not the larger and the loftier and the healthier for letting in air and light ; whether the grass can not grow under them for pasture, whether the alleys are not useful for the exportation and importation of what is profitable, and whether they do not enable the proprietor to watch that " no thieves break in and steal."

Teach people to rule themselves, and they will neither bear violence nor inflict it.

Something of consistency, one would desire, should appertain to those discreet and regular men who uphold the government of hereditary kings, unanswerable for their misdemeanours, both as the most lawful and the most convenient. If the gardener had pruned thy fruit-trees improperly, wouldst not thou admonish him or dismiss him ?

PETERBOROUGH. Certainly.

PENN. Thou thinkest it equitable and expedient.

PETERBOROUGH. Beyond a doubt.

PENN. If he seized thee by the throat for it, and protested he would hang thee, calling it atrocious, and insisting that only the devil could have instigated thee.

PETERBOROUGH. I would trip up the knave's heels, and cudgel him soundly.

PENN. There are those peradventure who would incline to say that he deserved no better at thy hands. Howbeit, suppose he should struggle and prevail against thee, and asseverate that not only he himself would continue to manage thy fruit-trees as beliked him, but that furthermore his son and grandson should do likewise, whether they had acquired a knowledge of horticulture or not ; for that, as his father had been thy father's gardener, it was undeniable that he ought to be thine, and his elder son thy elder son's ; waiving which argument, haply he would throw up a worm in thy face, and inform thee triumphantly, that if antecedently no fitness or reason had existed, yet both reason and fitness sprang up full-grown when he overthrew and smote thee.

PETERBOROUGH. Famous illustration.

PENN. Sneer not at what prelacy holds the most pertinaciously of her doctrines, and what, if thou wilt not swallow it from the pulpit, thou must gulp from the drum-head. Nay, Mordaunt, with all thy pride, impetuosity, and disdain, thou, even thou art the liveryman of this gardener : yea, thou who wert indignant to be designated as his master. Inconsistent creature !

PETERBOROUGH. It is something to have an influence on the fortunes of mankind : it is greatly more to have an influence on their intellects. Such is the difference between men of office and men of genius, between computed and uncomputed rank.

PENN. Thou art not among those who place Fortune above Nature, and the weakest work of the weakest mortals above the greatest work of Deity in his omnipotence. It is generous in thee to acknowledge what it would be expected from thee to deny, if thou wert not higher than a garter could lift thee.

PETERBOROUGH. I should be as mean as a man of fashion if I disallowed it, and as silly as a president of the council if I attempted to dissemble it. Only the first personage in the kingdom should be unenlightened and void, as only the first page in a book should be a blank one. It is when it is torn out that we come at once to the letters.

Your complimentary terms shall not preclude me from an attack on you, now we are away from your garden and gardener. You also in manners and regimen have your inconsistencies.

PENN. Let us correct them : we can do it, and are ready : what are they ?

PETERBOROUGH. I am not captious by nature, nor over-nice.

PENN. Thou beginnest well.

PETERBOROUGH. Really I am almost ashamed to take exceptions at mere words.

PENN. Better and better.

PETERBOROUGH. I will not spare you then. On my conscience, I do not see why your people, in reality so sincere, should use expressions in which there is no sincerity. *Friend*, on all occasions, is an abuse. A friend is a creature now extinct : we read of its petrified bones in distant regions, and those who would represent its figure in their persons, resemble it only in its petrifaction.

PENN. We call every man our friend because we wish to be every man's. Thou hast not found friendship in certain places, because

PENN AND PETERBOROUGH

thou wert looking for something else. Take virtue with thee, and thou wilt either find it or not want it. Here [1] thou art as unfair with us as thou wert on excommunication, of which I will now explain to thee our employment.

We admonish our younger brethren to omit no opportunity of pouring their ill actions and ill thoughts into quieter and more capacious minds, wherein the swells of their sorrows and the irregularities of their other affections may subside and sweeten. This practice remains with them through life. I see no similitude in it to that of the papist, when all the confidence a young man places in his father, and a young woman in her mother, is considered by the priest as not among the duties of life, unless both of them come before him, and submit the tenderer and purer mind to his hardened and intrusive touch. He tells them such confession, and such only, is necessary to their happiness in a future state. God, he says, accepts it not as a merit, but as an atonement : those who have been injured may be passed aside : he himself acts for these, without seeing them, without communicating with them, without making them reparation, without rendering them account.

PETERBOROUGH. There are creatures brought from other countries, as these priests were, and exhibited in fairs and markets and festivals (and wherever men and money are idly tossed about), as these priests are, which superintend each other's polls with much care and cunning, as these priests do, and pick out from them, and put between their grinders, the minute generations of incommodious things springing up innumerably from pruriency and scurf. What thinkest thou ? Thinkest thou that these animals, the bigger or the smaller, do the same for cleanliness ? No ; they do it for eating, as these priests do.

PENN. Inconveniences there may be in our manners, but not to us : inconsistencies there may be in our government, but not ours are those. In this country, where we are left to ourselves, we reconcile them gradually or remove them peaceably

PETERBOROUGH. If they were serious, and in your native country, you would find your religious scruples an impediment to every such exertion.

PENN. Thy indifference to modes of worship and to articles of faith is founded on the principle, I suppose, that a virtuous man will be virtuous in any of them.

[1] From " Here " to " employment " added in 2nd ed.

271

PETERBOROUGH. Unquestionably.

PENN. What maketh him virtuous ?

PETERBOROUGH. His inclination : the current and quality of his blood.

PENN. Hast thou reflected so little as not to know that inclinations are given by discipline and habit ; and that the quality and current of the blood are as much to be modified by indulgence or coercion, as they are by pepper or hemlock. I would never try to arouse thy soul from the only state of languor it is subject to, did not this indifference to externals, as thou callest them, cover in almost every breast (and might hereafter in thine) an equal indifference to what lies deeper. But, the thing being so, rise from thy apathy, from thy lethargic trance, if true courage, or even if false, be within thee ! Away to Piedmont ; away to the people of the Valley ! Doth the sword charm thee ? doth blood thrill thee ? or hath it lost its voice with thee when it crieth unto God ? Thousands had been cast into infected prisons ; yea, seventeen thousands. Winter stepped in between the pestilence and them ; and those whom the ice had not fastened to the floor were at last in number three thousand ; when it appeared to their prince to be a costly matter, and an offence to the Virgin, to feed any longer these heretics. Scourged from their dungeons, bayoneted from their country, they traverse Geneva ; they reach Berne. Not houses nor lands nor brotherly love, nor compassion, so sweet a stranger to them, so long unlooked for, could detain them there, nor the only alluring one of interdicted pleasures (for such it had ever been to them), the blessed communion of Christian faith. Their grain was growing yellow on its stalk, when they assembled by night in the wood of Nyon. The boldest of human enterprises was undertaken on the sixteenth of the eighth month, in the year of our redemption sixteen hundred and eighty-nine.

I designate the year particularly, although two have not since elapsed, because the existence of these persecuted men appears to be one of those glorious actions which both contemporary and future annalists may overlook. For History is now become as fond as Poetry ever was of the violent and powerful, and much more contemptuous of low condition. She loves better great nations than great actions, great battles than great examples, and is ready to emblazon no name under which she descries no shoulder-knot. Of these holy men, pursued like wolves, but never dropping in their flight the ark of true religion, fewer than nine hundred climb the hostile mountains of Savoy. Prudence and Justice guide them in their path : they pay their cruel enemies for everything needful, out of a pittance insufficient for perhaps another day. Between Suze and Brianson, at the bridge of Salabertrans, they are opposed by two thousand five hundred regular troops, and by a numerous armed peasantry. The bridge is barricaded : a battle of two hours renders them masters of this position. Weary with their conflict, hungered (for now those among them who had money can procure no subsistence with it, the peasantry being in the field against them), they still pursue their march, and attain the summit of the highest mountain on the road.

Why have they fallen on the earth ? and wherefore are they praising God ? Because they see again the land that nurtured them in the strength of holiness, the rafters (for some are unconsumed) of the churches wherein their parents were united, and the elder-tree in full flower upon their graves. Orchards and gardens had disappeared : flocks there were none, nor any beast whatever. The villages were to be conquered from the invader : in another day not a trace remained of them, excepting two black lines, where the fire had run along. Reduced at last to four hundred combatants, they threw up strong entrenchments, and resisted until winter the repeated assaults of their increasing enemies. Early in the spring an army of twenty-two thousand men attacked them, and was repulsed. Eight days afterward the entrenchment was cannonaded and bombarded, and there was on every side a pertinacious and most desperate assault. This too failed : but as the ill-constructed parapet was laid in ruins, they escaped down the precipices by night, amid the sentinels of the beleaguerer, and posted themselves at some distance, in the *Pré du Tour*, a small plain surrounded by the wildest mountains, where their ancestors like themselves had displayed such courage, as never was exhibited in any region of the earth, by any other portion of the human race.

PETERBOROUGH. Are you not ashamed of being so eloquent ?

PENN. I know nothing of oratory : I carry no piece of tape to measure periods ; but reflection shows me that the greater part of the most eloquent books that ever were written, might with more advantage be cast into the ovens of Paris and London, than placed in the hands of the young and inconsiderate. Philosophy, whatever it may do hereafter, has done little good at present : and History has reserved all her applauses for the destroyers of mankind. Point out to me one single schoolmaster or professor, in any age, who has not applauded the speech of Alexander to Parmenio : that if he were Parmenio he would sheathe the sword. Was the man so besotted as not to see clearly that Parmenio spoke in the interests of humanity and in the opinion of all nations, and that he himself spoke not even in his own interests, and directly against the well-being of the world ?

PETERBOROUGH. What an unfortunate man was Ludlow, not to have been present at the battles of these brave fellows ! He left their vicinity just before, and came into England, hoping to end his days among us. I met him in Westminster Abbey the morning of that memorable sitting when Sir Edward Seymour, who enjoyed the general's estate at Maiden Bradley, moved the House of Commons for an address to the king, praying that he should be arrested. Whiggism prevailed : and the soundest and sincerest friend of liberty went again into exile for the constancy of his attachment.

I was struck by the manly, calm, unassuming, military air, of a robust and fresh-coloured man, about seventy years of age, who stood before me with his eyes fixed downward on one spot. Being neither very shy, nor more disposed to balk my curiosity than my other propensities, I bowed to him respectfully, and expressed my persuasion that whoever was interred there, merited the sympathies of the nation.

" Young gentleman," answered he mildly, " you do not know, apparently, whose bones have lain here ? "

" Certainly not, sir," I replied ; " but probably many men's in many ages : for, whatever may be the respect which, in this place above others, is paid to the deceased, it will not ensure to their bones an undisturbed and permanent station."

" If it could," replied he, " surely those of the most prudent, humane, intelligent commander, that ever led Englishmen to victory, would not have been disinterred."

" The felonious Stuarts and their insatiable jackals," cried I, " prowled after rotten carcasses, and had more stomach to lap congealed blood than to fight for fresher. And there are sycophants yet among us who would excite our commiseration for their chastise-

274

ment. The same fellows, next week, will be just as loyal and religious in extolling the powers that be."

He seemed neither to notice my expressions nor to partake in my emotion, but, laying his hand gently on my shoulder, said, gravely and tenderly, " Even generous enthusiasm leaves men sometimes ungenerous. We have removed the evil ; let us pardon and forget it. Let us imitate, as far as we can, him whom we ought rather to think on than on the Stuarts. We are treading the ground that covered Blake ; the man of men."

Roused to higher enthusiasm by his calmness than I could have been by his eloquence, if he had any, I seized him by the hand, and swore by God the eulogy was merited and true.

PENN. And God will forgive thee ; for though thou didst (as many wise men will tell thee) take his name in vain, never was it taken in adjuration less in vain than then. Some admirals have maintained the glory of England ; some have increased it : he found it lower than that of Holland, of Spain, or even of France, and raised it by his genius and valour far above them all. The hope is more reasonable that we may never want such men again than that we shall ever see them.

PETERBOROUGH. Hold ! friend William ! With your leave, I will entertain both hopes alike ; little as is the probability that, if any admiral shall equal him in the union of nautical skill and moral bravery, the same person will be equally grave, disinterested, dispassionate, humble, and tender-hearted. I agree with you that no fighting man was ever at once so great and so good a man as Blake : and since History does not inform us that there has been, Reason does not encourage us to believe that there will be at any time hereafter : but Hope may whisper when these are silent. In all ages, party and self are the prime movers of human action, and never were they more busy than in the whole of his lifetime. Firm as he was in the principles of republicanism, he belonged to no party, and was as far removed from selfishness as from faction. He declined the honours of the state, he avoided the acclaim of popularity, he won battles against calculation, he took treasures above it, he lived frugally, he died poor.

Ludlow was moved by the earnestness of my language and demeanour, and said gracefully, " Sir ! I perceive you are a military man ; so was I, while I had any existence as an Englishman."

275

" How ! sir ! " exclaimed I.

" They under these stones," continued he, " inherit their place of rest : I come to seek it : and if rumours are to be trusted, I may fail to find it.   Again I behold my beloved country in the enjoyment of peace and freedom.   Much of my property, most of my days, all of my thoughts, designs, and labours, have been devoted to the consummation of this one event.   How gladly have I bestowed them ! how gladly shall I bestow the remainder !   To see the country I have served by my life and writings, is an ample recompense for any service I could render her, and almost comforts me under the privation of friends, associates, and comrades, swept away by the storm that split our island and convulsed all Europe."

An old beadle at this moment twitched me by the skirt of my coat, and drew me aside.   " Have a care," said he, in a tremulous voice ; " that is old Ludlow.   The Tories would pink him, and the Whigs poison him."

" Faith ! honest friend," said I, " you describe the two parties better than anyone in the land."   Then, turning to the general, I told him he had a right to reprove my forwardness ; and in order that he might know on what person the reproof should fall, I gave him my name.   He said many kind things, and added some compliments.   I regretted that he was not received in the country with public honours, as having been commander in chief, and against a family then excluded by a majority of the nation, and now expelled by the whole.   My indignation burst out against that wrangler and robber, Seymour, who a few days afterward drove him from the country, lest his virtues should be acknowledged, his sufferings pitied, his losses compensated, and his estates restored.[1]

Penn. We may discourse on better people and better things.

Peterborough. We will then

Away to the valleys, the mountains, and moors.

Pardon my bad singing.   Even your mare flinched at it.

Our accounts of the Valdenses in England have never been explicit and particular.

---

[1] 1st ed. reads : " restored.   In fact, William, was there ever an honest man or a modest woman in that family ? was there ever an individual of either sex, unstigmatized for guile and rapacity ?   Penn. I know not, but certainly we may . . . things.   Peterborough. Our," etc.

PENN AND PETERBOROUGH

PENN. Latterly the government has always been unfriendly to the growth of freedom in foreign countries, and to the purity of religion at home : wherefore [1], as we yield to the impulse it gives, their success or annihilation would concern fewer now than formerly. In the time of Cromwell this oppressed people was commiserated and protected.

PETERBOROUGH. I remember some verses written on their calamities by his Latin secretary, Mr. Milton, a strenuous advocate of their cause.

PENN. And of every cause in which the glory of God and the dignity of man are implicated. He spake with the enthusiasm of a prophet, he reasoned with the precision of a philosopher, and he lived with the purity of a saint.

PETERBOROUGH. I love all great men, and hate all counterfeits of them, particularly such as are struck and milled at a blow in the royal mint. Cromwell does not displease me, though I should have fought against him, unless [2] my uncle, who commanded the artillery under Essex, had led me preferably to that side.

PENN. Thou wouldst have judged ill in fighting against him, for his side was the righteous one, the side of the sufferer and the oppressed : and thou judgest no less ill in saying he doth not displease thee. He is thought to have been a hypocrite for the sake of power ; whereas in fact he was sincere, until power by degrees made him a hypocrite. How little then of it should be trusted to any man, when the wisest, and the bravest, and the calmest are thus perverted by it ! However, in no instance did he exercise his authority to the detriment of his country, which indeed he elevated as high in glory as the hereditary Charles immersed it in disgrace. So great and so desirable a prince as Cromwell never since the creation had been appointed by the Lord of it, to preserve the liberties and to moderate the passions of a turbulent, a factious, and a sinful people.

PETERBOROUGH. When so many high-minded men were against him, and those nearest him the most, I wonder how he could contrive to mount above them as he did.

PENN. Whoever is possessed of such a genius, or anything like it, and is resolved on deception, may rise to the first distinction : but

---

[1] From " wherefore " to " formerly " added in 2nd ed.
[2] From " unless " to " side " added in 2nd ed.

neither deception without genius, nor genius without deception, will elevate him to that wide prospect of dominion, at which the tempter in his breast says, " This, O my worshipper, shall be thine."

PETERBOROUGH. In general there is as much difference between a usurper and a hereditary king, as there is between a wild boar and a tame one : but Cromwell had nothing in him ferocious ; nor had Charles anything sordid, if we except the abandonment of his friends when they were distressed, and of his promises when they were inconvenient. I disapprove of the clownishness in some and of the levity in others, with which they treated the criminal on his trial ; nor do I less disapprove of the slavish baseness, the corrupt sycophancy, with which in his prosperity the king was served by his equals : for above an English gentleman there neither ought to be, nor is there, in character and dignity, anything upon earth. The king is the work of our hands, we are not the work of his : we existed before him, and shall exist after him : he may do much with us, without us nothing.

PENN. In this thou art wise ; and on this secure part of thy wisdom let thy bravery act and rest.

PETERBOROUGH. I know not upon what principle the chancellor Clarendon called Cromwell a *bold bad man*, unless it were to persuade us that he had read a play of Shakespeare's ; in which we find the same words, rather more happily applied. People are bad and good relatively and comparatively. Oliver would have been but a sorry saint, and no very tractable disciple or apostle ; nor do I imagine that you would have admitted him without a scrutiny into the Society of Friends : but he was a good father, a good husband, a good companion, a good soldier, and (taking up now the point on which we are to consider him) he was certainly the best usurper, if you can call him one at all, and perhaps the best prince, that ever lived. Mind, I speak of the functions of a prince, not of the accessaries, not of what belongs to the man or the philosopher. You will understand my reason for expressing a doubt of the Protector being a usurper. If he was one, so is the gentleman I helped to introduce from Holland, who is likewise a great man, and perhaps the next in dignity among our rulers. It is childish to talk of illegality because the army was the instrument. The army must always be the instrument in fundamental changes ; and is never so well employed ; not even in repelling an aggression. For we are liable to more mischief in our houses than out; liable to equal violence and greater depredation, and that depredation in costlier things; and the injury is the worse as coming from those about us, and trusted by us implicitly in our concerns.

Among such a people as the Valdenses, there is no danger of such a man as Cromwell obtaining an ascendency. They warned you; which is more than he ever did; I will answer for him.

PENN. The commands and the practice of our teacher do not permit me to applaud the bloodshedder, although in resistance. We hold it unlawful to kill a fellow creature for any offence whatever.

PETERBOROUGH. But if the laws enact it, then surely it is lawful.

PENN. There is a law, above the passions, above the mutabilities of man, from which whatever is lawful must emanate. Herein the commands of God are clear and definite.

PETERBOROUGH. Some of them; others not; or rather they run quite contrary. You feel greater horror at murder than any people do, and yet you would punish it less severely.

PENN. I deem that offence the worst which tends furthest to deteriorate our social condition. Were it lawful to punish anyone with death, it would be the conqueror, holding in subjection the people that has not injured him, and that consents not to his domination. If a traveller, who has been robbed and bound by a thief, can unbind himself and recover his property, ye deem him justified in so doing, although he can do it by no other way than by slaying the thief.

PETERBOROUGH. Certainly; and praise his spirit.

PENN. If a prince exacteth from his people any part of their substance, without asking their consent, or forces them to labour or fight, ye would deem that what is done by force may be resisted by force.

PETERBOROUGH. Princes who levy taxes and troops despotically, may justly be killed by those who suffer under them, whether born in that condition or not : but every kind of government has made conquests, and has retained them by treaty : these therefore are inviolable.

PENN. By whom were the treaties made?

PETERBOROUGH. By the governors.

PENN. But if the majority of the people, convoked and appealed to, did not consent, without force or fear, to pass under the new ruler, he who holds them in bondage may, according to thy principles, and according to worldly justice, be slain by any of the conquered. And until it is agreed and enforced, that no nation in Europe shall take possession of another, or of any part, international law will be no better than quibble and contradiction.

PETERBOROUGH.[1] He must be a legitimate fool, and of the purest breed, who believes that the powerful will ever cease to exercise their power for its propagation.

PENN. Ye defend the violence done by system, and punish by the gallows the same violence done by poor wretches incapable of reflection ; done perhaps from want of food, perhaps from neglect of education, criminal not in the robber, but in the ministers of the prince. If power is ever righteously to be exercised by one state toward another, it is in taking away the means of injustice and cruelty from the administrators, and in restoring to the people their rights. When they once have them, and find them acknowledged, they will fear to hazard the enjoyment of them, as they must do by assailing or injuring another state. For instance, if the French were free they would have no false appetite : being slaves, they are restless for something to buoy them up from their degradation. They are yet to be taught that Honour may dwell in houses as well as under tents ; and that, if they must boast for ever, they may boast of better things than having *served*.

PETERBOROUGH. Well said, my Quixote of orders grey ! The next proposal I expect from you, is the settlement of differences in the moon ; the second, the abolition of the slave-trade ; and the third, of the Inquisition.

PENN. As to the moon, thou hast more to look for there than I have, and I should gladly see thee righted : but O that God would grant both those abolitions ! I do indeed hold it just and reasonable in any powerful people to insist on them.

PETERBOROUGH. Insist ! when a nation insists on anything against another, it declares war.

PENN. There [2] is nothing in this life worth quarrelling for, and there is nothing to be gained by it in another : yet, apparently in the present state of things, we never can be long at peace. Our quarrels are as frequent and as irrational as those of children. Since however

[1] From " PETERBOROUGH " to " PENN " added in 2nd ed.
[2] From " There " to " apparently " added in 2nd ed.

the great evil of bloodshed must yet for some time continue, let us hope that, if the victory should be ours, the only punishment we inflict on the governors be the civilisation of the governed. Let us hope that we may exact the freedom of the Africans and of the Spaniards, and may empty for ever the holds of the slave-ship and the dungeons of the Inquisition. We have the same right to stipulate the one as the other, and a much greater than to demand the cession of a single village, or the transfer of a single man.

Abolish the slave-trade ! Ah, who can ever hope it ! Whoever shall effect this, will have effected more than the twelve apostles. *They* but threw a stone at a sparrow, and did not bring it to the ground ; he will have placed his foot upon a serpent, more venomous than ever was feigned by fear or poetry, and will have crushed it in all its folds from the setting sun to the rising. What in comparison have all the philosophers done, or what have all the religious ? they have raised much dust, and have removed little. He indeed hath conquered his enemy who binds him by moral obligations ; he indeed is great and good who knows how to make other men so ; and he is in a worse condition than a slave who reduces a higher mind to slavery. Incessant horrors haunt him, and eternal punishments (if there be any such) await him !

Princes of the earth ! will ye never hear a truth unless what is preached to you by your fellows at the scaffold ? Have ye forgotten so soon your last lesson ? Alas ! must it be repeated to you ?

PETERBOROUGH. The old admiral would not perhaps have been so civil as to ask the question of them. He would have preached to them when he had cropped the hair from both ears, and had erected a sounding-board to his liking at Whitehall.

PENN. Fools ! it is they who make such men as my father. He had his faults : but he feared God and loved his country. Let us honour him ! I must ever do it.

PETERBOROUGH. And I too. I admire and venerate many whom I should be glad to fight against.

PENN. Strange creature ! Are we then images of clay, baked by children in the sun, to be broken for their entertainment ?

PETERBOROUGH. The first of us are hardly worth a serious thought.

PENN. And yet how much happiness might even those who are not the first of us, confer !

PETERBOROUGH. I should have said *enjoy*.

PENN. I said it.

In the spirit of religion, which is humanity and nothing else, I may nevertheless demonstrate why these children of the mountains fought courageously. They believed that they were protecting the household and the house itself of God : they believed that their sufferings were trials, and that this life was given them for endurance, in proportion to which should be their happiness in the next. Hope is the mother of Faith.

PETERBOROUGH. Who [1] has a twin daughter very like her, named Folly.

PENN. Thy father may perhaps have said before thee, what mine often did, that good parents have sometimes worse children than one might have wished. It would however be inconsistent in thee to deny that energy and endurance are useful. Now nothing more certainly than Hope gives both endurance and energy to fighting men. If she can likewise give them to the suffering and imbecile, she must appear to thee still more admirable, as doing what is harder and better. Belief in a future state of happiness, as a recompense for unmerited and unavoidable evil, renders men patient and contented : and this effect neither their activity nor their ingenuity, neither their turbulence nor their eloquence, can bring about. It would be strange if that should be a weakness, which all the wisdom in the world can not equal in its efficacy.

PETERBOROUGH. I am glad to hear you talk in this manner upon energy, since it proves that you yourself are not, at heart, so indifferent to it as the generality of the sect. Their practices would destroy by degrees the vigour of the human intellect ; and the most energetic of our actions would be when we sneeze in the sunshine.

PENN. You, my friend, like the generality of mankind, seem to have formed to yourself no idea of energy but in acts of violence. Now there may be as much of it in saving a man from drowning as in drowning him. If indeed we are prone to evil, which you agree with us in believing, and on which supposition most sects of philosophy, and all religions and all laws, are founded, more energy is requisite in doing well than in doing ill. If the mind is subject to its tempests and tornadoes, more strength and firmness are shown amid

[1] 1st ed. reads : " She has . . . like this, who has several young ones growing up about her—Folly," etc.

them by immovability than by velocity. We yield to wrong and falsehood ; if indeed I may employ two terms upon one thing.

PETERBOROUGH. How is that ?

PENN. Wrong is but falsehood put in practice.

PETERBOROUGH. Would it not be better to expose the theoretical falsehood and to repress the practical ? or do you look only to the private harm done to yourselves, careless how far the evil may run on through its impunity ?

PENN. Falsehood is for a season : truth is eternal.

PETERBOROUGH. William ! William ! the eternity of truth is not yet begun : and the season of falsehood has existed from the creation of man. I do not believe that this will ever cease, or the other ever commence : if it should, nine-tenths of the world will rise against it and overthrow it. Your wild men here will be the only men neutral, not caring an elk's antler about the matter. Those who could disseminate truth, with a large and copious hand, through all the nations of the world, abstain from doing it : for there is no great mind without a share of foresight, and no share of foresight that does not glance down occasionally on the sharer. Hence those men calculate how much good the disseminating of truth will do to themselves, and how much good the garnering and secreting of it. Few of them come to any other conclusion, than that it is better to hold it back for the present. They put it off from the work-day to the market-day : they put it off from the market-day to the fair-day; and there they walk among the booths and benches, until they find a commodity to exchange for it : a sword-knot, a ribbon, a piece of purple or scarlet silk, or something that roughens in the hand, like gold. You, adverse as you are to the profession of war, or even to personal defence, are more enthusiastic about the Valdenses, and (I would swear for you) would fight better for them, than almost any of our noble generals, who would despise them because they fight without uniforms, and who would hate them because they fight for themselves.

You have related these battles with more spirit and energy than become your stoicism, and you leave me only to regret the want of *names* in the recital of heroism. This is the principal defect in modern historians, the worst of which are the English. They see only kings and ministers,[1] and when they should be busy in action,

---

[1] 1st ed. reads : " ministers, with a mistress or two peeping from behind the curtain. The courage," etc.

they sink to the knees in the heavy sands of disquisition. The courage, the firmness, the philosophy, which would have elevated men to the first station in a republic, are mentioned but in their effects. A victory is the king's or the nation's : the head that planned it, the hand that guided to it, are unseen, unknown. Self-devotion to any great cause is without a record ; and abstract principles lie among cold reflections. The immortal authors of antiquity chisseled out the more prominent characters, and traced the less : we have only white and black upon one smooth surface.

PENN. Beware ! beware ! Do not make me more of a republican than I am. Certainly we find the names of fewer great men in our English histories than in the ancient : yet if our nation had produced fewer, our institutions must have been worse. The assertion and the defence of freedom are never made without danger. Some are now living, and many have died lately, who hazarded their properties and lives for public law ;. and no few lost them for it. Instead of mentioning them with honour and reverence, we calumniate and revile them. This indeed will always be the case under the influence of party : but, taking a wider and fairer view of the subject, we find, as thou leadest me to remark, that English writers are less disposed to celebrate English worthies, than are the writers of any other country those who improved its condition and laboured for its glory. There are histories, and not deemed bad ones, wherein are omitted the names even of the great citizens by whom our freedom was founded. If the Greeks and Romans had done so, we should not have been supplied with that renovating spirit, which keeps alive in us the generous sentiment these ruder but stronger men implanted.

Why [1] dost thou cut the air with thy wand, spurring at once and coercing thy animal ?

PETERBOROUGH. I was recollecting with admiration the valour of your Valdenses. Glorious ! to make such a resistance against a regular force.

PENN. And is it for this only, or for this principally, that they are admirable ? Soldiers could not have acted so ; for even the best of them are vicious. The very names of vices were unknown for the most-part to these persecuted men ; insomuch that in the whole of their annals for many centuries, we find no instance of

---

[1] From " Why " to " animal " added in 2nd ed.

juridical animadversion on a single crime. Thuanus informs us that there was not a lawsuit among them until the sixteenth century ; when a peasant, richer than most others, sent his son to study the law at Turin, who on his return brought an action against his neighbour, for letting some goats eat his cabbage. Pope Innocent the Third was resolved on exterminating them. The French historian Girard saith hereupon, that nothing in fact drew down so heavily on them the hatred of His Holiness, as the freedom wherewith they reprehended the vices of ecclesiastics.

Now wilt thou tell me that it is a matter of indifference in religion, whether the professors of it persecute and murder us for the detection of iniquity, or search into it and reprove it ? Wilt thou tell me that it is better to keep a strong hand over others than over ourselves ? or to examine the secrets of their hearts rather than our own ? Lax morals may appear for a time opportune and convenient to thee : but wouldst thou wish thy son or thy daughter, if thou hadst one, to experience the utility of them ? or wouldst thou choose a domestic, in town or country, as being the wiser or the honester for thinking like thyself ?

PETERBOROUGH. It would bring him to the gallows within the year : for such fellows can have no sense of honour to direct them.

PENN. Sense of honour, it appeareth to me, is that exquisite perception, whereby a man apprehendeth how he may do the most injury to others for the longest time ; how he may be most acceptable to society at the least expense or pains. My own sense of it, on the contrary, I would desire to be such as may direct me how to do to others what shall both content and improve them, not concealing my own infirmities nor exposing theirs. Among you, a lofty spirit must be ever an inflammable one ; and Courage hath not room for Patience at the side of her. Ye pardon everything done against your God, and nothing done against yourselves : which maketh me sometimes doubt, whether those who are called liberal may not be peradventure the most illiberal of mankind.

In this country we must assist one another : and the necessity brings its blessing. Our religion and our polity spring alike from a virgin soil : in neither of them are we tethered to the stump of old superstitions. Haply [1] thou art listening so patiently because thou heedest so little ?

[1] From " Haply " to " vases. PENN " added in 2nd ed.

PETERBOROUGH. No, indeed. Not only do I listen to you with patience and pleasure, but even discuss with you such questions as I should nauseate with others ; because your religion does not teach you to seek for occasions of hatred on divergencies of opinion. Men, no longer in wolf-skin, but in velvet or brocade, and slit-sleeved and white-handed, still continue to sacrifice human victims ; not indeed with the knife, because the laws wrest it out of the fist, but with heart and soul ; and burn the offender in the fires of their evil passions. I do believe that many of the early Christians (for I know that some of the living) would listen calmly to the most inconsiderate doubts, and would rather suffer pain from them than inflict it for them. But such a spirit never was universal or prevalent. And why ? because, as I have said before, and as priests of all sects have agreed, Christianity has never yet taken root in any country under heaven. It resembles what we often see on our tables at the dessert, dwarf fruits in ornamental vases.

PENN. Idleness is no sign of dignity with us : ministerial prevarication no passport to princely trust. No man's luxuries are here so mischievous as to wring the mouldy morsel from the famished peasant, and to drill his son against him if he should demand it back. The smoke of our chimneys may rise above our roofs unpaid for ; and we may see the face of day and the works of God, without the demand of a shilling to the showman.

PETERBOROUGH. Dear William, no nation pays for light and air, although hearths in many countries are still taxed.

PENN. When human beings are so degraded by slavery as to pay another for the use of their own fire-places and fuel, they will in the next generation be coerced to pay even for the common air and light.

PETERBOROUGH. Your natural calmness, my worthy friend, softly as you speak, hath surely left you. No nation upon earth ever yet submitted to such branding ignominy, such heart-eating despotism. Abuses, however, and something of usurpation, will ultimately find entrance, or force it, even here. Decorations and distinctions are natural objects of desire throughout the world. Religion herself, so pretty and innocent in her girlish days, becomes, as she grows up,

A drab of state, a *cloth o' silver* jade :

and, in the midst of her finery, she tosses down her gin grenadierly ; cries " Come along with me " ; and kicks you if you hang back, in

286

going whither she would closet you. Who knows but that friend Penn, some time hence, may be found cutting out a pair of lawn-sleeves, from the most approved pattern at the milliners in Lambeth ! while the wenches are debating round, what colour is best for his more sanctified order of the garter, and whether a loop and button on the beaver might not, in all righteousness, be allowed to his house of peers. It is difficult to say what is the worst part of us : the best part is the possession of good easy fortunes, and the facility of mending them, when they want it, out of any man's shop we choose to enter. But the worst of Religion is, in my opinion, her wilfulness in having tragedies acted by her own servants, when there are so many fine pieces performed in other houses, with universal applause.

PENN. Friend Mordaunt, I do not require of thee to speak gravely ; thy high spirits and wittiness become thee : and truly I love to see every man as Nature formed him, bating his propensity to selfishness and injustice, by which we are most of us influenced, unless we check them. These are the causes why the decorations and distinctions thou mentionest are so generally the objects of desire, that thou deemest them naturally so, and universally. Men see them belonging to others who are without merit, and are angry at it ; yet would they themselves snatch them from people who have merit. But suppose that, instead of garters under the knee, like hoydens, and buttons big as sun-flowers on the left pap, ye substituted the hearty smile of every house ye entered, a pressure of the hand for every violence ye had calmed, and the thanks of your own hearts for every wrong ye had redressed, would the exchange be much against you ? These trappings and accoutrements, this holiday bravery of groom-boy harness, can influence our people no more than the feathers and ochre of our brethren in the woods. Where there is cleanliness and decency there is usually content : the same well-regulated mind produces both. Ambitious men I have always found disorderly and sordid.

Rising out of a condition so different from the barbarous one, wherein Feodality set up her lions and leopards and other wild creatures, real or feigned, which ye not unaptly call your supporters, we must undergo some ages of savage life in these forests, we must be hunters and murderers and oppressors, long before we can raise ourselves to the same line with you. And what advantages, I will not ask thee, can others derive from it, but what dost thou thyself ?

Art thou not indignant and scornful that others are preferred to thee ? This indignation and scorn could not arise, were your institutions good and fitting. Wherever institutions are not deplorably imperfect, a wise man will find employment for his wisdom. The best carpenter will have work given him, even in places where little judgment is exercised. Shall then he who is most capable of acting or of reasoning, be neglected or unemployed ?

A house of peers in Pennsylvania ! I have no mistresses ; nobody has cut another's throat for me ; nobody has increased my prerogative by his interpretation of my laws : on what grounds then can I erect a house of peers ! and on what other canst thou trace the foundation of one anywhere ?

PETERBOROUGH. It is wiser and pleasanter to look at the consequence than at the origin. Polished manners, and that mutual civility which you inculcate and exact, are acquisitions from aristocracy——

PENN. Made, no doubt, under those who, like lampreys, have always their heads on the ground, wriggling their bodies incessantly : and for what ? why, to suck a stone.

PETERBOROUGH. Faith ! there are many of them who suck better things than that : and whose suckers are of such strength and dimensions, they can wrinkle your pockets and bags across the seas. I am no courtier, nor ever shall be. Soldier [1] I am, and shall be always, and equally in readiness, whether in the field or out. This must depend upon the cabinet, as such things are fitly called.

> In games of politics and games of cricket
> Some must stand out while others keep the wicket.

There is a rhyme for you.

PENN. Truly I should have suspected it of being one.

PETERBOROUGH. Suspect as acutely that I did not take my seat to serve or to sleep on it. If I act and think for myself at present, dependent as I am and in pupilage, there is little danger that a place in the peerage will teach me the trade of a lackey.

PENN. Thou thinkest so ; and verily I think so too : but riches make some men vile, as poverty makes others proud. In England, good manners may grow perhaps only in high places ; where truly, in the finest seasons, I have met with but scanty crops : the gentry

[1] From " Soldier " to " sleep on it " added in 2nd ed.

288

imitate you ; the merchants them. Thus far thou art right. But dost thou imagine that good manners may not spring up from under every form of government ?   The Goths brought them into Europe ; the Moors perfected them : yet should we not have had them without the Goths or Moors ? or would we desire the Goths or Moors again with us, because we happened to derive from them a modification of good manners ?   Hast thou ever witnessed a single uncivil act or unbecoming speech, within the fortnight thou hast spent among us ?

PETERBOROUGH. I must acknowledge I never found anywhere such concession and conciliation.   In the French there is a glossiness of character : they are easily broken and easily fused again, and are the best when they are the most superficial.   What a scoundrel in scarlet was Richelieu, because he had one tendon more in him than the generality have, and was always springing upon it.

PENN. His intellect (if his writings are any proof) was indeed very limited : and its limits were contracted into a smaller compass by his jealousy and vanity : but his confidence gave him power, and power increased his confidence : so that he overthrew many men stronger than himself.   He however had them in a slippery place to trip them up in.   A mere child, with a king [1] in his hand, may break many heads and close many eyes about him.

I find, friend Mordaunt, thou wilt soon be one of us.

PETERBOROUGH. How so ?

PENN. Thou beginnest to speak plainly, albeit thou, in speaking of the man Richelieu, usest a term eschewed and dropt by us friends.

PETERBOROUGH. By another such deduction you may argue that I am growing old.

PENN. Nay, there the deduction is too fine for me : take it up and trace it, I pray thee.

PETERBOROUGH. I begin to speak plainly, and must therefore be soon one of you, since you speak so.   That I am growing old is as clear, since I have begun to be fond of young girls.

PENN. Out upon thee ! filthy man ! when wilt thou sober ? didst thou ride up so closely to me to whisper that ?   Away ! away ! Thou wilt not desert thy country for the French, I think : but we may discuss the matter of politeness, in which they excel, as they teach us.   Compared with one of our society, who claim none of it,

---

[1] So in 1st, 2nd, and Forster's and Crump's eds.

a Frenchman would appear to thee the more polite, from thy preconceived ideas of politeness; and an Englishman more hearty, from preconception also. For the foundation of civility it is requisite that all malignity be smoothened, and that evil-speakers be inhibited like evil-doers.

PETERBOROUGH. You must purify our English blood then. We have within us that acrid salt which effloresces eternally, and which, it appears, we must rub off one against the other. The French, and the continentals in general, indulge in evil-speaking, only as the groundwork of witticisms. The Englishman is contented with it crude and massy, and returns day after day to the identical dish, hot or cold, seasoned or unseasoned, with an incurious, equable, persevering, straightforward appetite. I have known even our women, and those the mildest and most religious, insinuate such things of their acquaintance, as would discredit the whole family, and render it wretched throughout its existence.

PENN. Yet thou couldst listen to these sirens; and not only while they sang, but while they were tearing the flesh from their prey.

PETERBOROUGH. We must take the evil with the good : the region of spices bears the *upas-tree*. Certain they will speak ill of me when I have turned my back, I defer the moment as long as I am able.

What is here ? Wheel round the black mare, William, or you will see what you would rather not.

PENN. Where ? show me it.

PETERBOROUGH. I did not believe that you countenanced any kind of gaming.

PENN. We forbid it rigorously.

PETERBOROUGH. What are those men about yonder, with several looking on ? They surely are drawing lots.

PENN. Those four men upon the bench under the old acacia ?

PETERBOROUGH. The same.

PENN. They are deputed to judge a cause. We have no solicitors, as thou knowest : every citizen stateth his own case : four intelligent men are appointed by lot as judges, in presence of the litigants : they draw a second time, and he to whom the lot falls, decides the question.

PETERBOROUGH. You disclaim all honours and distinctions ; yet do not you entitle these men judges ?

290

PENN AND PETERBOROUGH

PENN. While they are : to-morrow one of them may be called the hatter, another the mason, another the skinner.

PETERBOROUGH. Ha ! no wonder that fellow is upon the bench.

PENN. Thou knowest none more prudent in investigating, more patient in deliberating, or more upright in deciding. Despise him not because his skins are in his shop rather than upon his shoulder, nor because an ox's is not an ermine's.

PETERBOROUGH. What salaries have these people ? or rather, what compensation for loss of time ?

PENN. Thou speakest too good English. Loss of time ! this at least is not the portion of it that is lost. We repay them, as is reasonable, for the good they do.

PETERBOROUGH. That is what I asked : but how ?

PENN. By enabling them to do more good.

PETERBOROUGH. The honesty and rectitude of your people would induce those of every nation to a commercial intercourse with them, if your agricultural occupations allowed it.

PENN. It is untrue that nations can not be at once agricultural and commercial. That the most commercial are the most agricultural, the states of Holland and indeed the Netherlands at large are evidences, and, in another hemisphere, China. Attica, composed of rocks, was better cultivated than Sparta. Carthage and Alexandria, Bruges and Dantzic, put into motion fifty ploughs with every rudder.

Remove from mankind the disabilities that wrong systems of government have imposed, and their own interests will supply them both with energy and with morality. I speak of men as we find them about us, possessing the advantages of example and experience.

Here we are at home again. Thy valet is running hitherward with his hat off, beating the flies and gnats away. My helper Abel standeth expecting me, but knitting hose.

Abel ! Abel !

ABEL. Friend, what wouldst thou ?

PENN. Take my mare and feed her. Hast thou dined ?

ABEL. Nay.

PENN. Art hungry ?

ABEL. Yea.

PENN. Greatly ?

ABEL. In thy house none hungereth painfully : but verily at this hour my appetite waxeth sharp.

PENN. Feed then first this poor good creature, the which is accustomed to eat oftener than thou art, and the which haply hath fasted longer.

ABEL. Thou sayest well : it shall be done even as thou advisest.

PETERBOROUGH. There are only three classes of men that we in general have no patience with ; superiors, inferiors, and equals. You have given me abundant and perpetual proofs that you can bear the two latter ; and I am persuaded that you would place any decent one of the former in the same easy posture, if God, decreeing his happiness or amendment, should ever direct him toward you.[1]

---

[1] The chronology in this Conversation has been questioned by Crump, who considers it must be supposed to have taken place either in 1699 or in 1682. But from the passage, " I designate the year particularly," the true date would appear to be 1691.